MATHEMATICS FOR COLLEGE STUDENTS
ELEMENTARY CONCEPTS

Second Edition

MATHEMATICS FOR COLLEGE STUDENTS
ELEMENTARY CONCEPTS

Second Edition

A. William Gray and Otis M. Ulm
St. Petersburg Junior College
St. Petersburg, Florida

GLENCOE PRESS
A Division of Benziger Bruce & Glencoe, Inc.
Beverly Hills
Collier Macmillan Publishers
London

Copyright © 1975, Benziger Bruce & Glencoe, Inc.

Earlier edition copyright © 1969 by Glencoe Press, a
Division of Macmillan Publishing Co., Inc.

Printed in the United States of America

All rights reserved. No part of this book may be reproduced or
transmitted in any form or by any means, electronic or mechanical,
including photocopying, recording, or by any information storage
and retrieval system, without permission in writing from the Publisher.

GLENCOE PRESS
A division of Benziger Bruce & Glencoe, Inc.
8701 Wilshire Boulevard
Beverly Hills, California 90211
Collier-Macmillan Canada, Ltd.

Library of Congress Catalog Card Number: 73-7359

First printing, 1975

Contents

Chapter 1 The Language of Mathematical Reasoning

    1.1 The Development of Mathematical Language 1
    1.2 Inductive and Deductive Reasoning 2
    1.3 Statements in Deductive Reasoning 3
    1.4 Negation of a Simple Conjunctive and Disjunctive Proposition 5
    1.5 The Implication 6
    1.6 Negation of the Implication 7
    1.7 Deductive Argument 8
    1.8 Symbolic Representation of the Argument 8
    1.9 Quantifiers 11
    1.10 Negations of the Quantifiers 11
    1.11 Use of Diagrams to Represent the Argument 12
    1.12 Derived Implications 15
    1.13 Truth Value of Derived Implications 17
    1.14 Necessary and Sufficient Conditions 18
    1.15 Truth Tables 20
    1.16 The Nature of Mathematical Proof 22
    1.17 Disproof 24
    1.18 Review Exercise 25

Chapter 2 Sets and Relationships Between Sets

    2.1 Introduction to Sets 28
    2.2 Subsets 29
    2.3 Set Operations 32
    2.4 Cartesian Product 36

Chapter 13 The Mathematical System of Real Numbers

    3.1 Introduction 39
    3.2 The Set of Counting Numbers 39
    3.3 The System of Natural Numbers 41
    3.4 Postulates for Equality 43
    3.5 Postulates for Operation on Natural Numbers 44

- 3.6 The System of Integers   49
- 3.7 Classification of Natural Numbers   52
- 3.8 Tests of Divisibility   53
- 3.9 Greatest Common Divisor (GCD) and Lowest Common Multiple (LCM)   54
- 3.10 The System of Rational Numbers   56
- 3.11 The System of Real Numbers   63
- 3.12 The Axiom of Mathematical Induction   65

Chapter 4 Other Mathematical Systems

- 4.1 The System of Groups   69
- 4.2 The System of Modular Arithmetic   71
- 4.3 The System of Complex Numbers   75
- 4.4 The System of Matrices   81
- 4.5 The System of Vectors   86
- 4.6 Application of Vectors   93

Chapter 5 Concepts of Algebra

- 5.1 Introduction to Algebra   99
- 5.2 Algebraic Expressions   99
- 5.3 Algebraic Sentences   101
- 5.4 Solutions for Equations with One Variable   104
- 5.5 Solutions for Inequalities with One Variable   107
- 5.6 Absolute Value   109
- 5.7 Algebraic Sentences for Two Variables   112
- 5.8 Algebraic Statements for Two Variables and the Cartesian Plane   114
- 5.9 Graphs of Algebraic Statements for Two Variables   116
- 5.10 Simultaneous Solution of a System of Equations   124
- 5.11 Graphic Solutions to Systems of Linear Inequalities   133
- 5.12 Relations and Functions   138

Chapter 6 Exponents, Radicals and Quadratic Equations

- 6.1 Introduction   146
- 6.2 The Product of Powers   149
- 6.3 The Power of a Product   150
- 6.4 The Product of Two Polynomials   151
- 6.5 The Quotient of Powers   153
- 6.6 Division of Polynomial Expressions   156
- 6.7 Negative Exponents   158
- 6.8 Radicals (Fractional Exponents)   159

    6.9   Special Products and Factoring   162

    6.10 The Quadratic Function   163

    6.11 The Quadratic Equation   167

Chapter 7   Geometry

    7.1   Introduction   179

    7.2   History of Geometry   180

    7.3   Selected Geometric Concepts   187

    7.4   Other Geometric Concepts   199

Chapter 8   Probability and Statistics

    8.1   Probability   201

    8.2   Expected Probability   203

    8.3   Fundamental Principle of Counting   206

    8.4   Permutations and Combinations   208

    8.5   Probability Involving Arrangements   211

    8.6   Probability of Compound Events   213

    8.7   Mathematical Expectation   216

    8.8   Introduction to Statistics   218

    8.9   Numerical Description of Data   219

    8.10 The Normal Curve   224

Chapter 9   Introduction to Computers

    9.1   Historical Development of Computational Devices   230

    9.2   Types of Computers   231

    9.3   Computer Components   231

    9.4   Computer Arithmetic   233

Appendix A   Programming in BASIC

    A.1   Introduction   242

    A.2   Arithmetic Statements   242

    A.3   READ and DATA Statements   243

    A.4   PRINT Statement   244

    A.5   The Computer Program   244

    A.6   Looping   244

    A.7   Additional Printing Instructions   245

    A.8   Spacing the Printout   247

    A.9   Computer Decisions by Comparing Numbers   249

    A.10 Another Method of Looping   250

    A.11 Subscripted Variables   252

    A.12 Additional Basic Words   253

        A.13   Correcting Program Errors   254
        A.14   Program Input to the Computer   255

Appendix B   Student Research Topics   256
Appendix C   Selected Answers   258
Glossary   341
Symbols   346
  Index   349

Preface

Most college students major in fields in which mathematics is not of paramount importance. Nevertheless, many of these students desire—and sometimes are required—to achieve an understanding of the basic concepts of mathematics. It is these students that this text is addressed.

Readability, understanding, and continuous development have been stressed throughout. Whenever new concepts are introduced, an effort has been made to relate each concept to familiar ideas. In no instance has any sort of rigorous mathematical development been attempted at the expense of basic comprehension.

The process of *deductive reasoning* is the central theme of this text. But our classroom experience has taught us that students, regardless of background, are not initially responsive to the deductive approach to mathematics. Hence the opening chapter, "The Language of Mathematical Reasoning," describes both inductive and deductive reasoning as used in mathematical language. Symbolic logic is introduced as an aid to understanding mathematics rather than as an axiomatic system. Truth table manipulation is deemphasized.

The difficult task of encouraging student involvement in the study of mathematics has frequently been accomplished by making individual research assignments. So a list of student research topics has been included in the Appendices.

In some institutions, special mathematics courses are offered for the training of elementary and secondary teachers. This text is suitable for use in such courses. Also, it may be used in an "honors" course for the senior year of high school. This text is intended for use in a three or four semester-hour course.

In preparing this second edition, many changes recommended by users of the first edition have been included. The significant changes from the first edition are as follows.

1. The chapter on Mathematical Reasoning has been rewritten and organized so that daily assignments are facilitated.
2. The chapter on Sets has been expanded to include the Cartesian product.
3. More exercises have been included in the chapter on Real Numbers. Complex Numbers have been removed from the Real Numbers chapter and included with Other Mathematical Systems.
4. The chapters on Algebra have been expanded to include many new exercises.
5. The treatment of Probability has been expanded and Permutations and Combinations have been included.

6. An appendix on BASIC computer language has been added to the text.

We wish to express our deep appreciation to our colleagues for their help and encouragement. Again, we express our gratitude for the outstanding work of our typist, Mrs. John T. McAvoy.

St. Petersburg, Florida

A. William Gray
Otis M. Ulm

The Language of Mathematical Reasoning

1.1 THE DEVELOPMENT OF MATHEMATICAL LANGUAGE

Man's ability to communicate is his most distinguishing characteristic and the source of his most noble achievements. But success in communication depends on a mutual understanding of the words used. Mathematics, in particular, requires a precise and clear language through which complex ideas can be exchanged and understood.

The need for clarity in mathematical language is not new. The early Greek scholars made the first attempts to develop such a language. Euclid's *Elements*, written in the third century B.C., recorded working definitions of many mathematical terms for the first time. The *Elements* is still the most frequently published mathematics book and is second only to the *Bible* in actual number of publications.

When developing definitions for the language of mathematics, we rely on the generally accepted meanings of nonmathematical words as "between" and "above." We also use mathematical words that remain inadequately defined in regular language, for example, "point" and "line." No matter how rigorously a person intends to develop a mathematical system, he must use two types of undefined terms—technical and nontechnical.

As a guideline for defined terms, a good mathematical definition meets the following qualifications:

1. It uses only *undefined* words, *previously defined* words, or *nontechnical words* with a generally accepted meaning.
2. It establishes the *general category* into which the term falls. For example, with the term "square," the definition should place it in the general category of quadrilaterals.
3. It establishes the *special category* into which the term falls. For example, with "square," the definition should place it in the special category of quadrilaterals having four equal sides and four equal angles.
4. It uses the *simplest* and the most *concise* language possible. For example, with "square," if the definition states "a quadrilateral with equal sides and equal angles," it need not state that the angles are right angles.
5. The wording is such that either the term itself or the definition may be used *interchangeably* anywhere within the system.

By using both undefined and defined terms, we can develop our basic assumptions and set up fundamental rules. These so called "rules" are the assumptions upon which a mathematical system is based. The Greeks, considered the first people to have developed mathematics systematically, used the term "postulate" to refer to an accepted geometrical truth and "axiom" to refer to a truth having a more general application. We accept both postulates and axioms as true, although they may appear arbitrary.

The assumed truth of the axioms forms the base on which we "prove" theorems. If a mathematical system based on undefined terms, defined terms, and assumptions is to be useful, then these additional rules, the *theorems*, must be developed.

Not every mathematician since Euclid has used the same set of undefined terms or even the same set of axioms. The choice of axioms and undefined terms varies with the degree of rigor intended and the nature of the material being developed.

In summary, a mathematical system requires four essential features:

1. Undefined terms
2. Defined terms
3. Axioms
4. Theorems.

1.2 INDUCTIVE AND DEDUCTIVE REASONING

We have already said that a theorem is "proved." From the quotation marks, you may have wondered why this challenging word was singled out for special treatment. Our purpose is to emphasize the nature of a proof and the type of reasoning process employed to establish it. Observation and experimentation are important procedures in any development of human thought. The reasoning process employed in reaching a conclusion based on observation and experimentation is called *inductive reasoning*. For example, if we observe the occurrence of a given phenomenon under similar conditions ten times, then we might predict the outcome on the eleventh. We would have even greater assurance of the outcome if we had observed the phenomenon one hundred times, and we could be almost certain of the outcome after observing it one thousand times. Nevertheless, our prediction must allow for doubt and uncertainty. As long as we depend on observation and experimentation in reaching a conclusion, an element of doubt, however small, remains. Scientific development is usually based on the process of observation, experimentation, and conclusion. In other words, scientific development is based on inductive reasoning.

A mathematician relies on *deductive reasoning*, a form of reasoning that does not require observation and experimentation in forming conclusions. We refer to deductive reasoning as an orderly process of logical thinking. In the deductive process, conclusions are based on previously accepted statements. Drawing deductive conclusions occurs as a purely mental process. Doubt or uncertainty is excluded. For example, consider two statements:

1. The residents of Chicago live in Illinois.

2. Sue Brown lives in Chicago.

If we accept statements 1 and 2, we have no alternative but to accept a third statement:

3. Sue Brown lives in Illinois.

We do not have to observe Sue Brown to reach the proper conclusion. All we need do is apply logical deductive thinking to statements 1 and 2. Even if we had observed Sue Brown in Chicago, she might not be a resident—she could be visiting. Thus we cannot be sure of a conclusion if it is based on observation alone. Herein lies the essential difference between inductive and deductive reasoning—the doubt with inductive reasoning compared to the certainty with deductive reasoning.

1.3 STATEMENTS IN DEDUCTIVE REASONING

You have learned that sentences are classified as imperative, interrogative, exclamatory, or declarative. In our development of the deductive reasoning process, we shall limit ourselves to *declarative sentences*, which can be either true or false. The following definitions will therefore be extremely useful.

> **Definition 1.1** A *proposition* is a declarative statement that is either true or false.
>
> **Definition 1.2** A *simple proposition* is a proposition containing one independent clause.

From two or more simple propositions, we may form new propositions known as *composite propositions*. One such composite proposition, called a *conjunctive proposition*, joins two simple propositions by using the connective "and." Thus: "Fred will go home and Sam will stay at work." For our purposes, the order in which the simple propositions are written makes no difference. A conjunctive proposition is true only when both of the simple propositions are true. For example, consider the following simple propositions, both of which are considered to be true.

1. The earth is round.
2. Water is wet.

The true conjunctive proposition that may be formed from these two propositions is:

The earth is round, and water is wet.

At this point, we can introduce a simple rule of deductive logic. If we know that a conjunctive proposition is true, we can deduce that both simple propositions that make up the conjunctive proposition are true. This is called the *Rule of Simplification*. A similar rule, the *Rule of Conjunction*, states that if we know that two simple propositions are true, we can always form a true conjunctive proposition.

Another type of composite proposition, called a *disjunctive proposition*, joins two simple propositions by using the connective "or." In everyday language, the word "or" can be used in (1) the "and/or" (inclusive) sense or in (2) the "either but not both" (exclusive) sense.

The inclusive use of "or" is illustrated by the following: "In order to qualify for this position, an applicant must have a college degree or five years experience in the field. Sam, who has a college degree but no experience, qualifies. Tom, who has five years experience but no degree, also qualifies. And Fran, who has both a college degree and five years experience, qualifies. Only a person who fulfills *neither* of the requirements does not qualify."

The exclusive use of "or" is illustrated by the following: "The plane will be on time, or it will be late." Only *one* but not both of these simple propositions can be true. When "or" is used in the exclusive sense, the disjunctive proposition is true only when one of the simple propositions is true and the other is false.

In our development of the language of mathematical reasoning, we shall use only the inclusive "or."

EXERCISE 1.1

1. Identify the simple propositions.
   a) Napoleon defeated the British at Yorktown.
   b) The sum of two fractions is a fraction.
   c) Two plus four.
   d) The product of two numbers is a number.
   e) Add this sum.
   f) Come with me to the movie.
   g) All is well.
   h) Healthy, Wealthy and Wise.
   i) Two times six and four times seven.
   j) The sum of two and three is greater than two.
   k) Why is mathematics so fascinating?
   l) Multiplication is a simplified form of addition.

2. Form conjunctive propositions from the following pairs of simple propositions.
   a) Muldoon has poor eyesight.   Muldoon is a referee.
   b) Good books are friends.   I never get lonesome.
   c) Mathematics is important.   Arithmetic is its keystone.
   d) Two times four is equal to eight.   Four times two is equal to eight.
   e) Three times the sum of four and five is equal to twenty-seven.   The sum of four and five times three is equal to twenty-seven.
   f) The commutative law applies, and the distribution law applies.

3. Form disjunctive propositions from the following pairs of simple propositions.
   a) Four can be expressed as two times two.   Four can be expressed as four times one.

b) Four can be expressed as the quotient of twenty-four divided by six. Four can be expressed as the quotient of twenty-four divided by four.
c) Football players are sweet. Colds are sweet.
d) Theorems are proved. Axioms are assumed.
e) Geometry is the science of earth measurement. Geometry is abstract.

1.4 NEGATION OF SIMPLE, CONJUNCTIVE, AND DISJUNCTIVE PROPOSITIONS

The *negation of a proposition* is a proposition that denies the truth or falsity of a given proposition. If a given proposition is true, then its negation is false; if the proposition is false, then its negation is true. Consider the negation of the simple proposition: "Fred is an American." The negation of this proposition is "Fred is not an American." One and only one of these two simple propositions can be true at any given time.

Forming the negation of conjunctive propositions is more complicated than forming the negation of simple propositions. Consider the following conjunctive propositions.

1. The sky is blue, and the grass is green.

The negation of 1 is proposition 2.

2. The sky is not blue, or the grass is not green.

You should recall from our discussion of conjunctive propositions that 1 is true only when both simple propositions are true; thus, to form the negation of 1, we need to assert that at least one of the simple propositions is false, as we have done in proposition 2. The negation of a conjunctive proposition is always a disjunctive proposition.

A disjunctive proposition is true when either or both component simple propositions are true. The negation of a disjunctive proposition must assert that both simple propositions in the disjunctive proposition are false. For example, consider the following disjunctive proposition.

1. I will go to work or to the movies.

The negation of 1 is proposition 2.

2. I will not go to work, and I will not go to the movies.

The negation of a disjunctive proposition asserts that both simple propositions are false. The negation of a disjunctive proposition is always formed by first negating the two simple propositions and then forming a conjunctive proposition.

EXERCISE 1.2

Form the negations of the following propositions.
a) It is raining.
b) Fred is a teacher, or Fred is a bum.

c) John is happy and well fed.
d) Ten is larger than five.
e) All Irishmen wear green ties and live in Ireland.
f) I live in Ohio.
g) All heavenly bodies are planets or stars that shed no light.
h) Mr. Brown does not smoke cigars.
i) All men are cowards or heroes.
j) Paris is the largest city in France.

1.5 THE IMPLICATION

One of the most common and useful types of composite propositions in deductive logic is the *implication*. An implication takes the form of an "if-then" statement: "If it rains, then the sidewalks will be wet." This "if-then" proposition asserts that when the statement "it rains" is true, then the statement "the sidewalks are wet" is also true. The phrase "it rains" is called the hypothesis, and "the sidewalks are wet" is called the conclusion. To repeat, in a true *implication*, if the hypothesis is true, then the conclusion must be true. Much of our everyday conversation is stated in the form of implications, and many mathematical theorems are stated in this form. The following are a few examples.

1. If the sun shines, then I will go fishing.
2. If $x = 2$, then $x^2 = 4$.
3. If x is an odd number, then x^2 is an odd number.

Let us consider the various possibilities of the implication: "If the sun shines, then I will go fishing." If the sun shines and I go fishing, then I have told the truth. If the sun shines and I do not go fishing, then I have asserted a falsehood. However, if the sun does not shine, then whether or not I go fishing, I have told the truth. The implication is false only when the hypothesis is true and the conclusion is false.

An implication can be true even if there appears to be no relationship between the hypothesis and the conclusion. Most implications do assert a relationship between the hypothesis and the conclusion. The following examples should strengthen your understanding of this important concept.

Example 1. Several implications whose hypotheses lead to the same conclusion.

    a) If I am a physician, then I am a doctor.
    b) If I am a veterinarian, then I am a doctor.
    c) If I am a professor, then I am a doctor.

Example 2. Several false hypotheses followed by a true conclusion.

    a) If apples are identical to oranges, then $4 + 1 = 5$.
    b) If Volkswagens are bigger than Cadillacs, then $4 + 1 = 5$.
    c) If fleas are bees, then $4 + 1 = 5$.

Example 3. Some implications in which the hypothesis guarantees that the conclusion will be true.

a) If a person is a mother, then the person is a female.
b) If a student at St. Petersburg Junior College has less than 24-semester hours credit, then that student is a freshman.
c) If a figure has four equal sides and four equal angles, then it is a square.

In the implication, the word "then" is helpful in distinguishing the hypothesis from the conclusion. There are, however, other ways to state an implication. A comma is sometimes used in place of "then" (e.g., "If you leave, I will go home"). Sometimes the conclusion precedes the hypothesis (e.g. "I will go home if you leave"). Some implications employ neither "if" nor "then," but they can be paraphrased into a statement employing these words. For example, the proposition "all men are mortal" can be restated as "if he is a man, then he is mortal."

1.6 NEGATION OF THE IMPLICATION

Sometimes we may wish to form the negation of an implication. Thus negation of proposition 1,

1. If it rains, the sidewalks will be wet,

is conjunctive proposition 2.

2. It rains, and the sidewalks are not wet.

The *negation of an implication* results in a conjunctive proposition; the hypothesis is true and the negation of the conclusion is true. Consider another example.

1. If it snows, then Fred skis.

The negation of this proposition is conjunctive proposition 2.

2. It snows, and Fred does not ski.

Note that the hypothesis is unchanged and that the conclusion has been negated.

EXERCISE 1.3

1. In each following identify the hypothesis and the conclusion and transform the state- into the if-then form.
    a) You will not be admitted if you are a minor.
    b) If John makes good grades and does not miss the exams, he will make an A.
    c) It is always cloudy when it rains.
    d) The wind blows if the hurricane comes.
    e) I could relax and enjoy playing golf if I did not have to work.
    f) All politicians are honest.

g) Everything that goes up must come down.
h) College students are industrious.
i) Beggars would ride if wishes were horses.
j) A student who procrastinates should expect to fail.
2. Write the negation of each of the following propositions.
   a) If eight and four is twelve, then four and eight is twelve.
   b) If it is a theorem, then it has been proved.
   c) If it is an axiom, then it is assumed.
   d) If $x + 1 = 2$, then $x = 1$.
   e) If $a(b + c) = d$, then $(b + c)a = d$.

1.7 DEDUCTIVE ARGUMENTS

We will now develop three elementary rules of deductive logic. The first rule, known as the *Fundamental Rule of Inference*, states that *if we accept the implication as true* and *if we accept the hypothesis as true, then we must accept the conclusion as true*. For example, consider the following argument.

1. If it is snowing, then the streets are slick.
2. It is snowing.
3. Therefore the streets are slick.

In the preceding argument, the implication is "if it is snowing, then the streets are slick." The hypothesis is "it is snowing," and the conclusion is "the streets are slick." Acceptance of the hypothesis and the implication dictates the acceptance of the conclusion.

Our second rule states that *if an implication is true* and *the conclusion is false, then the hypothesis must also be false*. Consider the following example.

1. If Jan is a mother, then Jan is a female. (T)
2. Jan is a female. (F)
3. Therefore Jan is a mother. (F)

Our third rule, known as the *Chain Rule*, allows *several implications* to be "chained" *together before a conclusion is reached*. A Chain Rule argument is illustrated in the following example.

1. If the figure is a square, then it is a rectangle.
2. If the figure is a rectangle, then it is a parallelogram.
3. Therefore if the figure is a square, it is a parallelogram.

1.8 SYMBOLIC REPRESENTATIONS OF DEDUCTIVE ARGUMENTS

Writing the rules of deductive logic with symbols provides simple and concise statements. We represent each simple proposition in an argument with a letter of the alphabet. For connective words between propositions, we use one of the following symbols:

Connective Word	Symbol	Name
and	∧	Conjunction
or (inclusive)	∨	Disjunction
If . . . then	→	Implication

Example 1. Conjunctive propositions.

Proposition	Symbolic Representation
I am tired, and *I am irritable*	$p \wedge q$
$\quad\; p \qquad\qquad\qquad q$	

Example 2. Disjunctive proposition.

$\quad$ *I am tired* or *irritable*. $\qquad p \vee q$
$\quad\;\;\, p \qquad\quad\; q$

Example 3. Implication.

$\quad$ If *I am tired*, then *I am sick*. $\qquad p \to q$
$\qquad\;\; p \qquad\qquad\; q$

Example 4. The Fundamental Rule of Inference.

Argument	Symbolic Representation
1. If *I am tired*, then *I am sick*.	1. $p \to q$
2. *I am tired*.	2. p
3. Therefore *I am sick*.	*3. $\therefore q$

The negation of a given proposition p is "not p," which is symbolized by $\sim p$.

Example 1.

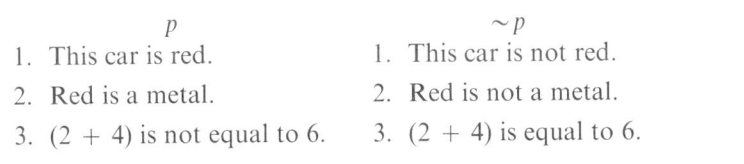

p	$\sim p$
1. This car is red.	1. This car is not red.
2. Red is a metal.	2. Red is not a metal.
3. (2 + 4) is not equal to 6.	3. (2 + 4) is equal to 6.

EXERCISE 1.4

1. Using the Fundamental Rule draw a valid conclusion from the following propositions.

   a) If John Brown lives in Dallas, then John Brown lives in Texas.
      John Brown lives in Dallas.
      Therefore

   b) Today is Monday.
      If today is Monday, then yesterday was Sunday
      Therefore

---

*The term "therefore" is symbolically represented by $\therefore$.

c) If dogs have 10 legs, then horses can fly.
   Dogs have 10 legs.
   Therefore

d) All dogs have fur.
   Fred is a dog.
   Therefore

2. Using the second rule write a conclusion for the following propositions with the indicated truth value.

   a) If Jack is a politican, Jack is a criminal.   (T)
      Jack is a criminal.   (F)
      Therefore   (F)

   b) If Mary owns 100 oil wells, then Mary is rich.   (T)
      Mary is rich.   (F)
      Therefore   (F)

   c) If you watch T.V. seven hours a day, then you are well informed.   (T)
      You are well informed.   (F)
      Therefore   (F)

   d) If If you can swim, then you can swim.   (T)
      You can swim.   (F)
      Therefore   (F)

3. Using the Chain Rule complete the following arguments to establish a valid conclusion.

   a) All rectangles are parallelograms.
      All parallelograms are trapezoids.
      Therefore

   b) If Jane is happy, then she is smiling.
      If Jane is smiling, then she is polite.
      Therefore

   c) If it rains, I'll get wet.
      If I get wet, I'll be sick.
      Therefore

   d) If a man marries, then he has troubles.
      If a man has troubles, then he is happy.
      If a man is happy, then he is a good husband.
      Therefore

4. Translate each of the following propositions into a symbolic representation.

   a) If Fred is late, Betty will not wait.
   b) If Jack is fired and loses his wallet, then he will be unhappy.
   c) I will stay home, or Fred will stay home.

d) If Jane dies, then Mary will celebrate.
   Mary does not celebrate; hence Jane does not die.
e) Pelicans are birds.

1.9 QUANTIFIERS

As we have already stated, an implication can be written in several forms. Consider, for example, the proposition "all trespassers will be shot." This statement tells us that if anyone is a trespasser, he will be shot. But note that this statement continues to be true even if no one ever trespasses. Now consider the proposition "no pillows are hard." This statement tells us that if an object is a pillow, then it is not hard. But it also tells us that no hard objects are pillows.

From these two examples, we can see then that propositions involving the words "all" and "none," called *quantifiers*, can be put into the implication form. There is, however, a third quantifier, "some," that cannot be written in the form of an implication. Thus the proposition "some cars are attractive" cannot be placed in the form "if it is a car, then it is attractive."

1.10 NEGATION OF THE QUANTIFIERS

Sometimes it is necessary to consider the negation of a quantified proposition employing "all," "none," or "some." To negate "all are," the phrase "some are not" is sufficient, since this phrase asserts that *at least one is not*.

Example 1. All girls are cute.

Negation. Some girls are not cute.

Example 2. All birds can fly.

Negation. Some birds cannot fly.

To negate quantified phrases employing "none," the phrase "some are" is sufficient, since this phrase asserts that *at least one is*.

Example 1. No student is lazy.

Negation. Some students are lazy.

Example 2. No teacher is clever.

Negation. Some teachers are clever.

To negate "some are," the phrase "none are" is sufficient.

Example 1. Some birds can sing.

Negation. No bird can sing.

Example 2. Some students make As.

Negation. No student makes an A.

1.11 THE USE OF DIAGRAMS TO REPRESENT DEDUCTIVE ARGUMENTS

A schematic method of representing the relationship among quantified propositions was invented by the Swiss mathematician Leonhard Euler (1707–1783). Euler used plane figures, usually circles, to indicate these relationships. Such diagrams are sometimes called *Euler's circles*.

We shall use Euler's method to analyze several propositions. For the first proposition, "all diamonds are hard," let p represent diamonds and q represent hard objects. The diagram is shown in Figure 1.1.

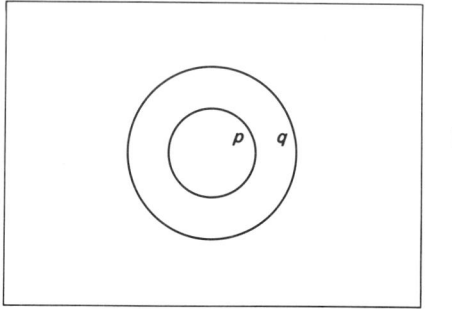

Figure 1.1

The circle and its interior represent all hard objects; the smaller circle p and its interior represent all diamonds. Because circle p lies entirely within circle q, we therefore conclude that if an object is a diamond, then it is hard.

For the second proposition, "no pillows are hard," let p represent pillows and q represent hard objects. The diagram is shown in Figure 1.2. The circle p and its interior represent all pillows; the circle q and its interior represent all

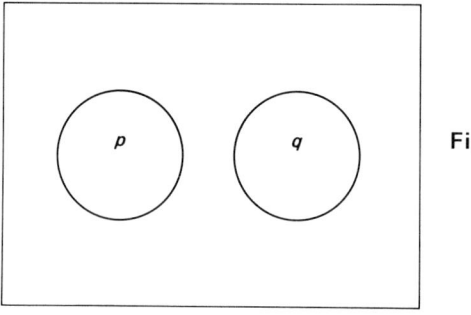

Figure 1.2

hard objects. Since circle p is entirely separate from circle q, we conclude that if an object is a pillow, then it is not hard.

For the third proposition, "some cars are attractive," let p represent all cars and q represent all attractive things. The diagram is shown in Figure 1.3. The circle p and the circle q have an intersection; thus at least one car—represented here by a dot—is common to both p and q. [Note: When we use the word "some," we mean at least one and possibly all.]

Figure 1.3

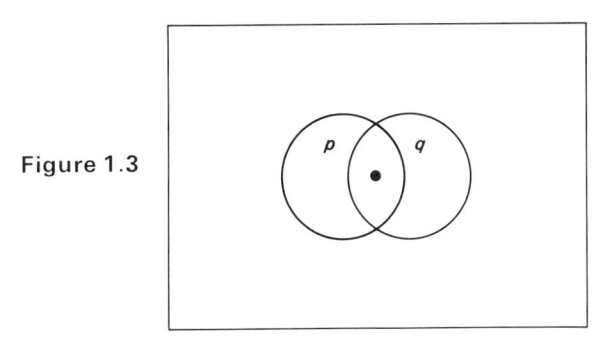

Finally, we should consider one other proposition, "some cars are not attractive." If p represents all cars and q represents all attractive things, then Figure 1.4 accurately depicts this proposition.

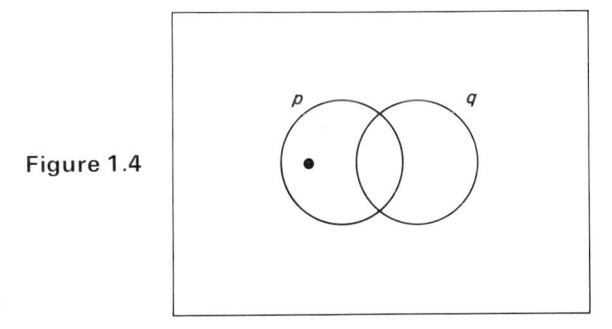

Figure 1.4

The dot in p indicates that there is at least one car that is not attractive.

We can now show how Euler's circles are used to test arguments involving quantifiers. For example, consider the following argument.

1. All football players drink milk.
2. All milk drinkers are healthy.
3. Therefore all football players are healthy.

Using Euler's circles to test the validity of this argument, we draw circles representing statements 1 and 2. Figure 1.5 illustrates statement 1—the p circle represents *football players* and the q circle represents *milk drinkers*.

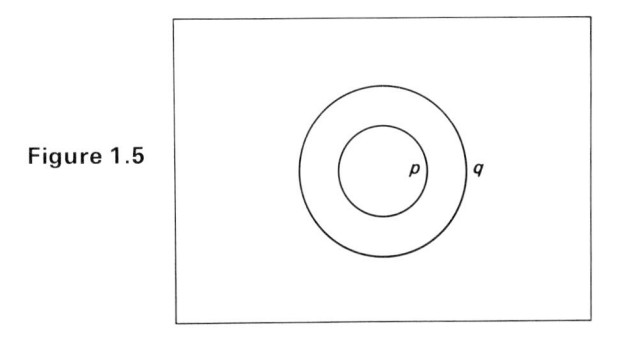

Figure 1.5

Figure 1.6 illustrates statement 2—the *q* circle represents *milk drinkers* and the *r* circle represents *the healthy*.

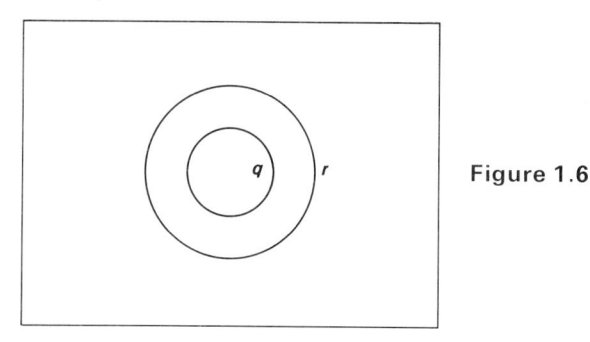

Figure 1.6

To this we add the *p* circle representing football players, as shown in Figure 1.7.

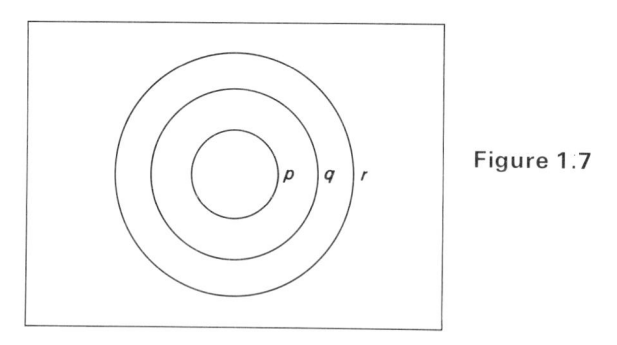

Figure 1.7

In this final diagram, we see that statement 3 of the argument is valid—all of the *football players*, represented by the *p* circle, are within the *r* circle, which represents *the healthy*.

EXERCISE 1.5

1. Using the appropriate Euler's circles, determine whether the conclusions of the following arguments are valid.

   a) All rabbits have long ears.
      My dog has long ears.
      Therefore my dog is a rabbit.

   b) Americans are heroic.
      Fred is an American.
      Therefore Fred is heroic.

   c) All women are fickle.
      Some women have blond hair.
      Therefore some blond-haired individuals are fickle.

   d) All college students are intelligent.
      No politicians go to college.
      Therefore no politicians are intelligent.

e) All good men die young.
   Ralph died young.
   Therefore Ralph was a good man.

f) All who live in Miami live in Florida.
   I live in Florida.
   Therefore I live in Miami.

g) All Catholics are religious.
   All those who are religious are good.
   Therefore some Catholics are good.

h) No scientists are well paid.
   No well-paid people are unhappy.
   Therefore no scientists are happy.

i) Some Germans are not evil.
   Some evil people are not from Europe.
   Therefore some Germans are not from Europe.

j) Everyone loves a fat man.
   Fred is a fat man.
   Therefore everyone loves Fred.

2. Find true conclusions, where possible, for the following sets of propositions.

   a) All college students are clever.
      Jack Blue is not clever.

   b) All squares are rectangles.
      All rectangles are plane figures.

   c) All roses are flowers.
      This is not a flower.

   d) No short boys are good ballplayers.
      Some fat boys are good ballplayers.

   e) If the workers are late, they will be fired.
      If they are fired, they will strike.
      The workers were not late.

   f) The shirt needs laundering if it is soiled.
      The shirt is soiled.

   g) All xs are ys.
      All ys are ws.
      Some zs are ys.

   h) No even number is odd.
      Some prime numbers are even.
      Some prime numbers are odd.

   i) Mathematics is logical.
      The logical is the true.

   j) Some tall men are dark and handsome.
      All dark and handsome men are romantic.

1.12 DERIVED IMPLICATIONS

Several associated statements are derived from the implication. One type of associated statement, the *converse* of the implication, reverses the hypothesis and the conclusion of the implication. For example, the converse of this implication, "if you use toothpaste, then your teeth are white" is this associated statement, "if your teeth are white, then you use toothpaste."

Another associated statement, the *inverse*, is formed by negating both the hypothesis and the conclusion of the implication. The inverse of the preceding implication is "if you do not use toothpaste, then your teeth are not white."

A third associated statement, which is more important to the mathematician, is called the *contrapositive*. The contrapositive of the implication is formed by first reversing the hypothesis and the conclusion and by then negating each of them. The contrapositive of the implication "if you use toothpaste, then your teeth are white" is "if your teeth are not white, then you do not use toothpaste."

Just as an implication is not always expressed in the "if–then" form, the derived implications may appear in different forms. For example, the implication "if it is a Chevrolet, then it was made by General Motors" can be properly stated as "all Chevrolets are made by General Motors." Similarly, the converse, inverse, or contrapositive of this implication may also be written as quantified statements. The following sentences illustrate:

1. All Chevrolets are made by General Motors. (The *implication*)
2. All cars made by General Motors are Chevrolets. (The *converse*)
3. All cars that are not Chevrolets are not made by General Motors. (The *inverse*)
4. All cars not made by General Motors are not Chevrolets. (The *contrapositive*)

We write the conditional, converse, inverse, and contrapositive of an implication in symbolic form.

Type of Statement	Symbolic Representation
Conditional	$p \to q$ (if p then q)
Converse	$q \to p$ (if q then p)
Inverse	$\sim p \to \sim q$ (if not p then not q)
Contrapositive	$\sim q \to \sim p$ (if not q then not p)

EXERCISE 1.6

1. Write the converse, inverse, and contrapositive of the following implications in both words and symbols.

    a) If a man is honest, he is good.

    b) If it rains, then it will turn cold.

    c) I will cut the grass if it rains.

    d) If the Democrats win, then Jones will be president.

    e) A student will not study if the course is too difficult or the instructor does not give exams.

2. Change the following statements to the "if–then" form and then write the converse, inverse, and contrapositive of the statements in both words and symbols.
   a) All roses are flowers.
   b) Dictators are undemocratic.
   c) The games of sport have a large following.
   d) No x is a y.
   e) Blue Grass cigarettes are more flavorful.

1.13 TRUTH VALUES OF DERIVED IMPLICATIONS

Let us examine the relationship between the truth values of the implication and its derived implications. Consider the following true implication.

    1. If it is an automobile, then it has wheels.

The converse of 1 is the following statement:

    If it has wheels, it is an automobile.

The converse of 1 is clearly false. For comparison, consider this true implication:

    2. If a figure has three sides and three angles, then it is a triangle.

The converse of 2 is the following statement:

    If this figure is a triangle, then it has three sides and three angles.

The converse of 2 is true. The truth value of the converse cannot be logically determined just by knowing the truth value of the implication. We must have prior knowledge of the relationship between the hypothesis and the conclusion.

Now consider the inverse of implication 1:

    If it is not an automobile, then it does not have wheels.

Obviously, the inverse of 1 is false. But consider the inverse of implication 2:

    If a figure does not have three sides or it does not have three angles, then it is not a triangle.

The inverse of 2 is true. Again, as in the case of the converse, we cannot determine the truth value of the inverse by logic alone. We must know the relationship between the hypothesis and the conclusion.

Consider the contrapositive of implication 1:

    If it has no wheels, then it is not an automobile.

The contrapositive of 1 is true.
Consider the contrapositive of implication 2:

    If a figure is not a triangle, then it does not have three sides or it does not have three angles.

The contrapositive of 2 is also true. From the second rule of logic (discussed earlier), we conclude that the truth value of the contrapositive can be determined by logic alone. It always has the same truth value as the implication.

The relationships we have seen between an implication and its inverse, converse, and contrapositive, are summarized here:

1. The truth value of the converse cannot be determined from the truth value of the implication.
2. The truth value of the inverse cannot be determined from the truth value of the implication.
3. The truth value of the contrapositive is always the same as the truth value of the implication.
4. Since the inverse is the contrapositive of the converse, the inverse and converse always have the same truth value.

1.14 NECESSARY AND SUFFICIENT CONDITIONS—THE BICONDITIONAL

Frequently, mathematicians write the implication $p \Rightarrow q$ in one of two ways:

1. q is a necessary condition for p. $(p \to q)$
2. p is a sufficient condition for q. $(p \to q)$

When we say q is a "necessary condition" for p, we mean that p cannot be true unless q is true. When we say that p is a "sufficient condition" for q, we mean that the truth of p is sufficient for the truth of q. These conditions are illustrated in Figure 1.8.

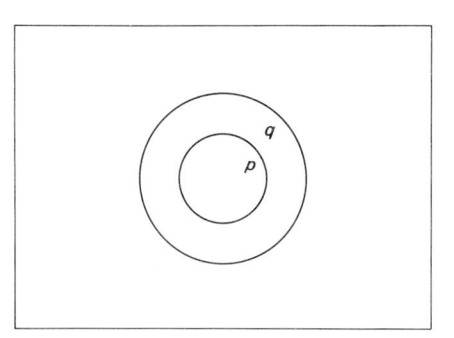

Figure 1.8

The following examples illustrate the terms necessary and sufficient as applied to mathematical propositions.

Implication. If the figure is a triangle then it is a polygon. $p \to q$.

Sufficient condition. A sufficient condition that a figure be a polygon is that it be a triangle. $p \to q$.

Necessary condition. A necessary condition that a figure be a triangle is that it be a polygon. $p \to q$.

1.14 Necessary and Sufficient Conditions—The Biconditional

When the hypothesis and the conclusion are interchangable, the following statements all convey the same meaning:

1. $(p \to q)$ and $(q \to p)$.
2. The hypothesis is both a necessary and sufficient condition for the conclusion.
3. The conclusion is both a necessary and sufficient condition for the hypothesis.

We write any of these statements symbolically as $p \leftrightarrow q$ and say that the implication is *biconditional*, which means both necessary and sufficient conditions are satisfied. We may say that p is true if and only if q is true; also, that p is equivalent to q.

Definitions, mathematical and nonmathematical, can always be expressed in biconditional form. Theorems, however, are not generally considered biconditional propositions. Here are three examples of biconditional statements:

Example 1. If $x = 2$, then $2x = 4$.
If $2x = 4$, then $x = 2$.

Example 2. A triangle is equilateral if and only if it has equal angles.

Example 3. If an integer is even, then it is divisible by two.
If an integer is divisible by two, then it is even.

EXERCISE 1.7

1. Assume the implication is true. From prior knowledge discuss the truth value of the converse and inverse and then write each.
    a) If it rains, then it is cloudy.
    b) It is wet if it is wet.
    c) If $x = 3$ then $2x = 6$.
    d) All right angles have 90°.
    e) All circles are perfectly round.
2. Make up two implications in which the converse and inverse are false and two in which they are true.
3. Make up three implications in which the converse, inverse, and contrapositive are true.
4. Use Euler's circles to illustrate the truth values of the implications and its converse, inverse, and contrapositive.
    a) If it is a horse, then it has four legs.
    b) If it is a Ford, then it is a car.
5. Express each of the following in words.
    a) $p \to q$
    b) $(p \to q) \to p$
    c) $(p \to q) \lor p$
    d) $(p \to q) \leftrightarrow (\sim q \to \sim p)$
    e) $(\sim p \lor q) \leftrightarrow (p \land \sim q)$

6 From your prior knowledge determine whether each of the following is biconditional.
   a) All squares are rectangles.
   b) If it is a digit, then it can be represented with one of the symbols from 0 through 9.
   c) If two lines are parallel, they never meet.
   d) If $3x + 2 = 5$ then $x = 1$.

1.15 TRUTH TABLES

By drawing *truth tables*, we can illustrate much of our presentation about deductive logic and the relationships between propositions. With truth tables, we can ascertain the truth value of a proposition, and determine the relationship between propositions. Tables 1.1, 1.2, 1.3, 1.4, and 1.5 are fundamental tools in the construction of truth tables.

In this system, when we assign a truth value to a given proposition p, then we must assign the opposite truth value to its negation $\sim p$. This is shown in in Table 1.1, where the "T" indicates a value of true and "F" false.

Table 1.1

p	$\sim p$
T	F
F	T

Table 1.2 shows the truth values of a conjunctive statement in which "and" or "but" or equivalent connectives are used.

Table 1.2

p	q	$p \wedge q$
T	T	T
T	F	F
F	T	F
F	F	F

The truth values of a disjunctive statement with "or" or equivalent connectives are shown in Table 1.3.

Table 1.3

p	q	$p \vee q$
T	T	T
T	F	T
F	T	T
F	F	F

The truth value of a conditional statement is shown in Table 1.4.

1.15 Truth Tables

Table 1.4

p	q	$p \rightarrow q$
T	T	T
T	F	F
F	T	T
F	F	T

The truth value of the biconditional is shown in Table 1.5.

Table 1.5

p	q	$p \leftrightarrow q$
T	T	T
T	F	F
F	T	F
F	F	T

If a compound statement is true for all possible truth values of its component propositions, then it is called a *tautology*. Table 1.6 shows that $(p \wedge q) \rightarrow \sim(\sim q \vee \sim p)$ is a tautology.

Table 1.6

p	$\sim p$	q	$\sim q$	$p \wedge q$	$\sim q \vee \sim p$	$\sim(\sim q \vee \sim p)$	$(p \wedge q) \rightarrow \sim(\sim q \vee \sim p)$
T	F	T	F	T	F	T	T
T	F	F	T	F	T	F	T
F	T	T	F	F	T	F	T
F	T	F	T	F	T	F	T

EXERCISE 1.8

1. Make truth tables for the following propositions.
    a) $(p \wedge \sim q)$
    b) $p \vee (p \wedge \sim q) \rightarrow q$
    c) $(p \wedge \sim p) \rightarrow (q \vee \sim q)$
    d) $(p \wedge q) \vee (\sim p \vee q)$
    e) $[(p \rightarrow q) \vee (q \rightarrow p)] \leftrightarrow (p \rightarrow q)$
2. Which propositions in problem (1) are tautologies?
3. Use truth tables to show that the following statements are negations of each other.
    a) If it purrs, then it is a cat.
    b) It purrs, and it is not a cat.
4. Write the contrapositive for the following propositions.
    a) If ten is larger than ten, then $2 + 2 = 4$.
    b) It is an alligator if it barks like a dog.

c) If Dallas is in Texas, then New York is in Canada.

d) All brilliant students are antisocial.

5. Write in words the negation of the following propositions.

   a) Mary goes to college, and Sue works in an office.

   b) If rabbits are furry, then squirrels are hairy.

   c) Jane is a senior, or John is a junior.

   d) A problem becomes a mountain or a molehill if you study and think.

6. Use truth tables to determine which, if any, of the following propositions are equivalent to this proposition:

   If Joe is over 21, he is a minor.

   a) If Joe is not a minor, he is not over 21.

   b) Joe is not over 21, or he is a minor.

   c) If Joe is not a minor, he is over 21.

   d) Joe is a minor if he is not over 21.

   e) Joe is not over 21, and he is not a minor.

   f) Joe is over 21, and he is not a minor.

7. Which propositions in Problem 6 are the negations of each other?

1.16 THE NATURE OF THE MATHEMATICAL PROOF

The mathematical concept we call *proof* originated in the age of Plato, Aristotle, and Euclid. It was during this time that the formal study of deductive reasoning began. The geometry of Euclid is based on a logical reasoning that uses a limited number of propositions assumed to be true. A proposition that can be deduced from the assumed proposition is called a *theorem*. The logical deductive process of deriving a theorem is called the *proof of the theorem*. This process can be briefly described as follows: (a) the proof of the proposition $p \rightarrow q$ is a sequence of statements that terminates in the conclusion q; (b) the first statement in the proof is the antecedent or some statement inferred from it; (c) the succeeding statements follow from the antecedent and are justified by a definition, postulate, or previously proved theorem; (d) the conclusion q is a logical result of the argument.

We may use any one of four styles to write a theorem and its proof: words, mathematical symbols, mathematical and logic symbols, and logic symbols only. We do not mix combinations of the four styles, as you see in the sample proofs that follow.

Theorem (in words): If a number is equal to two, then the number plus one is equal to three.

Proof:

Statements	Reasons
1. If a number is equal to two, then the number plus one is equal to two plus one.	Hypothesis and additive property of equality.

2. If a number plus one is equal to two plus one, then the number plus one is equal to three.　　Addition of $2 + 1$

3. If a number is equal to two, then the number plus one is equal to three.　　Chain Rule $p \to q$, $q \to r$, $\therefore p \to r$

Theorem (in mathematical symbols): If $x = 2$, then $x + 1 = 3$.

Proof:

Statements　　　　　　　　　　Reasons
1. $x = 2$　　　　　　　　　　　Hypothesis
2. $x + 1 = 2 + 1$　　　　　　　Additive property of equality
3. $x + 1 = 3$　　　　　　　　　Addition of $2 + 1$
4. If $x = 2$, then $x + 1 = 3$　　Chain Rule

Theorem (in mathematical and logic symbols): $(x = 2) \to (x + 1 = 3)$

Proof:

Statements　　　　　　　　　　　　　　Reasons
1. $(x = 2) \to (x + 1 = 2 + 1)$　　　Hypothesis and additive property of equality
2. $(x + 1 = 2 + 1) \to (x + 1 = 3)$　Addition of $2 + 1$
3. $(x = 2) \to (x + 1 = 3)$　　　　　Chain Rule

Theorem (in logic symbols only): $p \to r$

p : a number is equal to two
q : a number plus one is equal to two plus one
r : a number plus one equals three

Proof:

Statements　　　Reasons
1. $p \to q$　　　Hypothesis and additive property of equality
2. $q \to r$　　　Addition of $2 + 1$
3. $\therefore p \to r$　　Chain Rule

Each preceding proof is called a *direct proof* and is based on the Chain Rule of deductive reasoning. It may be more convenient to prove a theorem by an indirect proof. Several types of *indirect proofs* exist; the most widely used is based on the contrapositive of the given theorem.

Now let us prove our theorem indirectly. First, we shall use mathematical symbols and, secondly, the symbols of logic.

Theorem. $(x = 2) \rightarrow (x + 1 = 3)$.

Contrapositive. $(x + 1 \neq 3) \rightarrow x \neq 2$.

Proof of the contrapositive:

Statements	Reasons
1. $x + 1 \neq 3$	Hypothesis of the contrapositive
2. $x + 1 + (-1) \neq 3 + (-1)$	Additive property
3. $x \neq 2$	Addition of (-1) and 1, and 3 and (-1)
4. $(x + 1 \neq 3) \rightarrow x \neq 2$	Chain Rule
5. $\therefore (x = 2) \rightarrow (x + 1 = 3)$	Contrapositive of 4.

1.17 DISPROOF

Occasionally, we may attempt to prove a theorem that is not true. If we suspect that a theorem is not true, we can "test" for truthfulness by trying to disprove the theorem. To disprove a theorem, find an example for which the theorem fails. This method, called *proof by counter example*, is useful for testing theorems involving the quantifiers "all" and "none." Consider the following theorems as examples:

Example 1. For all values of x, $2x + 1 = 3$.

To disprove this theorem, we must find one value of x that fails to satisfy the statement of the theorem. A counter example of $x = 5$ disproves this theorem.

Example 2. For no x, $x + 2x = 5x$.

Counter example: $x = 0$.

Although we may disprove a theorem using a counter example, we cannot prove a theorem by using examples. As Einstein said: "A thousand examples won't prove me right but one can prove me wrong."

EXERCISE 1.9

1. a) Write (in words) the converse, inverse, and contrapositive of the implication, "If I study, I will pass the course."

b) Illustrate each of those statements with Euler's circles.
c) Using truth tables, show the truth value of each statement.
2. Use Euler's circles to classify the following arguments as valid or invalid:
   a) If you like mathematics, then you do not like this course.
      You do not like mathematics.
      Therefore you like this course.
   b) All girls are beautiful.
      Beautiful people seldom study.
      Therefore, if you seldom study, you are a beautiful girl.
3. Prove or disprove the following statements:
   a) For all values of x, $x + 2 = 4$.
   b) For no value of x, $2x + 3 = 4$.
   c) If $x + 2 = 7$, then $x = 5$.

1.18 REVIEW EXERCISES

1. Form the negation of each statement.
   a) All men are brave.
   b) Some men are brave, and some men are intelligent.
   c) Joe will either be on time, or he will not arrive at all.
   d) Some numbers are integers, and all integers are numbers.
   e) $2x = 4$, and $x = 2$.
   f) If a figure is a square, then it is not a triangle.
2. Identify the hypothesis and the conclusion in these statements:
   a) All who watch TV are well informed.
   b) Harry will not work unless he is paid.
   c) If I win the race or not, we will be happy.
   d) If x is more than z, then $2x$ is more than 4.
   e) If a is divisible by 3, then $6a$ is divisable by 3.
   f) All mathematics is not useful.
3. State a valid conclusion.
   a) If the sidewalk is icy, I will not fall down.
      I fell down.
      Therefore
   b) If $x + 2 = 1$, then $x = -1$.
      x is not equal to -1.
      Therefore
   c) If $A = B$, then $B = A$
      $A = B$.
      Therefore
   d) If a figure is geometric, then it is beautiful.
      This figure is not beautiful.
      Therefore
   e) If x is greater than z and y is greater than 3, then $x + y$ is greater than 5.

$x + y$ is not greater than 5.
Therefore

f) If one pair cost \$3.00, then four pair cost \$12.00.
Four pair do not cost \$12.00.
Therefore

4. Write the symbolic representation of the following statements:
   a) If money and men are offered, Joe will take them.
   b) Win or lose, those with a fighting spirit do not quit.
   c) All Americans were either born in the U.S., had parents born in the U.S., or are naturalized citizens.
   d) If $x = 3$, then $3x = 9$.
   e) All numbers greater than two are greater than one.

5. Write the inverse, converse, and contrapositive for the following statements:
   a) If baking soda is placed in vinegar, a quick reaction occurs.
   b) All penguins lack the ability to fly.
   c) If $x = 2y$, then $2x = 4y$.
   d) If $x = y$ and $x = z$, then $y = z$.

6. Use Euler's circles to determine whether the following are valid arguments:
   a) Some turtles have wings.
      Some things with wings are birds.
      Therefore some turtles are birds.
   b) No airplanes are lighter than air.
      All balloons are lighter than air.
      Therefore no balloons are airplanes.
   c) All hurricanes are horrid.
      Some storms are hurricanes.
      Therefore some hurricanes are horrid.
   d) All dogs have fleas.
      All things with fleas itch.
      Therefore dogs itch.
   e) Some circles are larger than some squares.
      All squares have four corners.
      Therefore some circles are larger than some things with four corners.

7. Make truth tables for the following propositions and note which of them are tautologies.
   a) $q \to [p \lor \sim p]$
   b) $[(q \lor r) \lor (\sim q \lor \sim r)] \to s$
   c) $(p \land q) \leftrightarrow (q \land p)$
   d) $(p \land \sim p) \to (q \to r)$
   e) $(p \lor s) \to (s \lor r)$

REFERENCES

Allendoerfer, C. B. and C. O. Oakley. *Fundamentals of Freshman Mathematics*. New York: McGraw-Hill, 1965.

Brant, Vincent and Mervin L. Keedy. *Elementary Logic.* New York: Holt, Rinehart and Winston, 1962.

Dinkines, Flora. *Introduction to Mathematical Logic.* New York: Appleton-Century-Crofts, 1964.

Kenelly, John W. *Informal Logic.* Boston: Allyn and Bacon, 1967.

Schaaf, William L. *Basic Concepts of Elementary Mathematics,* 2d ed. New York: Wiley, 1965.

Western, Donald W. and Vincent H. Haag. *An Introduction to Mathematics.* New York: Henry Holt, 1959.

2 Sets and the Relationship Between Sets

2.1 INTRODUCTION TO SETS

One of the most fundamental notions in mathematics is the concept of *set*. In a general sense, a set is a collection of objects, e.g., dishes, pencils, numbers, or people. Mathematically, a set consists of a *well-defined collection of objects*. A set is "well defined" only when there is no doubt that any given object "belongs to" or "does not belong to" the set. The objects that belong to a set are called its *elements*. The elements of a set are distinct; that is, each element differs from all other elements in the set.

Sets are called *finite*, *infinite*, *null* or *empty*. A finite set contains a limited number of elements. An infinite set contains an unlimited number of elements. An *empty* or *null* set (denoted by $\emptyset$) contains no elements.

We denote sets in several ways. One method is to list the elements and then enclose them with braces—for example, $\{1, 2, 3\}$. The order in which the elements are listed makes no difference. Set $\{1, 2, 3\}$ is the same as set $\{3, 1, 2\}$.

Another method of denoting a set is to state a rule that defines the set elements. Hence the set $\{1, 2, 3\}$ would be defined by this rule:

$$\{x \mid x \text{ is a natural number} < 4\}$$

This statement is read "the set of all x such that x is a natural number* less than 4."

Capital letters are used to designate sets and small letters to denote elements—for example, $A = \{x, y, z, w\}$. When we wish to indicate that the object x is an element of the set A (i.e., "belongs to" the set A), we do so by writing $x \in A$ (read: "x is an element of A"). Consider the following examples of set notation.

Example 1. Let A be the set of counting numbers.†

$$A = \{1, 2, 3, \ldots\}$$
$$A = \{x \mid x \text{ is a counting number}\}$$
$$1 \in A, \quad 2 \in A, \quad 3 \in A, \quad \text{etc.}$$

Example 2. Let B be the the set of integers.†

$$B = \{x \mid x \text{ is an integer}\}$$
$$B = \{\ldots, -3, -2, -1, 0, 1, 2, 3, \ldots\}$$

---

*The *set of natural numbers* is the set $\{1, 2, 3, \ldots\}$. [See Chapter 3.]
†See Chapter 3 for a complete description of these types of sets.

Example 3. Let C be the set of divisors of 80.

$$C = \{x \mid x \text{ is a divisor of } 80\}$$
$$C = \{1, 2, 4, 5, 8, 10, 16, 20, 40\}$$

In these examples of set notation, the elements have been numbers, but there is no limitation on the *composition* of an element. For example, the elements in a set may be composed of pairs of numbers:

$$A = \{(s, s), (s, f), (f, s), (f, f)\}$$
$$(s, s) \in A, \quad (s, f) \in A, \quad \text{etc.}$$

Each element of this set A consists of *two components*. Notice also that the *order* of the components of an element is significant. The ordered pair (s, f) with first component s and second component f is distinct from the ordered pair (f, s).

Two sets, A and B, are *equivalent* when both A and B contain the same number of elements. Two equivalent sets, A and B, are *equal* when each contains the same elements.

2.2 SUBSETS

In mathematics we often study individual "collections" of objects that all belong to one large set. For example, we are already somewhat familiar with the set of integers and the set of fractions that are both part of the set of real numbers.* A set that includes all of the elements under consideration is called the *universal set* (denoted by U). Any one collection of elements in U is called a *subset* of U. Consider the following examples.

Example 1. Let U be the set of families.

Subsets of U Let A be the set of families with 2 children.

Let B be the set of families with income above $10,000.

Example 2. Let U be the set of tires manufactured by Firestone.

Subsets of U Let A be the set of Firestone tires that fail after 30,000 miles.

Let B be the set of Firestone tires that cost $30.00.

Example 3. Let U be the set of TV viewers.

Subsets of U Let A be the set of viewers who watch sports.

Let B be the set of viewers who watch comedy.

Let C be the set of viewers who watch wrestling.

---

*Each of these sets is completely described in Chapter 3.

Note: Any subset in these examples could become the universal set if the totality of the objects under consideration were changed.

We can formalize the subset concept with a definition.

Definition 2.1 Set A is said to be a *subset* of B (denoted by $A \subseteq B$) if and only if each element of A is an element of B.

Now consider another group of subset examples.

Example 1. Let $A = \{(s,f), (f,s), (f,f)\}$.
If $B = \{(s,f), (f,s)\}$.
Then B is a subset of A.

Example 2. Let A = the set of freshman.
If B = the set of freshmen women.
Then B is a subset of A.

Example 3. Let A = the set of voters.
If B = the set of Republican voters.
Then B is a subset of A.

By definition 2.1, every set is a subset of itself. But each subset in these three examples is a *proper subset*. The following definition explains the distinction.

Definition 2.2 Set A is a *proper subset* of B (denoted by $A \subset B$) if and only if each element of A is an element of B and there is at least one element of B that is *not* an element of A.

Now verify that each of the subsets in the preceding examples actually satisfies Definition 2.2.

The universal set and its subsets may be geometrically represented by means of a *Venn diagram*,* as illustrated in Figure 2.1. The rectangle U in the diagram

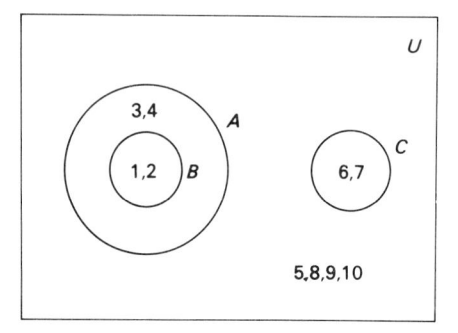

Figure 2.1 Venn Diagram:

$A \subset U, B \subset U, B \subset A, C \subset U$

---

*After its inventor John Venn, the nineteenth century English logician.

represents the universal set. The subsets of U are represented by circles or other closed geometric figures contained within the rectangle.

If we let $U = \{1, 2, 3, \ldots, 10\}$, $A = \{1, 2, 3, 4\}$, $B = \{1, 2\}$, and $C = \{6, 7\}$, the circle representing B must lie within the circle representing A, since $B \subset A$. Neither sets A and C nor sets B and C have any elements in common. Thus sets A and C are said to be *disjoint*; so are sets B and C.

EXERCISE 2.1

1. List the elements of the following sets.
    a) Integers from 5 through 10.
    b) Vowels including y.
    c) Talking catfish.
    d) The set of ordered pairs using the components 1, 2 and 3. [Repetition of components is permitted; i.e. (1, 1) is in the set.]
2. Which of these sets are equal to the first set listed?

    $$\{1, 2, 3\}, \quad \{2, 1, 3\}, \quad \{3, 2, 1\}, \quad \{3, 1, 2\}$$

3. Which of these sets are equal to the first set listed?

    $$\{(s, r), (r, s)\} \quad \{(r, s), (s, r)\} \quad \{s, r, r, s\}, \quad \{(s, r, r, s)\}$$

4. List all subsets of each of the following sets.
    a) $\{1, 2, 3\}$
    b) $\{(1, 2), (2, 1)\}$
    c) $\{(B, B, B), (G, G, G)\}$
    d) $\{(S, S), (S, F), (F, S), (F, F)\}$
5. List the subsets of the following sets.
    a) Football teams in the 1972 Super Bowl.
    b) Presidents of the U.S.A. since 1960.
    c) The set of positive odd integers less than or equal to 9.
6. Which of the following sets are infinite?

    Atoms in the ocean, counting numbers, stars in the sky.

7. How many subsets can be formed from the indicated set?
    a) $\{F, H, T\}$
    b) $\{(F, H), (H, F)\}$
    c) $\{(B, B), (B, G), (G, B), (G, G)\}$
    d) $\{(S, F, U), (S, U, F), (F, U, S)\}$
8. Represent the following sets in a Venn diagram.

    $$U = \{2, 4, 6 \ldots 24\}$$
    $$A = \{2, 8, 16\}$$
    $$B = \{4, 16\}$$
    $$C = \{2, 4, 6, 8, 16\}$$

9. Represent the following sets in a Venn diagram.

   Let U be the set of students at S.P. College.
   Let A be the set of students at S.P. studying English.
   Let B be the set of students at S.P. studying English and math.
   Let C be the set of students at S.P. studying English and history.
   Let D be the set of students at S.P. studying history and math.
   Let E be the set of students at S.P. studying history, English and math.
   Assume that no set is empty.

10. Write the following in set notation.
    a) A is a subset of B.
    b) x is a member of A.
    c) (x_1, y_1) is an element of F.
    d) $\{(B, B), (G, G)\}$ is a subset of $\{(B, B), (G, G), (B, G)\}$.

2.3 SET OPERATIONS

Given a universal set U, it is possible to "*operate*" on the subsets of U to form new sets. We define and study three set operations in this section.

In two of the following definitions of set operations, the words "or" and "and" appear. A clear understanding of the meaning of these words for our use is vital. When "or" is used in defining a set operation, it is always used in the *inclusive* sense. To say that the element "x is in set A or set B" means that x may be in A only, B only, or in both A and B. To say that the element "x is in A and B" means that A is simultaneously in both sets A and B.

The first operation that we shall consider is called *intersection*.

Definition 2.4 The *intersection* of A and B (denoted by $A \cap B$) is the set of all elements of U that belong to both A and B.

This definition may be written symbolically as

$$A \cap B = \{x \mid x \in A \quad \text{and} \quad x \in B\}$$

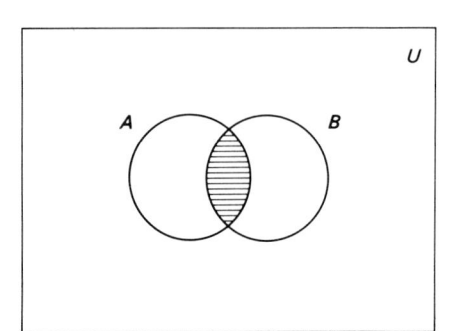

Figure 2.2 Intersection of A and B: $A \cap B$

The reason this operation is called "intersection" is apparent from Figure 2.2, where the shaded area represents $A \cap B$.

The second set operation that we shall define is called *union*.

Definition 2.5 The *union* of A and B (denoted by $A \cup B$) is the set of all elements of U that belongs either to A or to B or to both A and B.

This definition may be written symbolically as follows:

$$A \cup B = \{x \mid x \in A \quad \text{or} \quad x \in B \quad \text{or} \quad x \in \text{both } A \text{ and } B\}$$

The union of A and B is illustrated in Figure 2.3.

Figure 2.3 Union of A and B: $A \cup B$

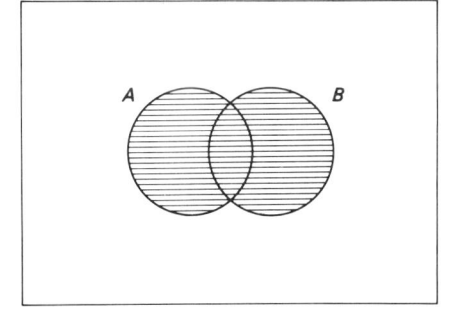

The last set operation that we shall consider now is called *complementation*.

Definition 2.6 The complement of A (denoted by A') is the set of all elements in U that are not in A.

Definition 2.6 may be symbolized as:

$$A' = \{x \mid x \in U \quad \text{but} \quad x \neq A\}$$

[Note: $\neq$ means "not an element of."] The shaded area of Figure 2.4 represents A'.

Figure 2.4 Complement of A: A'

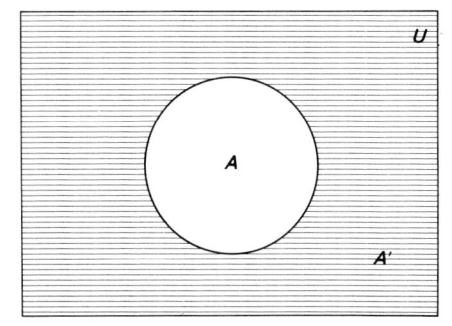

The operations of intersection, union, and complementation are illustrated in the following examples.

Example 1. Let $U = \{1, 2, 3, \ldots, 10\}$
$A = \{1, 2, 3\}$
$B = \{3, 4, 5\}$
Find a) $A \cap B$, b) $A \cup B$, c) A'

Solution: a) $A \cap B = \{x \mid x \in A \text{ and } x \in B\}$
$A \cap B = 3$

b) $A \cup B = \{x \mid x \in A \text{ or } x \in B \text{ or both}\}$
$A \cup B = \{1, 2, 3, 4, 5\}$

c) $A' = \{x \mid x \in U \text{ but } x \notin A\}$
$A = \{4, 5, 6, \ldots, 10\}$.

Example 2. Let $U = \{(s, s), (s, f), (f, s), (f, f)\}$
$A = \{(s, s), (s, f)\}$
$B = \{(s, f), (f, s)\}$
Find a) $A \cap B$, b) $A \cup B$, c) A'

Solution: a) $A \cap B = \{(s, f)\}$
b) $A \cup B = \{(s, s), (s, f), (f, s)\}$
c) $A' = \{(f, s), (f, f)\}$

Example 3. Let U = the set of U.S. presidents
Let A be the set of U.S. presidents from 1932–1972
Let B be the set of U.S. presidents who were assasinated
Find a) $A \cap B$, b) $A \cup B$

Solution: a) $A \cap B = \{\text{Kennedy}\}$
b) $A \cup B = \{\text{Roosevelt, Truman, Eisenhower, Kennedy, Johnson, Nixon}\}$

EXERCISE 2.2

1. Given: $U = \{1, 2, 3, \ldots, 14\}$
   $A = \{1, 2, 3, \ldots, 10\}$
   $B = \{2, 4, 6, 8, 10, 12, 14\}$
   $C = \{1, 3, 5, 7, 9\}$

   Find:
   a) $A \cup B$
   b) $B \cup C$
   c) $A \cup C$
   d) $(A \cup B) \cup C$
   e) $A \cup (B \cup C)$
   f) $A \cup (B \cap C)$
   g) A'
   h) B'
   i) C'
   j) $A' \cap (B' \cap C')$

2.3 Set Operations

2. Given: $U = \{(s, s, s), (s, s, f), (s, f, s), (f, s, s), (s, f, f), (f, s, f), (f, f, s), (f, f, f)\}$
   $A = \{(s, s, s), (s, s, f)\}$
   $B = \{(s, s, s), (s, f, s)\}$
   $C = \{(s, f, f), (f, s, s), (s, s, f)\}$

   Find:
   a) $A \cup B$
   b) $B \cup C$
   c) $A \cup C$
   d) $(A \cup B) \cup C$
   e) $A \cup (B \cup C)$
   f) $A \cup (B \cup C)$
   g) A'
   h) B'
   i) C'
   j) $A' \cup (B' \cup C')$

3. If set A has 5 elements and set B has 5 elements, what is the maximum number of elements in (a) $A \cup B$, (b) $A \cap B$?

4. If set A has 10 elements, set B has 5 elements, and set C has 3 elements, determine
   a) the maximum number of elements in $A \cup B \cup C$
   b) the minimum number of elements in $(A \cup B) \cup C$
   c) the maximum number of elements in $(B \cap C) \cup A$
   d) the minimum number of elements in $A \cap B \cap C$

5. Given: $U = \{(x, y) | x = s \text{ or } x = f, \; y = s \text{ or } y = f\}$
   $A = \{(s, x) | x = f \text{ or } x = s\}$
   $B = \{(x, f) | x = f \text{ or } x = s\}$

   Find:
   a) $A \cup B$
   b) $A \cap B$
   c) A'
   d) B'

6. Given: $U = \{(b, b), (b, g), (g, b), (g, g)\}$

   A is the set of elements with the first component b

   C is the set of elements with first component b or g

   D is the set of elements with first component b and second component b or g.

   Find:
   a) the elements in A
   b) the elements in C
   c) the elements in D
   d) the elements in $A \cup C$
   e) the elements in $A \cap C$
   f) the elements in $A \cap (C \cap D)$

7. Given: $U = \{x | x \text{ is a human being}\}$
   $A = \{y | y \text{ is a human being 21 yrs. of age or older}\}$
   $B = \{z | z \text{ is Caucasian}\}$
   $C = \{w | w \text{ is Negroid}\}$

   Describe each of the following in words.
   a) $A \cap B$
   b) $A \cup B$
   c) $B \cup C$
   d) $A \cup C$
   e) $(B \cap C)$

8. Using diagrams similar to that shown here, shade those portions indicated by the set specified in (a)–(h).

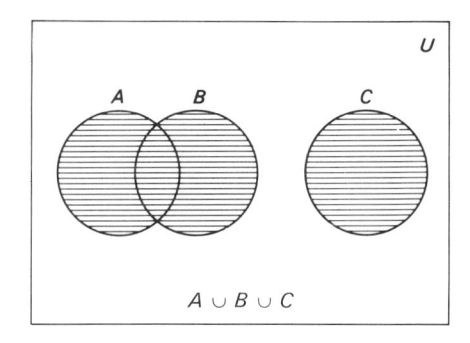

$A \cup B \cup C$

a) $A \cup (B \cap C)$
b) $A \cap B$
c) $A \cap C$
d) $B \cap C$
e) $(A \cap B) \cup C$
f) $(A \cup B) \cap C$
g) $C \cap (A \cup B)$
h) $A \cap (B \cup C)$

9. Referring to your answers to Problem 8, determine
   a) which diagrams illustrate the commutative property of union or interesection
   b) which diagram illustrates the associative property of union or intersection
   c) which diagrams indicate closure of union or intersection
   d) which diagrams illustrate the distributive property

2.4 THE CARTESIAN PRODUCT SET

The fourth and final set operation we define is called the *Cartesian product*. This operation differs from the other three because it is based on *ordered pairs*.

Definition 2.7 The *Cartesian product* of two sets A and B (denoted by $A \times B$) is the set of all ordered pairs (a, b) such that $a \in A$ and $b \in B$.

Symbolically, we express definition 2.7 like this:

$$A \times B = \{(a, b) | a \in A \text{ and } b \in B\}$$

Example 1. If $A = \{1, 2, 3\}$ and $B = \{a, b, c\}$, find $A \times B$ and $B \times A$.

Solution: $A \times B = (1, a), (1, b), (1, c), (2, z), (2, b), (2, c), (3, a), (3, b), (3, c)\}$
$B \times A = \{(a, 1), (a, 2), (a, 3), (b, 1), (b, 2), (b, 3), (c, 1), (c, 2), (c, 3)\}$

Each element of A is matched with each element of B to yield $3 \times 3 = 9$ elements in $A \times B$. Similarly, each element of B is matched with each element of A to yield $3 \times 3 = 9$ elements in $B \times A$.

Example 2. If $A = \{(s, s), (s, f)\}$ and $B = \{(f, s), (f, f)\}$, find $A \times B$ and $B \times A$.

Solution: Each element of A is matched with each element of B to yield $2 \times 2 = 4$ and elements in $A \times B$, and vice versa.

$$A \times B = \{((s, s), (f, s)), ((s, s), (f, f)), ((s, f), (f, s)), ((s, f), (f, f))\}$$
$$B \times A = \{((f, x), (s, s)), (f, s), (s, f), ((f, f), (s, s)), ((f, f), (s, f))\}$$

The two-dimension coordinate system was first introduced by René Descartes. We have borrowed from his name to call $A \times B$ the "Cartesian product." The entire set of coordinates—integral, rational, and irrational—can be found in the following manner:

Let $A = \{1, 2, 3 \ldots\}$ and find $A \times A$. The product is

$$A \times A = \{(1, 1), (1, 2), (1, 3), \ldots, (1, n), (2, 1), (2, 2), (2, 3), \ldots,$$
$$(2, n), (n, 1), (n, 2), (n, 3), \ldots, (n, n)\}$$

The Cartesian product concept can be extended to any finite number of sets. The product $A \times B \times C$ is the set

$$A \times B \times C = \{(a, b, c) | a \in A, b \in B, \text{ and } c \in C\}$$

The number of elements in a product set $A \times B$ may be found by computing the arithmetic product of the number of elements in A and the number of elements in B. For example, if A has m elements and B has n elements, then $A \times B$ has $m \times n$ elements.

EXERCISE 2.3

1. Given: $A = \{1, 2, 3\}$
   $B = \{x, y, z\}$
   Find: a) $A \times B$ c) $A \times A$
   b) $B \times A$ d) $B \times B$

2. Given: $A = \{a, b, c, d\}$
   $B = \{1, 5, 7, 9\}$
   $C = \{a, 2, b, 3$
   Find: a) $A \times B$ c) $B \times C$
   b) $A \times C$ d) $A \times B \times C$ (list 4 elements)

3. Set A has 3 elements, set B has 5 elements, and set C has 7 elements. How many elements are in each of the following sets?
   a) $A \times B \times C$
   b) $B \times A \times C$
   c) $C \times A \times B$

4. Based on your answers to the preceding problems, what conjecture can be made regarding the relationship of the Cartesian product to ordinary multiplication?

REFERENCES

Allendoerfer, C. B. and C. O. Oakley. *Fundamentals of Freshman Mathematics.* New York: McGraw-Hill, 1965.

Denkines, Flora. *Elementary Theory of Sets.* New York: Appleton-Century-Crofts, 1964.

Gray, James F. *Sets, Relations and Functions.* New York: Holt, Rinehart and Winston, 1962.

Horner, Donald R. *A Survey of College Mathematics.* New York: Holt, Rinehart and Winston, 1967.

Sachs, Jerome M., Ruth B. Rasmusen, and William J. Purcell. *Basic College Mathematics.* Boston: Allyn and Bacon, 1960.

Zehna, Peter W. and Robert L. Johnson. *Elements of Set Theory.* Boston: Allyn and Bacon, 1962.

The Mathematical System of Real Numbers

3.1 INTRODUCTION TO NUMBER SETS

Everyday, we use a set of *numbers* $\{1, 2, 3, 4 \ldots\}$ to count objects. In addition, we often use another set of numbers, called *fractions*, $\{\frac{1}{2}, \frac{5}{6}, 2\frac{1}{4}, 33\frac{1}{3} \ldots\}$ to measure objects. These two sets of numbers suffice for most purposes. But a third set of numbers may also be encountered in our daily lives—one that is larger than the other two sets combined. If we could always make *exact* measurements, the set $\{\sqrt{2}, \sqrt{3}, \sqrt{5} \ldots\}$ would probably be as familiar to us as the set $\{1, 2, 3, 4 \ldots\}$.

For each element in these three sets of numbers, there exists a negative in the *set of negative numbers*. The negative set $\{-1, -\frac{1}{2}, -1\frac{1}{2}, -2 \ldots\}$ conveys the same message to a mathematician as red ink does to an accountant. To represent these numbers mathematicians have found that putting a minus sign with the number is more convenient than changing colors.

We have created a special ruler, shown in Figure 3.1, to indicate the relative positions of a few selected numbers.

Figure 3.1

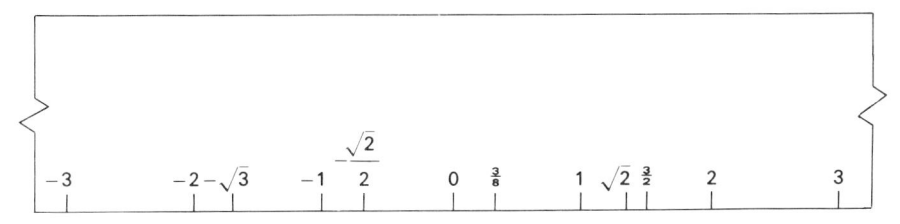

All four sets of numbers that we have just discussed are actually part of the larger *set of real numbers*. The purpose of this chapter is to develop this mathematical system of real numbers, starting with one of its subsets—the set of counting numbers.

3.2 THE SET OF COUNTING NUMBERS

The Counting Numbers

The numbers that we represent with the set of symbols 1, 2, 3, ..., 100, ..., 1000, ... are called *counting numbers*. These are the first numbers that we learn to use. A person learns to count by associating physical objects with these numerical symbols. They represent a *quantity*—pennies, beads, or objects—

in daily life. Soon, the beginner learns to associate a single number symbol with many different physical sets of objects. For example, the symbol 4 is matched with four marbles, four birds, and four boys. Each of the sets that we can match with the symbol 4 has the same *cardinal number*, which is the designation for how many elements are in a set. All sets having the same cardinal number have an *identical number of objects* in the set. So we can always determine whether two sets, A and B, have the same cardinal number by matching the elements in the sets. If we can match each element of set A with a unique element of set B and each element of set B with a unique element of set A, the two sets can then be put into a *one-to-one correspondence*. This concept is illustrated in Figure 3.2.

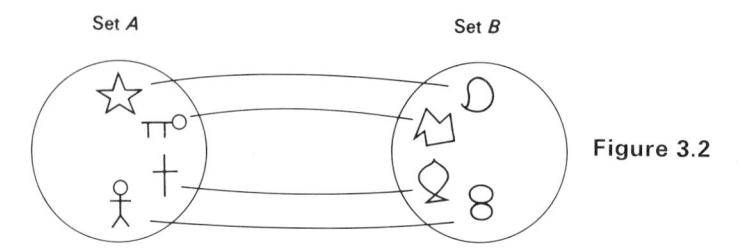

Figure 3.2

Representing the cardinal number of a set is not dependent on the same symbols used for the number of elements in the set. For example, a set with one element and another with four elements can be represented symbolically as shown in Table 3.1.

Table 3.1

Set	Symbols for the Cardinality of the Set			
	Hindu-Arabic	Roman	Greek	Mayan
*	1	I	α	●
	Hindu-Arabic	Roman	Babylonian	Egyptian
****	4	IV	𒁹𒁹𒁹𒁹	||||

In addition to knowing how many elements are in a given set, we often want to know the order or position of each particular element, whether first, second, third, and so forth. This is called the *ordinal concept of numbers*. Consider the following statements.

Cardinal concept: There were *three* men in the race.
Ordinal concept: John was *first*.
Cardinal concept: There are *six* exercises in this chapter.
Ordinal concept: The *first* exercise follows Section 5.

Sum and Product of Counting Numbers

We are now ready to discuss the *sum* of two counting numbers. Picture two disjoint sets: one has cardinal number 2 and the other has cardinal number 3.

Place the two sets side by side and then find a set with the same cardinality as the combined set. The answer, of course, is the set of cardinality five. Our experience tells us that no other set with a different cardinality can be put in a one-to-one correspondence with the combined set. We could forever go through the physical process of finding the sum of two numbers by combining the sets and then counting the elements to determine the sum. But this procedure becomes tiresome with small sets and impossible with large sets. When trying to combine sets totalling more than a hundred elements, our caveman ancestors probably threw in the sponge. Fortunately, over a millennium ago, people discovered a better way to find the sum of the elements of two sets. We call this summing procedure *addition*, and we describe it further in another section.

We explain the *product* of two counting numbers in much the same way as we did the sum. To find the product of a set with two elements and one with three elements, place two sets with three elements in each set side by side and, counting the elements, observe that the union of the sets has the cardinality six. We can illustrate this process by setting up a rectangular array of elements in two rows with three elements in each row, thus yielding a set of cardinality six.

$$\begin{array}{ll} \text{Row 1:} & * \quad * \quad * \\ \text{Row 2:} & * \quad * \quad * \end{array}$$

It is obvious that we could always use the physical process of setting up rectangular arrays to find the product of counting numbers. However people learned long ago to find the product of two counting numbers by the process we now call *multiplication*.

Our presentation of the set of counting numbers has emphasized its relationship with sets of physical objects. But the set of counting numbers also has several important *properties* that govern its operations, each time we find the sum or product of two of these numbers. In the next section, we shall state these observed properties and then develop from them an abstract mathematical system called the system of natural numbers.

3.3 THE SYSTEM OF NATURAL NUMBERS

In Chapter 2, we studied the mathematical system of sets. We are now ready to study a second system—the *mathematical system of natural numbers*. These are the essential elements of a number system.

1. A set of elements
2. Two operations
3. Undefined terms
4. Defined terms
5. Postulates
6. Theorems

The Elements of the Natural Number System

The set of elements of the natural number system is the set of counting numbers. When the counting numbers become the elements of the system of natural numbers, it is customary to call them *natural numbers*. In this sense, the two sets are identical, since every element of each set is an element of the other set. But, although the two sets are mathematically identical, there is a profound difference in our concept of them. We treat natural numbers as abstract ideas, whereas our concept of the counting numbers is based on experience with real objects. It may be helpful to recall that our emphasis in the discussion of counting numbers was on the set itself. In this section, our emphasis will be on the *system* rather than on the set of natural numbers.

Two Operations on Natural Numbers

The procedure for finding the sum of two counting numbers is based on observation and counting. When this procedure is systematically repeated, the results can be recorded in a table called an *addition table*. Thereafter, whenever we wish to find the sum of two numbers, we do not have to combine sets of objects—we merely refer to the table (or our memory), regardless of what the symbols in the table initially represented. When the sum is found, we say that the mathematical operation of addition has been performed.

Let us examine a partial addition table (see Table 3.2). Of course, it is *impossible* to prepare a complete table, since the set of natural numbers is infinite.

Table 3.2 Addition Table

+	1	2	3	4	5	6	7	8	9
1	2	3	4	5	6	7	8	9	10
2	3	4	5	6	7	8	9	10	11
3	4	5	6	7	8	9	10	11	12
4	5	6	7	8	9	10	11	12	13
5	6	7	8	9	10	11	12	13	14
6	7	8	9	10	11	12	13	14	15
7	8	9	10	11	12	13	14	15	16
8	9	10	11	12	13	14	15	16	17
9	10	11	12	13	14	15	16	17	18

We shall now use our addition table to perform an addition operation. We begin by selecting an element from the left column and then pair the selected element with an element from the top row of the table. For example, let us select the number 3 from the left column and the number 5 from the top row. We record our addition selections as

$$3 + 5$$

Now find the intersection of the row in which 3 appears and the column in which 5 appears. The element at this intersection is the number 8, the sum of 3 and 5. So we record this result as

$$3 + 5 = 8$$

This operation is called a *binary operation* because two elements are involved and the result is unique.

We turn now to the product of natural numbers. Using our experience in finding the product of counting numbers, we prepare a *multiplication table* (see Table 3.3).

Table 3.3 Multiplication Table

x	1	2	3	4	5	6	7	8	9
1	1	2	3	4	5	6	7	8	9
2	2	4	6	8	10	12	14	16	18
3	3	6	9	12	15	18	21	24	27
4	4	8	12	16	20	24	28	32	36
5	5	10	15	20	25	30	35	40	45
6	6	12	18	24	30	36	42	48	54
7	7	14	21	28	35	42	49	56	63
8	8	16	24	32	40	48	56	64	72
9	9	18	27	36	45	54	63	72	81

We shall now use our table to perform a multiplication operation. Again, we select an element from the first column and then pair the selected element with elements from the top row. Let us select 2 from the first column and 3 from the top row. We record our multiplication selection as

$$2 \times 3$$

Now find the intersection of the column in which 3 appears and the row in which 2 appears. The element at this intersection is, of course, 6. So we record our result as

$$2 \times 3 = 6$$

3.4 POSTULATES FOR EQUALITY

Throughout this text, we have employed the concept of *equality*. So far, an intuitive grasp of the meaning of this term has been adequate. Now, however, a "common" understanding of this concept is needed to proceed with a logical development of the natural number system. The properties of equality are contained in five postulates.

Postulates for Equality

1. Any natural number, a is equal to itself; that is, $a = a$. This is called the *reflexive property of equality*.
2. If a and b are two natural numbers and $a = b$, then $b = a$. This is called the *symmetric property of equality*.

3. If a, b, c are natural numbers and if $a = b$ and $b = c$, then $a = c$. This is called the *transitive property of equality*.
4. If a, b, c are natural numbers and $a = b$, then $a + c = b + c$. This is called the *additive property of equality*.
5. If a, b, c are natural numbers and $a = b$, then $ac = bc$. This is called the *multiplicative property of equality*.

3.5 POSTULATES FOR OPERATIONS ON NATURAL NUMBERS

Using our experience with counting numbers, we have constructed partial tables for both addition and multiplication. By carefully studying these tables and by applying *inductive reasoning*, we can determine the probable behavior of the entire set of natural numbers under the operations of addition and multiplication. By finding the sum and product of counting numbers (outlined in Section 3.3), we soon conclude that natural numbers and counting numbers behave the same way. Most of all however, our experience with the physical sets lends credence to the set of postulates that we shall adopt for the set of natural numbers.

Postulates for Closure

Closure for Addition. For every pair of natural numbers, a and b, there exists a unique natural number, c, that is called the *sum* of a and b; that is, $a + b = c$.

Closure for Multiplication. For every pair of natural numbers, a and b, there exists a unique natural number, d, that is called the *product* of a and b; that is, $a \times b = d$.

Perhaps the concept of closure can be understood best by exhibiting a set that is closed for one operation only. Consider the following operation tables for the set (0, 1).

+	0	1
0	0	1
1	1	2

×	0	1
0	0	0
1	0	1

It should be apparent that addition on the set (0, 1) is not closed, since a result appears in the table that is not in the given set. On the other hand, the set is closed for multiplication, since all entries in the table are elements of the given set.

Postulates for Addition

Commutative Addition: If a and b are natural numbers, then $a + b = b + a$

This postulate tells us that the order of addition is not important. We examine this postulate more closely by returning to Table 3.2 on p. 42. Consider the sum $3 + 5$, where we selected 3 in the left column and 5 in the first row and found the result 8 in the table. We now reverse our selections. We select 5 from the first column and 3 from the first row. Again we find the sum to be 8. We conclude that

$$3 + 5 = 5 + 3 = 8.$$

Associative Addition: If a, b and c are natural numbers, then

$$(a + b) + c = a + (b + c).$$

This postulate tells us that in adding three natural numbers we may add the sum of the first two numbers to the last or the sum of the last two to the first. For example,

$$(2 + 3) + 4 = 2 + (3 + 4)$$
$$5 + 4 = 2 + 7$$

It is this postulate, together with the commutative property and the following definition that permits us to add a column of figures in any order. $a + b + c = (a + b) + c$.

Postulates for Multiplication

Commutative Multiplication: If a and b are natural numbers, then

$$a \times b = b \times a.$$

This postulate permits us to reverse the order of multiplication.

Associative Multiplication: If a, b, and c are natural numbers, then

$$a \times (b \times c) = (a \times b) \times c$$

This postulate provides a method for multiplying three numbers. We define the product of three natural numbers as

$$a \times b \times c = (a \times b) \times c$$

Postulates for Multiplication over Addition

Distributive Multiplication: If a, b, and c are natural numbers, then
$$a \times (b + c) = (a \times b) + (a \times c)$$

This postulate provides the basis for multiplication of numbers with more than one digit. The following example illustrates its applicability.

Example:
$$\begin{aligned} 5 \times 17 &= 5 \times (9 + 8) \\ &= (5 \times 9) + (5 \times 8) \\ &= 45 + 40 = 85 \end{aligned}$$

EXERCISE 3.1

1. State the postulate upon which each of the following equations are based.
   a) $3 + 5 = 5 + 3$
   b) $(2 + 3) + 4 = 2 + (3 + 4)$
   c) $(2 + 3) + 4 = 4 + (2 + 3)$
   d) $4 + 12 = 12 + 4$
   e) $a + b + c = b + a + c$

2. Which of the following sets are closed under the addition operation?
   a) $\{2, 4, 6, \ldots, 2n, \ldots\}$ $n \in$ natural numbers
   b) $\{3, 5, 7, \ldots, 2n + 1, \ldots\}$ $n \in$ natural numbers
   c) $\{1, 2, 3, 4\}$
   d) $\{0, 1\}$

3. When adding a column of figures, the operation can be performed by starting either at the top or at the bottom of the column. Show how this statement is based on two of the postulates.

4. Under the operation *followed by*, which of the following are commutative?
   a) Putting on socks, followed by putting on shoes.
   b) Depressing the clutch, followed by shifting gears.
   c) Reading the newspaper, followed by eating breakfast.
   d) Falling asleep, followed by snoring.
   e) Studying the lesson, followed by reciting.

5. Consider the word "nature" and assume that every possible arrangement of all or part of the letters in this word forms another word. Does the operation of forming words with the set $\{n, a, t, u, r, e\}$ follow:
   a) closure?
   b) associativity?
   c) commutativity?

6. How many different ways can the elements of $A = \{a, b, c\}$ be paired with the elements of $B = \{1, 2, 3\}$?

7. Distinguish between cardinal numbers and ordinal numbers.

8. Distinguish between cardinal numbers, counting numbers, and natural numbers.

9. Classify each of the following statements as true (T) or false (F).
   a) Every cardinal number is a counting number.
   b) Every cardinal number is a natural number.
   c) The natural number system is the same as the set of natural numbers.
   d) Only one operation is required for any number system.

Theorems for Natural Numbers

In higher mathematics, no additional postulates are necessary to characterize the operations of addition and multiplication on the set of natural numbers. The postulates we discussed serve as a firm basis for developing a *set of theorems* used to solve problems involving natural numbers. From observing the behavior of counting numbers, we can accept the postulates. Using the deductive reasoning we studied in Chapter 1, or a combination of deductive and inductive reasoning, we must prove the theorems. Our purpose in this section is to show how a few of the basic theorems for natural numbers may be proved.

Theorem 3.1 If a, b and c are natural numbers, then

$$a + (b + c) = b + (a + c)$$

Proof:

Statements	Reasons
$a + (b + c) = (a + b) + c$	Associativity for addition
$(a + b) + c = (b + a) + c$	Commutativity for addition
$(b + a) + c = b + (a + c)$	Associativity for addition
$a + (b + c) = b + (a + c)$	Transitivity for equality

Application of the theorem:
$$2 + (3 + 4) = 3 + (2 + 4)$$
$$2 + 7 = 3 + 6$$
$$9 = 9$$

We begin with $a + (b + c)$, the left-hand side of the equation, and continue to change this side by applying postulates, until we reach a form that is identical to the right-hand side of the equation. Conversely, we could have started with the right side of the equation and continued until we reached a form identical to the left side. Why? In proving a theorem, we must be careful *not* to assume at the start that the two sides are equal. Since we want to prove that at the outcome. The last statement in the proof is based on the *transitive property of equality*; that is, if $a = b$ and $b = c$, then $a = c$. This is the fundamental principle employed in a direct proof—no matter how many steps appear in the proof. Look at the different steps in Theorems 3.2 and 3.3:

Theorem 3.2 If a, b, and c are natural numbers, then
$$(b + c)a = ba + ca$$

Proof:

Statements	Reasons
$(b + c)a = a(b + c)$	Commutativity for multiplication
$a(b + c) = ab + ac$	Distributivity
$ab + ac = ba + ca$	Commutativity for multiplication
$(b + c)a = ba + ca$	Transitivity for equality

Application of the theorem:
$$(2 + 3)4 = 2 \times 4 + 3 \times 4$$
$$5 \times 4 = 8 + 12$$
$$20 = 20$$

Theorem 3.3 If a, b, and c are natural numbers, then
$$(ab)c = c(ba)$$

Proof:

Statements	Reasons
$(ab)c = (ba)c$	Commutativity for multiplication
$(ba)c = c(ba)$	Commutativity for multiplication
$(ab)c = c(ba)$	Transitivity for equality

Application of the theorem:
$$(3 \times 4)5 = 5(3 \times 4)$$
$$12 \times 5 = 5 \times 12$$
$$60 = 60$$

EXERCISE 3.2

1. What is a mathematical proof?
2. Distinguish between a postulate and a theorem.

Two proofs are given in Problems 3 and 4. State the reason for each step in the proof.

3. **Theorem.** If a, b, and c are natural numbers, then $ab + c = c + ba$.

3.6 The System of Integers

Proof:

Statements	Reasons
$ab + c = c + ab$	
$c + ab = c + ba$	
$ab + c = c + ba$	

4. **Theorem.** If a, b, c are natural numbers, then $b + (a + c) = c + (a + b)$.

   Proof:

Statements	Reasons
$b + (a + c) = (a + c) + b$	
$(a + c) + b = (c + a) + b$	
$(c + a) + b = c + (a + b)$	
$b + (a + c) = c + (a + b)$	

5. Prove or disprove the statement: $a + (b + c) = (a + b) + (a + c)$.
6. Write the statement in Problem 5 in words.

3.6 THE SYSTEM OF INTEGERS

We are now ready to develop our third mathematical system—*the system of integers*. The procedure will parallel the format used in developing the system of natural numbers.

The Set of Integers

In our development of the system of natural numbers, the set of counting numbers became the elements of the natural number system. Unfortunately, no such simple set is available for the system of integers. So we must introduce a new set. One reason that we require more elements in this set is to provide solutions for statements such as $x + a = 0$, where a is a natural number and 0 the cardinality of the empty set. The number "x" when added to the number "a" yields the sum of 0. At this point, you might recall our special ruler in Section 3.1, a part of which is reconstructed in Figure 3.3.

Figure 3.3

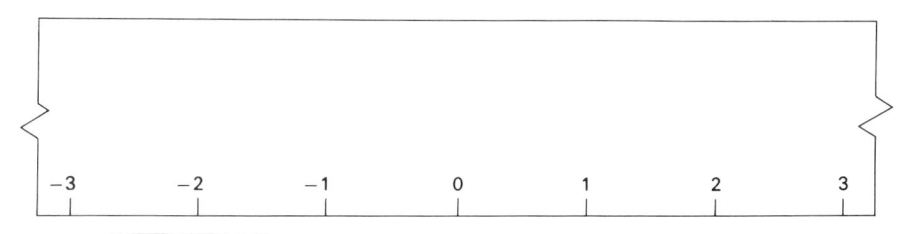

$$-3 \quad -2 \quad -1 \quad 0 \quad 1 \quad 2 \quad 3$$

Notice that the symbols $-1, -2, -3$, lie on one side of 0, and symbols 1, 2, 3, lie on the opposite side. We say that -1 (read "negative 1") and 1 are opposites, -2 and 2 are opposites, -3 and 3 are opposites. That is, each number on one side of zero has an *opposite* on the other side.

We call the elements of this new set $\{\ldots, -3, -2, -1, 0, 1, 2, 3, \ldots\}$ *integers*. This set consists of three disjoint subsets: positive integers, zero, and negative integers.

This seemingly simple change has added an important new concept to the idea of number—*the concept of direction*. To illustrate, suppose a person walks 4 blocks east, turns, and walks 4 blocks west. The net change in his position is 0 blocks. Using both symbols and words, we would write: 4 east + 4 west = 0. Using only mathematical symbols, we would write: $4 + (-4) = 0$. Similarly, if the individual had walked first west and then east, the mathematical symbols would be $(-4) + 4 = 0$.

Special Properties of Integers Zero and One

If we add 0 to any integer, a, the sum is the integer a; that is, $a + 0 = a$. This statement is true even when a itself is 0; that is, $0 + 0 = 0$. Because of this property, zero is called *the identity element for addition*.

When we multiply any integer, a, by 1, the product is the integer a; that is, $1 \times a = a$. Because of this property, 1 is called *the identity element for multiplication*.

Operations for Integers

The *binary operations of addition and multiplication* still hold for the set of integers. A rigorous development of the properties of integers customarily defines these operations in a special way and then proceeds to prove that the postulates we assumed for natural numbers hold for integers. However we are principally concerned with the *sign of the result*, when we add or multiply positive and negative integers. So, when the integers are both positive, they obey the same rules as the natural numbers, but when the signs are opposite or both are negative, a new set of definitions for addition and multiplication is required. Before stating these definitions, we need the following definition of subtraction of natural numbers.

Definition 3.1 If a, b are natural numbers and a is larger than b, then the *difference* between a and b (designated $a - b$) is a natural number c such that $b + c = a$.

Example. 5 is larger than 3

$$3 + 2 = 5$$
$$\therefore 5 - 3 = 2.$$

We can now state the definitions for addition and multiplication of integers, when the signs are opposite or both are negative. In each definition, a, b, c are natural numbers, while $(\pm a)$, $(\pm b)$, and $(\pm c)$ are integers.

Addition of Integers:

Definition 3.2 If a is larger than b, then $(+a) + (-b) = +(a - b)$.

Example. If 3 is larger than 2, then $(3) + (-2) = +(3 - 2) = 1$.

Definition 3.3 If a is smaller than b, then $(+a) + (-b) = -(b - a)$.

Example. If 4 is smaller than 5, then $(4) + (-5) = -(5 - 4) = -1$.

Definition 3.4 For all $a, b, (-a) + (-b) = -(a + b)$.

Example. $(-2) + (-3) = -(2 + 3) = -5$.

Multiplication of Integers:

Definition 3.5 $(+a)(-b) = -(a \cdot b)$.

Example. $(+2)(-3) = -(2 \cdot 3) = -6$.

Definition 3.6 $(-a)(-b) = +(a \cdot b)$.

Example. $(-2)(-3) = +(2 \cdot 3) = 6$.

Postulates for Integers

All the postulates for the natural numbers apply to the set of integers. In addition, we now can add the following postulates.

Identity for Addition. There exists an integer (designated 0) with the property $a + 0 = 0 + a = a$, where a is any integer.

Identity for Multiplication. There exists an integer (designated 1) with the property that for any natural number, $a, a \times 1 = 1 \times a = a$.

Inverse for Addition. There exists a unique integer for the integer a (designated $-a$) such that $a + (-a) = (-a) + a = 0$.

EXERCISE 3.3

1. Perform the indicated operations. In each case, state the postulate, definition, and/or theorem on which the operation is based.
   a) $(-5) - (+8)$
   b) $(-9) - (-9)$
   c) $(-2) + (+1) - (-3)$
   d) $(-4) - (-1) - (-3)$
   e) $(+10) - (-2) - 5 + (-3)$
   f) $(-a) + (-5b) + (-6a) - (-b)$
   g) $2x - 3x + 4y - 2y$

2. Perform the indicated operation. In each case, state the postulate, definition, and/or theorem on which the operation is based.
   a) $(-2)(-3)$
   b) $(+1)(-5)$
   c) $(-2)(+1)(-3)$
   d) $(-1)(-3)(-5)(-2)$
   e) $(-2)(-3)(-5)$

3. Which of the following are binary operations?
   a) Addition of even numbers $\{2, 4, 6, \ldots\}$.

b) Addition of odd numbers $\{1, 3, 5, \quad \}$
c) Multiplication of even numbers.
d) Multiplication of odd numbers.

4. Construct a figure like Figure 3.3, starting at -5 and counting to $+5$. Trace a path with your pencil beginning at 0 and proceeding in the following manner:
   a) From 0 go to -4,
   b) then to -2,
   c) then to 5,
   d) then to 3, and
   e) finally to -3.

   How far has your pencil traveled, assuming that each unit represents one inch? In arriving at your answer, on what set did you perform addition? You stopped at (-3). Using the set of integers, write (in symbols) the operations that you performed with your pencil.

5. What is the additive inverse of each of the following:
   a) -2 b) a c) $6x$
   d) $(2 + x)$ e) $(-3 - 2)$ f) $(2x - 2)$

6. You walk six miles east, six miles west, six miles north and three miles south. Write this statement using mathematical symbols.

7. If we had so wished, the definitions for integer operations could have been proved as theorems. Now see if you can prove the following. In each case, a, b, c are natural numbers while $+a, -a, +b, -b$ are integers.
   a) $(-a)(-b) = ab$ [*Hint:* Try $(-a)(b + (-b)) = 0$.
   b) $(-a)(+b) = -ab$ [*Hint:* Try $a(b + (-b)) = 0$.]
   c) $a < b$ then $a - b = -(b - a)$ [*Hint:* Use Definition 3.1.]

3.7 CLASSIFICATIONS OF NATURAL NUMBERS

Man's first attempts at classifying natural numbers were based on his desire to determine what—if any—were the "mystical powers" of each number. Even today, some people believe in this pseudoscience, called *numerology* (e.g., 7 is lucky, while 13 is unlucky). So, our modern classification of numbers as *even* or *odd* stems from the age-old superstitious beliefs that surrounded numbers.

The investigations of ancient mathematicians led to the discovery of the so-called *perfect number*—a number that possesses a sum, derived from its proper divisors, that equals the number itself. For example, the smallest perfect number is 6; the proper divisors of 6 are 3, 2, and 1, so their sum is $1 + 2 + 3 = 6$. Two other perfect numbers are 8128 and 496. There is also a perfect number (other than 6) that is less than 30—can you find it? No one has yet determined a general formula for finding perfect numbers, although the final proposition in Euclid's *Elements* deals with finding certain types. We do not know how many perfect numbers exist. Nor do we know if all of them are even—in spite of the fact that no odd ones have yet been found. By definition, however, *no number* can be a *proper divisor of itself*, just as no set can be a proper subset of itself.

Numbers were also classified by early mathematicians as *excessive* (those smaller than the sum of their proper divisors) and *defective* (those larger than the sum of their proper divisors). For example, 18 is an excessive number, since $1 + 2 + 3 + 6 + 9 = 21$, and 10 is a defective number, since $1 + 2 + 5 = 8$.

The concept of *amicable* or *friendly numbers* is another curious notion that ancient mathematicians had about numbers. A pair of numbers was considered "amicable," if each were equal to the sum of the proper divisors of the other. The Greeks knew of the pair 220 & 284, and they considered them symbols of harmony, friendship, and love. In 1636, the pairs 17 & 296 and 18 & 416 were discovered. In 1886, another pair, 1184 & 1210 was discovered (perhaps by accident) by a 16-year-old Italian boy, Nicolo Paganini. Recently numerous pairs* have been discovered with the aid of computers.

The early mathematicians also discovered that some numbers had only *two* divisors: 1 and the number itself. These were called *prime numbers*. Other numbers with three or more divisors were called *composite numbers*. One was placed in a special class by itself. Every natural number is either prime itself or can be expressed as the product of prime numbers.

3.8 TESTS OF DIVISIBILITY

The determination of the *prime factors of a number* is extremely important in some operations. But the process of determining primes can be laboriously time-consuming. To facilitate the procedure, we have provided several *tests of divisibility*.

Test of Divisibility by 2. A number is divisible by 2 when the units digit is divisible by 2.

Example 1. 324 is divisible by 2, since 4 is divisible by 2.

Example 2. 421 is not divisible by 2, since 1 is not divisible by 2.

Test of Divisibility by 3. A number is divisible by 3 when the sum of the digits is divisible by 3.

Example 1. 243 is divisible by 3, since the sum of its digits is 9—which is divisible by 3.

Example 2. 139 is not divisible by 3, since the sum of the digits is 13—which is not divisible by 3.

Test of Divisibility by 4. A number is divisible by 4 when the number formed by the last two digits on the right is divisible by 4.

Example 1. 568 is divisible by 4, since 68 is divisible by 4.

Example 2. 193 is not divisible by 4, since 93 is not divisible by 4.

---

* A complete listing, along with the discoverers, has been published.

Test of Divisibility by 5. A number is divisible by 5 only when the last digit on the right is divisible by 5.

Example 1. 545 is divisible by 5, since 5 is divisible by 5.

Example 2. 367 is not divisible by 5, since 7 is not divisible by 5.

Tests of divisibility can be devised for any number. However, in most cases, "the cure is worse than the disease." A test of divisibility by 7 is a good example, since the actual division is much simpler than any divisibility test yet devised.

3.9 GREATEST COMMON DIVISOR (GCD) AND LOWEST COMMON MULTIPLE (LCM)

In discussing the *greatest common divisor* (GCD), let a and b be two integers. If a number, c, divides both a and b, then c is a common divisor of a and b. And among the common divisors, there must exist the *largest* one, which we call the GCD. For example, if a and b are relatively prime, then the GCD is 1. But, when a and b are not relatively prime, there exists some positive integer that will be a factor of both. To find this factor, we must return to the set concept, studied in Chapter 2.

In forming new sets from old sets under the operation $A \cap B = C$, we listed in C the elements that were common to both A and B. So, to find the GCD of two numbers, *we write the prime factorization of each as elements in a set* and *form the intersection of the two sets*. The elements in the intersection will be the prime factors of the GCD. When the intersection is empty, the numbers are relatively prime.

Example. Find the GCD of 8 and 12. Since, $8 = 2_1 \cdot 2_2 \cdot 2_2$, the prime factorization forms the set $(2_1, 2_2, 2_3)$. And, since $12 = 2_1 \cdot 2_2 \cdot 3_1$, the prime factorization forms the set $(2_1, 2_2, 3_1)$.

$$\{2_1, 2_2, 2_3\} \cap \{2_1, 2_2, 3_1\} = \{2_1, 2_2\}$$

Hence $2 \cdot 2 = 4$, so the GCD of 8 and 12 is 4.

This concept is extended to give the GCD of three or more numbers.

Example. Find the GCD of 18, 24, and 42. Since $18 = 2_1 \cdot 3_1 \cdot 3_2$, the prime factorization forms the set $2_1, 3_1, 3_2$. Since $24 = 2_1 \cdot 2_2 \cdot 2_3 \cdot 3_1$, the prime factorization forms the set $2_1, 2_2, 2_3, 3_1$. And, since $42 = 2_1 \cdot 3_1 \cdot 7_1$, the prime factorization forms the set $2_1, 3_1, 7_1$.

$$\{2_1, 3_1, 3_2\} \cap \{2_1, 2_2, 2_3, 3_1\} \cap \{2_1, 3_1, 7_1\} = \{2_1, 3_1\}$$

Hence $2 \cdot 3 = 6$, so the GCD of 18, 24, and 42 is 6.

We may approach the *lowest common multiple*, LCM, in much the same manner, A number, m, is a common multiple of two integers, a and b, when both a and b are divisors of m. The product ab will always be a common multiple of a and b. Among the common multiples, there must exist one, called the LCM, that is the "least."

The *union operation* used on sets provides a simple means of obtaining the

LCM. As an illustration, we will arbitrarily select the numbers 6 and 8 and then find the LCM by the union of the sets of prime factors.

Example. Find the LCM of 6 and 8. Since $6 = 2_1 \cdot 3_1$, $\{2_1, 3_1\}$ is the set of factors of 6. And, since $8 = 2_1 \cdot 2_2 \cdot 2_3$, $\{2_1, 2_2, 2_3\}$ is the set of factors of 8.

$$\{2_1, 3_1\} \cup \{2_1, 2_2, 2_3\} = \{2_1, 2_2, 2_3, 3_1\}$$

Hence $2 \cdot 2 \cdot 2 \cdot 3 = 24$, so the LCM of 6 and 8 is 24.

As with finding the GCD, the procedure for finding the LCM can be extended to three or more numbers.

Example. Find the LCM of 6, 10, and 20. Since $6 = 2_1 \cdot 3_1$, $10 = 2_1 \cdot 5_1$, and $20 = 2_1 \cdot 2_2 \cdot 5_1$

$$\{2_1, 3_1\} \cup \{2_1, 5_1\} \cup \{2_1, 2_2, 5_1\} = \{2_1, 2_2, 3_1, 5_1\}$$

Hence $2 \cdot 2 \cdot 3 \cdot 5 = 60$, so the LCM of 6, 10, and 20 is 60.

The separation of numbers into prime factors to find the GCD can be a slow process. To reduce the work, a procedure credited to Euclid may be used. The procedure outlined here will find the GCD of two numbers, a and b.

1. Divide the smaller number into the larger number. If the numbers divide evenly, the smaller is the GCD.
2. If the numbers do not divide evenly, a remainder exists. Divide this remainder into the smaller number. If the smaller number is evenly divisible by the remainder, the remainder is the GCD.
3. If Step 2 does not yield the GCD, divide the remainder from Step 1 by the remainder in Step 2. If the numbers divide evenly, the last remainder is the GCD.
4. If Step 3 does not yield the GCD, continue the process until the GCD is found.

Example 1. Find the GCD of 90 and 60.

$$90 | 60 = 1, \text{ remainder } 30$$
$$60 | 30 = 2$$
$$\therefore \quad 30 \text{ is the GCD}$$

Example 2. Find the GCD of 121 and 44.

$$121 | 44 = 2, \text{ remainder } 33$$
$$44 | 33 = 1, \text{ remainder } 11$$
$$33 | 11 = 3$$
$$\therefore \quad 11 \text{ is the GCD.}$$

Example 3. Find the GCD of 191 and 33.

$$191 | 33 = 5, \text{ remainder } 26$$
$$33 | 26 = 1, \text{ remainder } 7$$

$$26 | 7 = 3, \text{ remainder } 5$$
$$7 | 5 = 1, \text{ remainder } 2$$
$$5 | 2 = 2, \text{ remainder } 1$$
$$2 | 1 = 2$$
$$\therefore \quad 1 \text{ is the GCD}$$

EXERCISE 3.4

1. Express the given numbers as the product of primes.
   a) 75   b) 25   c) 105
   d) 117   e) 221   f) 1209
   g) 1728 h) 51,862   i) 259,308
2. Find the GCD for the following:
   a) 14 and 35   b) 39 and 52
   c) 69 and 97   d) 243 and 324
   e) 384 and 256   f) 34, 51, and 85
   g) 28, 63, and 84 h) 18, 42, 54, and 78
3. Find the LCM for the following:
   a) 6 and 15   b) 12 and 33
   c) 28 and 56   d) 14, 21, and 35
   e) 38, 57, and 95 f) 16, 32, 96, and 128
4. If 1 is the GCD of two numbers, what can you say about the LCM?
5. Laurie Masters has four guests for dinner and only one pie for dessert. For the first serving, she cuts one-fourth of the pie. Realizing there must be five servings, she decides to make each subsequent serving four-fifths as large as the previous one. If Laurie served herself last, what portion of the pie did she get? How much of the pie was left for her husband?
6. What is the largest prime you would need to divide by in order to determine whether a natural number is prime?

3.10 THE SYSTEM OF RATIONAL NUMBERS

The ancient words *mile* (1000 paces of a Roman regiment), *foot*, and *inch* (width of a man's thumb) provide evidence that man has *measured* objects almost as long as he has counted them. Prior to 2000 B.C., both the Egyptians and the Babylonians had already developed a *concept of fractions*. This, in turn, has provided the foundation for developing the *system of rational numbers*.

Definition 3.7 A *rational number* is a number that can be expressed in the form a/b, where a and b are integers and b is not equal to 0.

The set of rational numbers includes the set of integers as a subset. Sometimes, a rational number may be a fraction with a value less than one. However a rational number may be greater than one; it may be negative; or it may be an integer. Some Examples of rational numbers are

$$-4, \quad 5, \quad 1/5, \quad 21/9, \quad 25, \quad 90\%$$

The numbers -4 and 5 may be written in the form $-4/1$ and $5/1$ or even in the form $8/-2$ and $-10/-2$. Many fractions symbolize the *same* rational number.

Operations of the Rational Number System

Before defining the operations on rational numbers, we must first define the *equality of rational numbers*.

Definition 3.8 $a/b = c/d$ if and only if $ad = bc$.

Example 1. $2/3 = 4/6$ if and only if $2 \cdot 6 = 4 \cdot 3$.

Example 2. $2/y = 3/x$ if and only if $2 \cdot x = 3 \cdot y$.

To perform operations on the set of rational numbers, we begin by defining *addition and multiplication*.

Definition 3.9 (Addition). $a/b + c/d = (ad + bc)/bd$.

Example. $\dfrac{2}{3} + \dfrac{3}{4} = \dfrac{2 \cdot 4 + 3 \cdot 3}{3 \cdot 4} = \dfrac{17}{12}$

Definition 3.10 (Multiplication). $a/b \times c/d = ac/bd$.

Example. $\dfrac{2}{3} \times \dfrac{3}{4} = \dfrac{2 \cdot 3}{3 \cdot 4} = \dfrac{6}{12}.$

We may then define *subtraction and division* of rational numbers.

Definition 3.11 (Subtraction). $a/b - c/d = (ad - bc)/bd$.

Example. $\dfrac{3}{4} - \dfrac{2}{3} = \dfrac{3 \cdot 3 - 4 \cdot 2}{4 \cdot 4} = \dfrac{1}{12}.$

Definition 3.12 (Division). $a/b \div c/d = ad/bc$.

Example. $\dfrac{2}{5} \div \dfrac{3}{7} = \dfrac{2 \cdot 7}{5 \cdot 3} = \dfrac{14}{15}.$

Division With Zero

Before discussing division with zero, we should provide the following definition.

Definition 3.13 For any integer a, $a \times 0 = 0$.

In our definition of rational numbers, one restriction made on a/b was that $b \neq 0$. Now let us examine the following cases involving zero.

1. $\dfrac{0}{a}$ 2. $\dfrac{a}{0}$ 3. $\dfrac{0}{0}$

where $a \neq 0$. In Case 1, the result must be a number such that a times the number is zero. We have defined the product $a \times 0$ to be 0; hence $0/a = 0$. In Case 2, there is an implication that 0 times some number is a, when $a \neq 0$. This is obviously false; so we conclude that there is no rational number $a/0$. Mathematically, we say that $a/0$ is *undefined*. In Case 3, there is an implication that zero times some number is zero. This is obviously true for all numbers; hence $0/0$ can be any rational number. Mathematically, we say that $0/0$ is *indeterminate*.

Postulates for the Rational Number System

We can prove that the properties postulated for natural numbers and for integers also hold for rational numbers. Let us first prove the closure property for addition. If the rational numbers satisfy this property, then addition of two rational numbers must produce a unique rational number.

Proof

Statements	Reasons
$\dfrac{a}{b} + \dfrac{c}{d} = \dfrac{ad + bc}{bd}$	Definition of addition of rational numbers
where a, b, c, d are integers and $b \neq 0, d \neq 0$.	
$ad = e$	Closure of integers for multiplication
$bc = f$	Closure of integers for multiplication
$bd = g$	Closure of integers for multiplication
$\dfrac{ad + bc}{bd} = \dfrac{e + f}{g}$	Postulates for equality
$e + f = h$	Closure for addition of integers
$\dfrac{e + f}{g} = \dfrac{h}{g}$	Postulates for equality

$$\frac{a}{b} + \frac{c}{d} = \frac{h}{g}$$ Transitive property

Using the same procedure, we can prove that the commutative, associative, and distributive properties also apply to the set of rational numbers.

The postulates originally added for the system of integers were the identity elements for addition and multiplication and the inverse for addition. We verify these postulates for integers as they apply to the rational number system.

Postulates for the system of rational numbers:

Identity for Addition. There exists an element $0/a = 0$, $a \neq 0$, that when added to any element yields the element as the sum.

Identity for Multiplication. There exists an element $a/a = 1$, $a \neq 0$, that when multiplied by any element yields the element as the product.

Inverse for Addition. For every element a/b, $b \neq 0$ in the set of rational numbers, there is a unique element of opposite sign that when added to the given element yields the identity element for addition.

$$\frac{a}{b} + \left(-\frac{a}{b}\right) = 0.$$

In addition to the ten properties that can be proved, we may add another postulate for the system of rational numbers:

Inverse for Multiplication. For every nonzero element of the rational numbers, there exists another nonzero element of this set, called the *multiplicative inverse* of the original element, such that the product of the original element and its inverse is the identity element for multiplication.

$$\frac{a}{b} \times \frac{b}{a} = 1 \qquad a, b \neq 0$$

Theorems for the Rational Number System

Many of the theorems for *arithmetic* and *elementary algebra* are applicable to the system of rational numbers. We shall prove one basic theorem here to help you do the Exercise at the end of this section.

Theorem 3.4 $a/b = ax/bx$, where a, b, x, are integers, and $b \neq 0$, $x \neq 0$.

Proof:

Statements	Reasons
$\dfrac{ax}{bx} = \dfrac{a}{b} \cdot \dfrac{x}{x}$	Definition of multiplication of rational numbers
$\dfrac{a}{b} \cdot \dfrac{x}{x} = \dfrac{a}{b} \cdot \dfrac{x}{1} \cdot \dfrac{1}{x}$	Definition of multiplication of rational numbers
$\dfrac{x}{1} \cdot \dfrac{1}{x} = 1$	Inverse postulate for multiplication
$\dfrac{ax}{bx} = \dfrac{a}{b} \cdot 1$	Property of equality
$\dfrac{ax}{bx} = \dfrac{a}{b}$	Identity for multiplication
$\dfrac{a}{b} = \dfrac{ax}{bx}$	Symmetric property of equality

This theorem is called the *Fundamental Principle of Fractions*. It enables us either to change a fraction to lowest terms or to raise it as desired.

Example 1. Reduce 2/4 to lowest terms.

$$\frac{2}{4} = \frac{2 \cdot 1}{2 \cdot 2}$$

$$\frac{2 \cdot 1}{2 \cdot 2} = \frac{2}{2} \times \frac{1}{2} = 1 \cdot \frac{1}{2} = \frac{1}{2}$$

Example 2. Change 2/3 to a fraction with the denominator 12.

$$\frac{2}{3} \times \frac{4}{4} = \frac{8}{12}$$

Representing Rational Numbers in Decimal Notation

When calculations involve rational numbers, we often find it more convenient to write the numbers in *decimal form*. For example, we could write the rational number 1/4 as .25 (read "twenty-five hundredths")—just as if we were reading the fraction 25/100. So we are able to convert the rational number a/b to decimal form by dividing b into a.

Example. Determine the decimal equivalent of 3/5.

$$\begin{array}{r} .6 \\ 5\overline{)3.6} \\ \underline{30} \end{array}$$

Sometimes, when this division is performed, a continuous decimal with a *repeating block of digits* results. For example,

$$\frac{1}{3} = .333 \ldots$$

$$\frac{1}{37} = .027027027 \ldots$$

or

$$\frac{1}{7} = .142857142857142857 \ldots$$

This repeating block may also be written with a bar over the first repeating block; then the other blocks are omitted. For example,

$$\frac{1}{37} = .\overline{027}$$

$$\frac{1}{7} = .\overline{142857}$$

A repeating decimal may be converted to a rational fraction by using the technique in the following examples.

Example 1. Convert $.027027\ldots$ into the form a/b, where $a, b,$ are integers.

$$\text{Let} \quad N = .027027 \ldots$$
$$\text{Then} \quad 1000\,N = 27.027027 \ldots$$
$$-N = -.027027 \ldots$$
$$\overline{999\,N = 27.}$$
$$N = \frac{27}{999} = \frac{3 \cdot 3 \cdot 3}{3 \cdot 3 \cdot 3 \cdot 37} = \frac{1}{37}$$

Example 2. Convert $.\overline{14}$ into the form a/b, where a/b are integers.

$$\text{Let} \quad N = .\overline{14}$$
$$\text{Then} \quad 100\,N = 14.\overline{14}$$
$$-N = -.\overline{14}$$
$$\overline{99\,N = 14}$$
$$N = \frac{14}{99}$$

The method that we have used multiplies (in multiples of ten) the given number by a sufficiently large number to move the decimal the same number of places as appear in the repeating block. In Example 1 the decimal had to be moved three places, thus necessitating multiplication by 1000. The original number is then subtracted. As a result, the repeating block drops out and the rational fraction may be obtained. So we may now redefine a rational number.

Definition 3.14 A *rational number* is a number of the form a/b, where a and b are integers and $b \neq 0$, or is a number that may be expressed in the form of a repeating decimal.

Example 1. $\dfrac{1}{4} = .250\overline{0}$

Example 2. $\dfrac{3}{2} = 1.50\overline{0}$

Example 3. $5 = 5.\overline{0}$

Example 4. $\dfrac{1}{3} = .\overline{3}$

EXERCISE 3.5

1. Perform the following additions of rational numbers by using the definition of addition.

   a) $\dfrac{2}{-5} + \dfrac{-2}{-3}$ b) $\dfrac{1}{3} + \dfrac{-3}{1}$

   c) $\dfrac{6}{7} + \dfrac{-1}{1}$ d) $\dfrac{2a}{3} + \dfrac{3b}{2}$

2. Perform the following multiplications

   a) $\dfrac{-6}{5} \times \dfrac{7}{2}$ b) $-3 \times \dfrac{6}{-5}$

   c) $\dfrac{1}{ab} \times \dfrac{-ab}{1}$ d) $\left(-\dfrac{1}{7}\right) \times \left(+\dfrac{3}{2}\right) \times \left(-\dfrac{6}{5}\right)$

   e) $.013 \times 1.09$

3. Reduce to their lowest terms.

   a) $\dfrac{63}{84}$ b) $\dfrac{2.0}{.5}$ c) $\dfrac{.75}{.05}$

   d) $\dfrac{.3}{21}$ e) $\dfrac{-1.5}{-.3}$

4. Change to a rational number with an indicated denominator—if possible.

   a) $\dfrac{3}{4} = \dfrac{}{16}$ b) $\dfrac{7}{8} = \dfrac{}{1000}$ c) $\dfrac{1}{37} = \dfrac{}{1000}$

   d) $\dfrac{5}{16} = \dfrac{}{64}$ e) $\dfrac{7}{64} = \dfrac{}{1000}$

5. Find the quotient for the following divisions.

   a) $\dfrac{2}{3} \div \dfrac{7}{-5}$ b) $-\dfrac{7}{4} \div \dfrac{7}{4}$ c) $\dfrac{3}{2} \div 3$

   d) $-\dfrac{1}{2} \div -\dfrac{1}{4}$ e) $1.73 \div .21$

6. Convert the following numbers into decimal form.

   a) $\dfrac{9}{16}$ b) $\dfrac{3}{12}$ c) $\dfrac{16}{24}$ d) $\dfrac{351}{770}$ e) $\dfrac{231}{1000}$

7. Find the indicated inverse for the following.

   a) $-\dfrac{7}{3}$ for addition   b) $\dfrac{2}{5}$ for multiplication

   c) $\dfrac{-2}{-3}$ for multiplication   d) $\dfrac{-7}{-8}$ for addition

   e) $\dfrac{15}{-7}$ for multiplication

8. Determine whether the following equation represents a true statement for some value of a and b.

   $$\dfrac{1}{a} + \dfrac{2}{b} = \dfrac{3}{a+b}$$

9. What is the meaning of each of the following

   a) $\dfrac{0}{4}$ b) $\dfrac{0}{0}$ c) $\dfrac{a}{0}$, $a \neq 0$

   d) $\dfrac{a}{a}$, $a \neq 0$ e) $\dfrac{(1/3)}{0}$

10. Find the decimal equivalents for the following fractions.

    a) $\dfrac{1}{6}$ b) $\dfrac{5}{8}$ c) $\dfrac{1}{9}$ d) $\dfrac{3/4}{7/8}$ e) $\dfrac{17\ 3/5}{3\ 4/9}$

11. Write the following in the form a/b, where a and b are integers.

    a) .4999 ...   b) $.\overline{9}$ c) .31   d) 1.040   e) 14.303

12. Find the decimal equivalents for the following fractions.

    a) $\dfrac{.5}{.2}$ b) $\dfrac{-1.03}{.12}$ c) $\dfrac{1.11}{-2.3}$ d) $\dfrac{-21.3}{-2.5}$

13. Are noninteger rational numbers desirable for recording measurements?
14. It can be shown that the set of rational numbers has the same cardinality as the set of natural numbers. By what method?
15. Is there a largest rational number? What is the rational number closest to zero?
16. Prove that the following pairs of rational numbers are unequal.

    a) $\dfrac{11}{391}$ and $\dfrac{21}{781}$ b) $\dfrac{2a}{17}$ and $\dfrac{5a}{42}$, $a \neq 0$

17. Prove the commutative property for addition of rational numbers.

3.11 THE SYSTEM OF REAL NUMBERS

All the numbers studied so far have been known to us since elementary school days. But, when we combine this familiar set, which we call rational numbers, with the set of irrational numbers, which we shall define here, we get the so-called *set of real numbers.*

The Set of Irrational Numbers

Before defining an irrational number, let us first examine the diagonal of a square whose sides are one foot in length. Try to recall the basic geometry of a square. We would like to know the length of the diagonal. Obviously, it has a definite length, as shown in Figure 3.4.

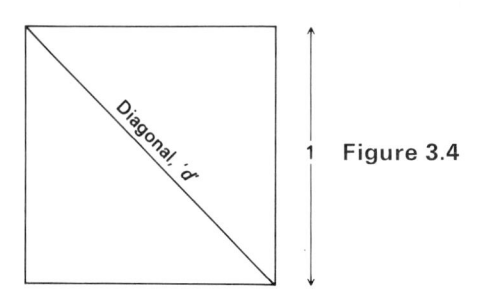

Figure 3.4

To find the length of d, the diagonal, we use the Pythagorean theorem,* which simply states that the square of the hypotenuse of a right triangle is equal to the sum of the squares of the other two sides. For the square shown, this tells us that $d^2 = 1^2 + 1^2 = 2$. We can prove, however, that there is no rational number that when multiplied by itself gives a product of 2. The symbol customarily used to represent d is $\sqrt{2}$. But the number $\sqrt{2}$ cannot be expressed in the form a/b, where a, b are integers. Following this duscussion, we can now define an irrational number.

Definition 3.15 An *irrational number* is a number that can be expressed as an infinite, nonrepeating decimal. Such numbers are not expressible in the form a/b, where a and b are integers and $a \neq 0$.

Examples. $\sqrt{3}$, $\sqrt{5}$, $\sqrt{6}$, $\dfrac{1}{\sqrt{3}}$, $\dfrac{\sqrt{2}}{2}$, $\sqrt{6}$, $\sqrt{10}$, $2 + \sqrt{33}$.

Do not conclude, however, that *any* number written with the symbol $\sqrt{}$ is irrational. For example: $\sqrt{4} = 2$, $\sqrt{25} = 5$, $\sqrt{.16} = .4$. Another method of writing irrational numbers, called *exponential notation*, has been devised and will be discussed in Chapter 6.

An irrational number may be *approximated by a decimal*. For example, we can approximate $\sqrt{2}$ by the decimal 1.4. If greater accuracy is desired, we could represent $\sqrt{2}$ to three decimal places, i.e., 1.414. Even if we expressed it as 1.414213562, this is only an approximation of the number $\sqrt{2}$. In higher mathematics, we can prove that an irrational number cannot be expressed as a repeating decimal.

---

*The Pythagorean theorem is discussed further in Chapter 7.

The Set of Real Numbers

The set of numbers expressible as infinite decimal expansions (repeating and nonrepeating) is called the *set of real numbers*. This set may be classified as shown in Figure 3.5.

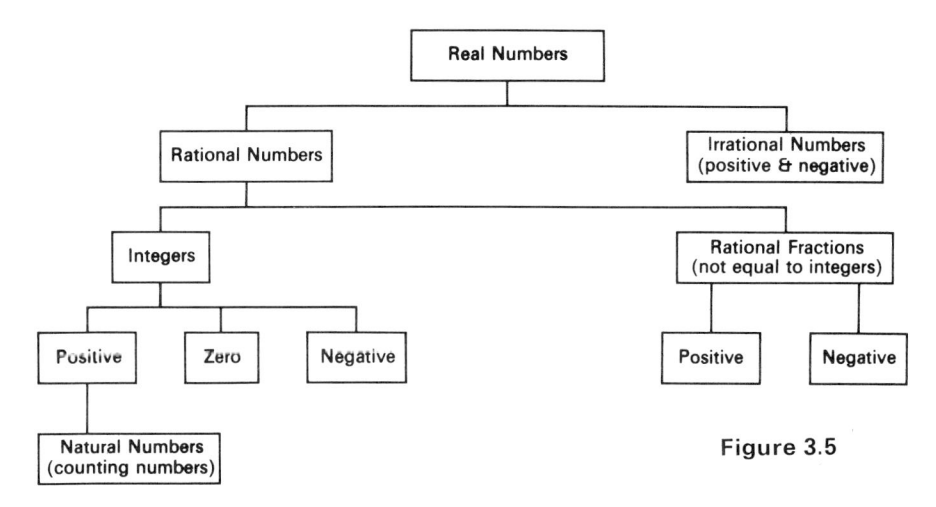

```
                          Real Numbers
                         /            \
              Rational Numbers    Irrational Numbers
              /           \       (positive & negative)
          Integers    Rational Fractions
         /   |   \    (not equal to integers)
   Positive Zero Negative    /        \
      |                  Positive   Negative
 Natural Numbers
(counting numbers)
```

Figure 3.5

Postulates for the Real Numbers

Eleven of the postulates that characterize the rational number system apply to the real numbers. In addition, an important new postulate will be added. You will recall that we began our study of the real number system by stating that this system provided a number for every point on the special "ruler" that we constructed. We now give this ruler a name, *the real number line*. Assuming a one-to-one correspondence between the elements in the set of real numbers and the points on the real number line, gives us the *postulate of continuity* of the real number line. Its algebraic equivalent is called the *completeness property*. Because of this property, the real number system is said to be complete.

3.12 THE AXIOM OF MATHEMATICAL INDUCTION

In Chapter 1, we defined inductive reasoning as "the process of drawing a general conclusion based on a limited number of observations." Inductive reasoning plays a role in the selection of fundamental statements, called postulates, as well as in the selection of theorems to be proved. Beyond these functions, however, inductive reasoning plays no part in the formal proof of mathematical statements. Mathematical reasoning is primarily *deductive reasoning*. This concept is sometimes obscured in applications of the so-called *Axiom of Mathematical Induction*, which we shall now discuss.

Axiom of Mathematical Induction

When we listed the postulates for the natural numbers, two postulates were left unstated: one is the Axiom of Mathematical Induction, and the other is the Axiom of Order, which appears in Chapter 6.

Axiom of Mathematical Induction. If S is a set of natural numbers with the properties that (a) S contains the number 1 and (b) if S contains a number k, then S contains the number $k + 1$, then S is the set of natural numbers.

We shall now show how this axiom is used in reaching a mathematical conclusion. Consider the set of natural numbers. Next speculate how the sum of a finite number of consecutive natural numbers (starting with 1) might be determined without actually adding the numbers. Notice the pattern in the following addition sequence:

$$1 + 2 = 3 = \frac{2(3)}{2}$$

$$1 + 2 + 3 = 6 = \frac{3(4)}{2}$$

$$1 + 2 + 3 + 4 = 10 = \frac{4(5)}{2}$$

$$1 + 2 + 3 + 4 + 5 = 15 = \frac{5(6)}{2}$$

From the last entry in each row, an intelligent guess is that $n(n + 1)/2$ is equal to the sum of the first n consecutive natural numbers.

At this point, the process of inductive reasoning ceases (unless we make another "guess"). We have observed four cases and stated a conjecture. We do not know whether our conclusion holds for the nth natural number. But it is here that the mathematical reasoning—deductive reasoning—enters the picture to prove or disprove our conjecture. Although the entire procedure is called *Proof by Mathematical Induction*, the actual proof is entirely deductive. Four basic steps form our procedure for proving our conjectured theorem for the sum of n natural numbers, $\frac{n}{2}(n + 1)$.

Proof by Mathematical Induction:

1. The proposed theorem is verified by the number 1.

$$\frac{n(n + 1)}{2} = \frac{1(1 + 1)}{2} = \frac{2}{2} = 1$$

In this case, the sum of one natural number is, of course, 1.

2. The proposed theorem is assumed true for the kth natural number.

$$1 + 2 + 3 + \cdots + k = \frac{k(k + 1)}{2}$$

3. The proposed theorem must then be proved true for the $(k + 1)$th natural number; that is, we must prove that $1 + 2 + 3 + \cdots + k + (k + 1) = (k + 1)(k + 2)/2$.

Proof: $1 + 2 + 3 + \cdots + k + (k + 1) = \dfrac{k(k + 1)}{2} + (k + 1)$

$$= \dfrac{k(k + 1) + 2(k + 1)}{2}$$

$$= \dfrac{k^2 + k + 2k + 2}{2}$$

$$= \dfrac{k^2 + 3k + 2}{2}$$

$\therefore \quad 1 + 2 + 3 + \cdots + k + (k + 1) = \dfrac{(k + 1)(k + 2)}{2}$

Hence the formula is true for the $(k + 1)$th term.
Therefore the formula is true for the nth natural number by the Axiom of Mathematical Induction.

Discussion of the proof: The axiom of Mathematical Induction specifies a set of natural numbers, S. In each case, S is the set of natural numbers for which the proposed theorem holds. Obviously, in the proof, 1 is the set S. We assumed that k was in the set S for which the theorem holds. (This is step 2.) Then, we added a $(k + 1)$th natural number to the sum of k natural numbers. By algebraic manipulation, we were able to show that the proposed formula is true for the $(k + 1)$th natural number in the set S, if it is true for the kth natural number in S. The Axiom of Mathematical Induction tells us that the set S for which the proposed theorem holds is the set of natural numbers.

In particular: Since it holds for 1, it holds for $1 + 1 = 2$. Since it holds for 2, it holds for $2 + 1 = 3$. Since it holds for 3, it holds for $3 + 1 = 4$, etc.

EXERCISE 3.6

1. List the set of postulates that apply to the real numbers.
2. Complete the table. The first row has already been filled in. (See next page, too.)

Type of Number

Number	Natural	Integer	Rational	Irrational	Real
2	X	X	X		X
-3					
$-7/3$					
$2 + \sqrt{3}$					

$\sqrt{9}$

$\sqrt{9/4}$

$2\sqrt{3}$

$\sqrt{7/2 + 2}$

3. Demonstrate geometrically the existence of the number $\sqrt{3}$, using the Pythagorean theorem.
4. By exhibiting several cases, we might conjecture that the sum of n odd integers is n^2.

$$1 = 1$$
$$1 + 3 = 4$$
$$1 + 3 + 5 = 9, \text{ and so forth}$$

See if you can prove this conjecture by mathematical induction.
5. Draw a conjecture for the sum of n even integers and prove your conjecture.
6. Locate the following on the real number line.

$$\sqrt{2}, \quad \sqrt{25}, \quad \sqrt{\frac{2}{3}}, \quad -\sqrt{2}, \quad \sqrt{36}$$

7. Carry out the indicated operations.

   a) $(2 + \sqrt{2})(\sqrt{2} + 3)$ b) $\dfrac{3 + \sqrt{2}}{5}$

   c) $2 + \sqrt{2} + \frac{1}{2} - \sqrt{25} + \dfrac{-3}{2}$ d) $.\overline{3} + .\overline{9} + .25\overline{0}$

   e) $.1\overline{66} \times .12\overline{5}$

8. From the following numbers select those that are integers, those that are rational but not integers, those that are irrational, and those that are real.

   a) $\dfrac{-4}{-2}$ b) $.12\overline{5}$

   c) $.999\ldots$ d) 1.101001000100001, etc.

   e) $\dfrac{22}{7}$

Other Mathematical Systems 4

4.1 THE SYSTEM OF GROUPS

The number system that we studied in Chapter 3 is, in many respects, a very complicated mathematical structure. We began with the real number system, however, because you were already familiar with many of its properties and its uses. Now we shall turn our attention to several other systems—some will be simpler than the real number system and some will be more complicated. The first system that we shall study is called a *group*.

Anyone who has learned to tell time with an ordinary timepiece has learned the elementary concepts of a group. For example, consider the numbers 1 through 12 on the clock's face and then study the following examples.

Example 1. It is now 10:00 o'clock. What time will it be in 3 hours?

Solution. $10 + 3 \equiv 1$. It will be 1:00 o'clock.

Example 2. Tom begins work at 7:00 A.M. and works 8 hours. What time will he quit?

Solution. $7 + 8 \equiv 3$. Tom stops work at 3:00 P.M.

Example 3. It is now 12:00 o'clock. What time will it be in 12 hours?

Solution. $12 + 12 \equiv 12$. It will be 12:00 o'clock.

Table 4.1 Operation Table

$\oplus$	1	2	3	4	5	6	7	8	9	10	11	12
1	2	3	4	5	6	7	8	9	10	11	12	1
2	3	4	5	6	7	8	9	10	11	12	1	2
3	4	5	6	7	8	9	10	11	12	1	2	3
4	5	6	7	8	9	10	11	12	1	2	3	4
5	6	7	8	9	10	11	12	1	2	3	4	5
6	7	8	9	10	11	12	1	2	3	4	5	6
7	8	9	10	11	12	1	2	3	4	5	6	7
8	9	10	11	12	1	2	3	4	5	6	7	8
9	10	11	12	1	2	3	4	5	6	7	8	9
10	11	12	1	2	3	4	5	6	7	8	9	10
11	12	1	2	3	4	5	6	7	8	9	10	11
12	1	2	3	4	5	6	7	8	9	10	11	12

We used a new symbol, ≡, in the solutions of these above examples. The meaning of this symbol will be explained in the following section, but as it was used here, it may be thought of as being closely "related" to the concept of equality, defined in Chapter 3.

Obviously, the operation performed in the solutions of Examples 1, 2, and 3 was *not* regular addition, since this operation ensures that when we add hours on the clock, the result will always be a numeral on the face of the clock. So let us symbolize this operation by $\oplus$ and prepare an operation table for a regular 12-hour clock (see Table 4.1).

In examining the table, we see that the operation $\oplus$ is *binary*; i.e., two elements are involved and the result is unique. We also see that the number 12 is the identity element for the operation; e.g., $6 \oplus 12 \equiv 6$, $12 \oplus 12 \equiv 12$, etc. In addition, for each element in the set, there exists an element such that their sum is 12. Thus each element has an additive inverse; e.g., $1 \oplus 11 \equiv 12$, $5 \oplus 7 \equiv 12$, etc. Although it is not apparent in the table, the associative property for the operation also holds. For example,

$$1 \oplus (2 \oplus 3) \stackrel{?}{\equiv} (1 \oplus 2) \oplus 3$$

$$1 \oplus 5 \stackrel{?}{\equiv} 3 \oplus 3$$

$$6 \equiv 6$$

This set of numbers on the face of the clock under the operation $\oplus$ (*clock addition*) is an example of the mathematical system of groups—it should not be confused with the ordinary meaning of a "collection."

Definition 4.1 A *group*, G, is a mathematical system consisting of a set of elements and a single binary operation, o, that satisfy four basic postulates:

If $a, b \in G$, then $a \circ b$ is an element in G.

If $a, b, c \in G$, then $a \circ (b \circ c) = (a \circ b) \circ c$.

There is a unique identity element, symbolized by e, in the set G. If $a \in G$, then $a \circ e = e \circ a = a$.

For each $a \in G$, there is a unique element, symbolized by a', in G such that $a \circ a' = a' \circ a = e \cdot a'$ is the inverse of a

The operation o, characterized by these postulates, is *unrestricted*—the elements may be numbers, letters, geometric changes, sets, or just abstract symbols.

Often, a fifth postulate (the commutative property) holds for an operation on a group. When this is true, the group is called an *Abelian group*, after the Norwegian mathematician Niels Henrik Abel (1802–1829).

A group may be considered to be the "atom" of mathematical systems. Using the group as a building block, many mathematical systems can be constructed simply by changing the operation and the elements. For example, the following is a list of a few familiar group systems.

1. The set of integers under the operation of addition.
2. The set of rational numbers under the operation of addition.
3. The set of rational numbers (excluding zero) under the operation of multiplication.

EXERCISE 4.1

1. Prepare an addition table for a 5-hour clock.
2. Determine if the numbers on a 5-hour clock form a group.
3. Consider the set of elements a, b, c and the operation $\square$ that yields the following results.

$$a \square a \equiv a$$
$$b \square b \equiv b$$
$$c \square c \equiv c$$
$$a \square b \equiv a$$
$$a \square c \equiv c$$
$$b \square a \equiv b$$
$$b \square c \equiv c$$
$$c \square a \equiv c$$
$$c \square b \equiv c$$

   a) Using these results, prepare an operation table for $\square$.
   b) Is a, b, c a group under $\square$? Why
4. Find the following such that x will be a number on the 12-hour clock.
   a) $8 + x \equiv 3$ b) $x \equiv 9 + 7$
   c) $6 \equiv x + 2x$ d) $3x \equiv 12$
   e) $4 - x \equiv 5$ f) $5 - 7 \equiv x$
   g) $3x \equiv x + 6$ h) $5x \equiv 8$
5. An operation table for the days of the week could be constructed by numbering the days 1 through 7. Show that this operation forms a group. Is it an Abelian group?
6. Under what operation is the set of positive integers a group?
7. Under what operation is the set of even integers a group?

4.2 THE SYSTEM OF MODULAR ARITHMETIC

Let us imagine that our 5-hour clock has had its "face lifted" by replacing the 5 with the 0, as shown in Figure 4.1.

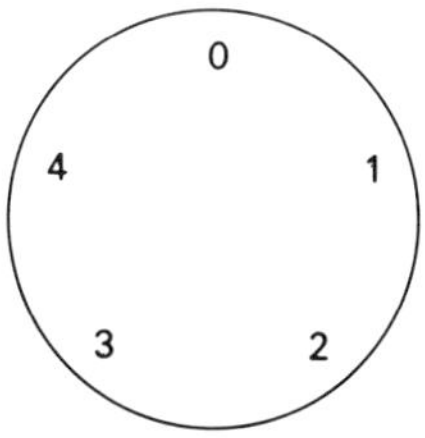

Figure 4.1

72 Other Mathematical Systems

The addition table for the 5-hour clock that you constructed in Problem 1, Exercise 4.1, would be modified to fit our "new" clock, as shown in Table 4.2.

Table 4.2

$\oplus$	0	1	2	3	4
0	0	1	2	3	4
1	1	2	3	4	0
2	2	3	4	0	1
3	3	4	0	1	2
4	4	0	1	2	3

So far, clock discussions have utilized only the operation of addition, $\oplus$. But can also perform *clock multiplication*. To do so, we use our knowledge of regular multiplication and quickly recognize that the result must always be a number on the clock. We may symbolize this form of multiplication by $\otimes$ and construct a table that would look like the one shown in Table 4.3.

Table 4.3

$\otimes$	0	1	2	3	4
0	0	0	0	0	0
1	0	1	2	3	4
2	0	2	4	1	3
3	0	3	1	4	2
4	0	4	3	2	1

Now let us examine these two operations, addition and multiplication, for group characteristics.

	$\oplus$		$\otimes$	
1. *Closure*	Yes		Yes	
2. *Identity*	0		1	
3. *Inverse*	Yes	$0 \oplus 0 \equiv 0$	Yes (except for zero)	
		$1 \oplus 4 \equiv 0$		$1 \otimes 1 \equiv 1$
		$2 \oplus 3 \equiv 0$		$2 \otimes 3 \equiv 1$
		$3 \oplus 2 \equiv 0$		$3 \otimes 2 \equiv 1$
		$4 \oplus 1 \equiv 0$		$4 \otimes 4 \equiv 1$
4. *Associative*	Yes		Yes	

The associative property can be shown to hold by listing each case. We show one case for each operation.

$$2 \oplus (3 \oplus 4) \stackrel{?}{\equiv} (2 \oplus 3) \oplus 4 \qquad 2 \otimes (3 \otimes 4) \stackrel{?}{\equiv} (2 \otimes 3) \otimes 4$$
$$2 \oplus 2 \stackrel{?}{\equiv} 0 \oplus 4 \qquad\qquad 2 \otimes 2 \stackrel{?}{\equiv} 1 \otimes 4$$
$$4 \equiv 4 \qquad\qquad\qquad 4 \equiv 4$$

The modified clock operation $\oplus$ meets the group requirements of closure, identity, inverse, and associativity. And, except for the element "o," the operation $\otimes$ also meets the requirements for a group.

We shall now develop an abstract mathematical system that is not associated with physical objects. This abstract system is called *modular arithmetic*.

In section 4.1, we introduced the symbol $\equiv$, without a definition. Now we can say that the symbol $\equiv$ represents an *equivalence relationship* and has the same five properties as does equality—i.e., reflexive, symmetric, transitive, additive, and multiplicative. This symbol is read "is equivalent to" or, more commonly, "is congruent to." In modular arithmetic, when we say that two numbers, a and b, are congruent, we mean that a given number divides $a - b$ evenly.

Let us return briefly to clock arithmetic. When we performed an operation, it was essential for us to know whether we were working with a 12-hour clock, a 5-hour clock, etc. In modular arithmetic, the clock number is replaced by a number called the *modulus*, which does not actually appear in the table. Remember that in our modified 5-hour clock, the number 5 was replaced by zero and did not appear.

Tables 4.2 and 4.3 can now become operation tables for addition and multiplication for modulus 5 (usually called "modulo 5" and then abbreviated to "mod 5"). The elements in our set are 0, 1, 2, 3, 4, which represent all sums (multiples) under the two operations $\oplus$ and $\otimes$.

We can determine each entry in an addition table for modular arithmetic by following three simple steps.

1. Add the two numbers by regular addition.
2. Divide the sum by the mod.
3. Discard the quotient and enter the remainder in the table.

Example 1. Add 3 + 4 in mod 5.

Solution. $\dfrac{3+4}{5} = \dfrac{7}{5} = 1$ with a remainder of 2.

Discard the quotient 1 and enter the remainder 2 in the table as the result of 3 + 4.

Example 2. Add 4 + 4 in mod 5.

Solution. $\dfrac{4+4}{5} = 1$, remainder 3.

Discard the quotient 1 and enter the remainder 3 in the table as the result of 4 + 4.

Entries for a multiplication table follow a similar procedure.

Example 3. Multiply 2 × 3 in mod 5.

Solution. $\dfrac{2 \times 3}{5} = 1$ remainder 1.

Discard the quotient 1 and enter the remainder 1 in the table as the result of 2 × 3.

Example 4. Multiply 4 × 4 in mod 5.

Solution. $\dfrac{4 \times 4}{5} = 3$ remainder 1.

Discard the quotient 3 and enter the remainder 1 in the table as the result of 4 × 4.

Operation tables in modular arithmetic are also called "remainder tables." In preparing these tables, it is helpful to keep this point in mind.

The mathematical system in mod 5 has a *double group structure*—except for zero. Let us now see if we can promote this system to a number system having the same requirements as that outlined in Chapter 3. To do so, we must show that both the commutative and distributive postulates apply.

Because we are dealing with a finite set, these two postulates (commutative and distributive) do apply—if we try all cases for each postulate as we have in the following two cases.

Commutative: a) $\quad 2 \oplus 3 \stackrel{?}{\equiv} 3 \oplus 2 \qquad 2 \otimes 3 \stackrel{?}{\equiv} 3 \otimes 2$
$$0 \equiv 0 \qquad\qquad 1 \equiv 1$$

b) $\quad 4 \oplus 2 \stackrel{?}{\equiv} 2 \oplus 4 \qquad 4 \otimes 2 \stackrel{?}{\equiv} 2 \otimes 4$
$$1 \equiv 1 \qquad\qquad 3 \equiv 3$$

Distributive: a) $\quad 2 \otimes (3 \oplus 4) \stackrel{?}{\equiv} (2 \otimes 3) \oplus (2 \otimes 4)$
$$2 \otimes 2 \stackrel{?}{\equiv} 1 \oplus 3$$
$$4 \equiv 4$$

b) $\quad 4 \otimes (2 \oplus 3) \stackrel{?}{\equiv} (4 \otimes 2) \oplus (4 \otimes 3)$
$$4 \otimes 0 \stackrel{?}{\equiv} 3 \oplus 2$$
$$0 \equiv 0$$

We have now shown that a group satisfying only four postulates can sometimes be promoted to a number system. The technical name for this system is a *field*. A field is a "double" Abelian group (excluding 0 for multiplication) that also satisfies the distributive property. The mod-5 field is an example of a *finite field*, whereas the system of rational numbers and the system of real numbers are both examples of an *infinite field*.

EXERCISE 4.2

1. Construct modular arithmetic tables $\oplus$ and $\otimes$ for thet 0, 2, 3, 4, 5, 6.
2. Using the tables from Problem 1, solve the following:
   a) $2 \otimes (3 \oplus 4) \equiv$
   b) $(2 \otimes 3) \oplus (2 \otimes 5) \equiv$
   c) $4 \otimes (4 \oplus 3) \equiv$
   d) $(4 \otimes 4) \oplus (4 \otimes 3) \equiv$
3. Prepare a list of inverses for each element under both $\oplus$ and $\otimes$ for mod 7.
4. Solve the following problems in the mod indicated.
   a) $4 \otimes 3 \equiv x \pmod{5}$
   b) $3 \otimes 6 \equiv x \pmod{5}$
   c) $5 \oplus x \equiv 1 \pmod{7}$
   d) $2x \oplus 3 \equiv 4 \pmod{7}$
   e) $x \otimes 4 \equiv 3 \pmod{5}$
   f) $3 \oplus 3x \equiv 1 \oplus x \pmod{5}$
5. Solve the following problems in the mod indicated.
   a) $5x - 3 \equiv 4 \pmod{12}$
   b) $7 - x \equiv 2 \pmod{12}$
   c) $9 - 11 \equiv x \pmod{12}$
   d) $8x \equiv 8 \pmod{12}$
   e) $11x \equiv 1 \pmod{12}$
6. A number a is said to be a zero divisor in mod 16, when $a \times b \equiv 0 \pmod{16}$. For example, 2 is a zero divisor in mod 16, since $2 \otimes 8 \equiv 0 \pmod{16}$, and 8 is not congruent to 16. Are there other zero divisors of 16? If so, what are they?
7. July 4th is the 185th day of the year and falls on Friday. On what day would Christmas fall? Explain.
8. A flight is scheduled to arrive at 16 o'clock on a 24-hour clock. The flight is 8 hours late. At what time does it arrive?
9. The 15th of July falls on Wednesday. On what date does the 15th of August fall?
10. Find the modulus in each of the following.
    a) $4 \otimes 5 \equiv 5$
    b) $2 \otimes (3 \oplus 4) \equiv 4$
    c) $4 \oplus 5 \otimes (1 \oplus 3) \equiv 6$
    d) $(7 \oplus 3) \otimes (6 \oplus 4) \equiv 1$
    e) $(4 \oplus 5) \otimes (0 \otimes 3) \equiv 3$

4.3 THE SYSTEM OF COMPLEX NUMBERS

In Chapter 3, one of our objectives was to find a number for *every point* on a line. We reached this objective with the set of real numbers and postulated that the real number line is complete—which is true, as long as we stay on this line. If we venture into the plane, however, we do *not* have a set of numbers to describe each point in the plane.

Those who live in a city with rectangular blocks and numbered streets (and avenues) will appreciate the desirability of having a number to describe all street intersections. Such a "number" might actually be a *pair* of numbers; that is, if you live at 66th Street and 5th Avenue, you could represent the location by (66, 5). If all the citizens understood the first number to be the street and the second to be the avenue, the message conveyed by the number pair (66, 5) would be unquestionable. If we interchanged the elements of the pair and wrote (5, 66), however, an entirely different intersection would become the focus. We shall use this pair concept to establish a set of numbers, called *complex numbers*, to match every point in the plane. But, before proceeding with the development of complex numbers, we must understand what is meant by the phrase "points in the plane."

The Cartesian Plane

More than three hundred years ago, the French mathematician and philosopher René Descartes (1596–1650) discovered a profound mathematical concept, which is based on using two perpendicular real number lines. The intersection of the lines is called the *origin*, 0. One of the lines is *horizontal* (usually called the *x*-axis), and the other is *vertical* (usually called the *y*-axis). The right side of the *x*-axis is *positive*, and the left side is *negative*. On the vertical or *y*-axis, positive numbers appear above, negative numbers below the *x*-axis. The two lines divide the plane into four sections, called *quadrants*, that are numbered as shown in Figure 4.2.

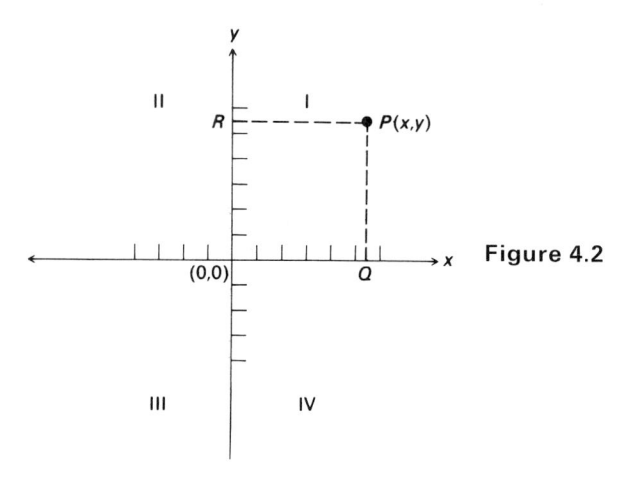

Figure 4.2

We represent any point, P, in this system by an *ordered pair* (x, y). If we project P onto the *x*-axis at the point Q so that the line PQ is perpendicular to the *x*-axis, then the distance from 0 to Q is x. Similarly, if we project P onto the *y*-axis, then the distance from 0 to R is y. The pair (x, y) is called an ordered pair, since x is the first and y is the second element. We are now ready to describe the set of complex numbers.

The Elements of the Complex Number System

Definition 4.1 A *complex number* is an ordered pair of real numbers (a, b).

Complex numbers include a *subset*, written in the form $(a, 0)$, where a is a real number. This subset represents the points on the *x*-axis, which is called the *real axis*. All real numbers may be expressed in the $(a, 0)$ form. For example, we can write 5 as $(5, 0)$, 2 as $(\sqrt{2}, 0)$, 1/2 as $(1/2, 0)$, and -7 as $(-7, 0)$. When the complex number is a real number, the second element is *always* zero.

We have a special name for complex numbers that appear along the y-axis—they are called *imaginary numbers*. We write these numbers as $(0, a)$, where a is a real number; for example, $(0, 2)$, $(0, \sqrt{3})$, $(0, 1)$, $(0 - 5)$. These numbers, however, are no more "imaginary" in the physical sense than are the "real" numbers.

The ordered pair (a, b), where a and b are both nonzero real numbers, is neither a real nor an imaginary number. It is a new concept that describes a point in the plane. Hence the elements of the set of complex numbers include: the set of real numbers, with all its subsets, the set of imaginary numbers, and the set of complex numbers that is neither real nor imaginary (see Figure 4.3).

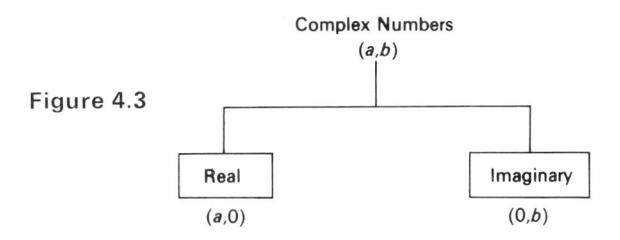

Figure 4.3

```
            Complex Numbers
                 (a,b)
          ┌────────┴────────┐
        Real              Imaginary
        (a,0)               (0,b)
```

Operations for Complex Numbers

If the set of complex numbers is to form a number system, *the binary operations of addition and multiplication must apply*. Since leaving the natural numbers, we have added definitions to ensure that the binary operations hold for each expansion of our system. We now do the same for the complex numbers.

Definition 4.2 If a, b, c and d are real numbers, then

$$(a, b) + (c, d) = (a + c, b + d).$$

Example. $(2, 3) + (-4, 5) = [2 + (-4), 3 + 5] = (-2, 8).$

Definition 4.3 If a, b, c and d are real numbers, then

$$(a, b) \cdot (c, d) = (ac - bd, ad + bc).$$

Example 1. $(5, 6) \cdot (3, 4) = (5 \cdot 3 - 6 \cdot 4, 5 \cdot 4 + 6 \cdot 3)$
$= (15 - 24, 20 + 18) = (-9, 38).$

Example 2. $(3, -2) \cdot (-5, 3) = [3(-5) - (-2)(-3), 3(-3) + (-2)(-5)]$
$= (-15 - 6, -9 + 10) = (-21, 1).$

At this time, it is not feasible to explain the significance of the sum and product of complex numbers. The source of our concepts of addition and multiplication is still the set of counting numbers, and these initial concepts can be traced through the set of real numbers. Beyond this point, we need new concepts to explain the sum and product of complex numbers of the form (a, b), where $a, b \neq 0$ and $(0, b), b \neq 0$.

So we require one more definition before proceeding to the postulates for complex numbers. This is the definition for the *equality of complex numbers*.

> **Definition 4.4** If a, b, c and $d \neq 0$ and are real numbers, then
> $$(a, b) = (c, d) \quad \text{if and only if} \quad a = c \quad \text{and} \quad b = d.$$

Example. $(4, 8) = (2x, 4y) \leftrightarrow 2x = 4$ and $4y = 8$.

Postulates for Complex Numbers

No new postulates are required for the complex number system. The eleven basic postulates for closure, associativity, commutativity, distributivity, identity, and inverse apply and can be rigorously proved. To save time, we shall prove only the associative and commutative properties for addition—proofs for the other nine follow a similar pattern.

Associativity for addition:

We must show that

$$[(a, b) + (c, d)] + (e, f) = (a, b) + [(c, d) + e, f)]$$

Statements	Reasons
From the left side,	
$[(a, b) + (c, d)] + (e, f) =$ $(a + c, b + d) + (e, f)$	Definition of addition of complex numbers
and	
$(a + c, b + d) + e, f) =$ $(a + c + e, b + d + f)$	Definition of addition of complex numbers
From the right side,	
$(a, b) + [(c, d) + (e, f)] =$ $(a, b) + (c + e, d + f)$	Definition of addition of complex numbers
and	
$(a, b) + (c + e, d + f) =$ $(a + c + e, b + d + f)$	Definition of addition of complex numbers
Therefore	
$[(a, b) + (c, d)] + (e, f) =$ $(a, b) + [(c, d) + (e, f)]$	Transitive property of equality

Commutativity for addition:

We must show that
$$(a, b) + (c, d) = (c, d) + (a, b).$$

Statements	Reasons
From the left side,	
$(a, b) + (c, d) = (a + c, b + d)$	Definition of addition of complex numbers
$(a + c, b + d) = (c + a, d + b)$	Commutative for addition of real numbers
From the right side,	
$(c, d) + (a, b) = (c + a, d + b)$	Definition of addition of complex numbers
Therefore	
$(a, b) + (c, d) = (c, d) + (a, b)$	Transitive property of equality

Theorems for Complex Numbers

All the theorems for the set of real numbers apply to complex numbers of the form $(a, 0)$, since this is merely another way of symbolizing the real number a. For complex numbers that are not real, special courses have been devised to develop the necessary theorems. Such courses usually contain the phrase "complex variables" in the title. Engineers, physicists, mathematicians, and other scientists are required to pursue such courses.

An Alternate Method of Writing Complex Numbers

Historically, the representation of a complex number as an ordered pair of real numbers (a, b) is comparatively new. Originally, the set of complex numbers was invented to provide solutions for certain types of equations, such as $x^2 + 1 = 0$. Any attempt to find a real number that can be squared and added to 1, yielding zero, is predestined to be fruitless. The only number we can substitute for x in the equation $x^2 + 1 = 0$ is $\sqrt{-1}$. So let us try

$$(\sqrt{-1})^2 + 1 = -1 + 1 = 0.*$$

Now let us try another substitution for x. We substitute the complex number $(0, 1)$ for x.

$$\begin{aligned} x^2 + 1 &= (0, 1) \cdot (0, 1) + 1 = 0 \\ &= [(0 \cdot 0) - (1 \cdot 1), (0 \cdot 1) + (1 \cdot 0)] + 1 = 0 \quad \text{(Def. 4.3)} \\ &= (-1, 0) + 1 = 0 \\ &= -1 + 1 = 0 \end{aligned}$$

---

*$(\sqrt{-1})^2 = -1$; see Chapter 6.

Since both $\sqrt{-1}$ and $(0, 1)$ provide a solution to $x^2 + 1 = 0$, we can reasonably define $\sqrt{-b}$, where b is a nonnegative real number.

Definition 4.4 $\quad \sqrt{-b} = (0, \sqrt{b})$.

Example 1. $\sqrt{-4} = (0, \sqrt{4}) = (0, 2)$.
Example 2. $\sqrt{-5} = (0, \sqrt{5})$.

When b is the number one, then $\sqrt{-b} = \sqrt{-1}$. This number, $\sqrt{-1}$, is denoted by i. We are now able to represent every complex number of the form $(0, b)$ in terms of i. For example,

$$(0, 2) = (0, \sqrt{4}) = \sqrt{-4} = 2i \quad \text{(Def. 4.3)}$$

Explanation:
$$(2, 0) \cdot (0, 1) = (0, 2)$$
$$(2, 0) = 2$$
$$(0, 1) = i$$
$$2i = (0, 2).$$

Before continuing with this alternate notation, let us return to the definition of the sum of complex numbers and add

$$(1, 0) + (0, 1) = (1 + 0, 0 + 1) = (1, 1)$$
$$= (a + 0, 0 + b) = (a, b)$$

and $(a, 0) + (0, b)$

In place of $(a, 0)$ and $(0, b)$, we now substitute their equals. [Recall: $(a, 0)$ is the real number a, and $(0, b)$ is the number bi.]

$$(a, 0) = a \quad \text{and} \quad (0, b) = bi$$

Hence
$$(a, 0) + (0, b) = (a, b) = a + bi$$

This notation appears in many texts. Thus we can show that operations on complex numbers apply when the numbers are defined in the form $a + bi$.

EXERCISE 4.3

1. Perform the indicated operation.
    a) $(2, 0) + (3, 4)$
    b) $2 + (3 + 4i)$
    c) $(0, 3) + (0, -5)$
    d) $(5, 1) + (2, 3) + (1, 1)$
    e) $(2, 3) + (3, 4) + (4, 5)$
2. Represent each result of problem 1 as a point in the plane.
3. Write the powers of i through i^{12}, that is, i, i^2, i^3, etc.
4. See if you can find a pattern in the powers of i. What is i^{32}, i^{63}?
5. Have we studied any other sets of numbers that may be represented by an ordered pair?
6. In complex number form, is it possible to write a number such as $2 + \sqrt{3}$?

7. What is the multiplication inverse of i?

8. Assume that we define the magnitude of a complex number (a, b) to be the positive of $\sqrt{a^2 + b^2}$. Use this definition to answer the following questions.

   a) Is it possible for more than one complex number to have the same magnitude?

   b) Can complex numbers be arranged in order from the smallest to the largest?

9. We now have a set of numbers for points on a line and a set for points in a plane. How could we represent points in space? Conjecture about whether we could develop a number system for these points in space.

10. Prove that the set of complex numbers satisfies the commutative postulate.

4.4 THE SYSTEM OF MATRICES

The relatively new *system of matrices*, was invented in 1858 by the English mathematician Arthur Cayley (1821–1895). Since World War II, the system has been applied extensively to economics, business, statistics, engineering, physics, and the behavioral sciences. The widespread application of matrices to these diverse fields of study has been hastened by the sophisticated development of the computer.

Definition 4.5 A *matrix* is a rectangular array (arrangement) of real numbers, written in the following manner

$$\begin{pmatrix} a_{11} & a_{12} & \ldots & a_{1n} \\ a_{21} & a_{22} & \ldots & a_{2n} \\ . & . & & . \\ . & . & & . \\ . & . & & . \\ a_{m1} & a_{m2} & & a_{mn} \end{pmatrix}$$

Each horizontal line in the array is called a *row*, and each vertical line is called a *column*. The numbers in the array, e.g., a_{11}, a_{12}, are elements of the matrix, and each is a real number in our development. Lowercase letters usually represent elements of a matrix, while capital letters represent the entire matrix.

The double subscript shown with each element identifies the location of the element in the array. (The first subscript identifies the row and the second identifies the column.) For example, a_{23} is the element in the second row and third column. The matrix displayed above has m rows and n columns and is called an ($M \times N$) matrix (read "M by N"). Some examples of matrices of different dimensions are the following:

Example 1. The matrix $\begin{pmatrix} 1 & 2 \\ 3 & 5 \end{pmatrix}$ is a (2×2) matrix.

Example 2. The matrix $\begin{pmatrix} 2 & 1 & 5 \\ 6 & 7 & 9 \end{pmatrix}$ is a (2 × 3) matrix.

Example 3. The matrix $\begin{matrix} 4 & 5 & 6 \\ 1 & 2 & 3 \\ 9 & 6 & 1 \end{matrix}$ is a (3 × 3) matrix.

Example 4. The matrix (1 3 4) is a 1 × 3 matrix.

If a matrix has the same number of rows and columns, it is called a *square matrix*. We shall confine ourselves to the study of (2 × 2) matrices.

Definition 4.6 (Equality of Matrices). Two matrices are *equal* if and only if the elements in the corresponding positions are equal.

Example 1. $\begin{pmatrix} a & b \\ c & d \end{pmatrix} = \begin{pmatrix} e & f \\ g & h \end{pmatrix}$

Therefore $a = e$, $b = f$, $c = g$, and $d = h$.

Example 2. $\begin{pmatrix} x+2 & 0 \\ 0 & y+3 \end{pmatrix} = \begin{pmatrix} 2 & 0 \\ 0 & 3 \end{pmatrix}$

Therefore $x + 2 = 2$, $0 = 0$, $0 = 0$, and $y + 3 = 3$.

Definition 4.7 (Addition of Matrices). The *sum of two matrices* is a matrix whose elements are the sum of the corresponding elements of the two matrices.

Example. $\begin{pmatrix} 2 & 3 \\ 5 & 6 \end{pmatrix} \cdot \begin{pmatrix} 1 & 5 \\ 2 & 4 \end{pmatrix} = \begin{pmatrix} 2+1 & 3+5 \\ 5+2 & 4+6 \end{pmatrix} = \begin{pmatrix} 3 & 8 \\ 7 & 10 \end{pmatrix}$

This definition means that we cannot add matrices of different sizes. We can prove that *matrix addition* of (2 × 2) matrices follows the same postulates as addition of real numbers. The operation is closed, associative, and communicative. There is an identity matrix, and each matrix has an addition inverse matrix. The identity matrix is the *zero matrix*

$$\begin{pmatrix} 0 & 0 \\ 0 & 0 \end{pmatrix}$$

The additive inverse matrix for

$$\begin{pmatrix} a & b \\ c & d \end{pmatrix} \text{ is } \begin{pmatrix} -a & -b \\ -c & -d \end{pmatrix}$$

Why?

EXERCISE 4.4

1. Find the value of x that makes the following pairs of matrices equal.

4.4 The System of Matrices

a) $\begin{pmatrix} x & 2 \\ 3 & 4 \end{pmatrix} = \begin{pmatrix} 5 & 2 \\ 3 & 4 \end{pmatrix}$ b) $\begin{pmatrix} 3 & x + \frac{1}{2} \\ 1 & 2 \end{pmatrix} = \begin{pmatrix} 3 & 1 \\ 1 & 2 \end{pmatrix}$

c) $\begin{pmatrix} \frac{3}{6} & \frac{4}{5} \\ \frac{2}{3} & x+2 \end{pmatrix} = \begin{pmatrix} \frac{1}{2} & \frac{8}{10} \\ \frac{4}{6} & 0 \end{pmatrix}$ d) $\begin{pmatrix} 2x & .5 \\ .3 & .2 \end{pmatrix} = \begin{pmatrix} .8 & .5 \\ .3 & .2 \end{pmatrix}$

2. Find the sum of the following matrices.

a) $\begin{pmatrix} 2 & 7 \\ 4 & 9 \end{pmatrix} + \begin{pmatrix} -5 & 1 \\ 3 & 7 \end{pmatrix}$

b) $\begin{pmatrix} 6 & 11 \\ 21 & -9 \end{pmatrix} + \begin{pmatrix} x-3 & x+5 \\ x-12 & x-7 \end{pmatrix}$

c) $\begin{pmatrix} x+3 & 5 \\ x-2 & 7 \end{pmatrix} + \begin{pmatrix} x-3 & x+5 \\ x+2 & x-7 \end{pmatrix}$

d) $\begin{pmatrix} 1.4 & .2 \\ 7.9 & .5 \end{pmatrix} + \begin{pmatrix} .6 & .8 \\ .1 & .5 \end{pmatrix}$

3. Solve for x, y, z and w.

a) $\begin{pmatrix} 1 & 3 \\ 5 & 7 \end{pmatrix} + \begin{pmatrix} x & 2 \\ y & 3 \end{pmatrix} = \begin{pmatrix} .2 & 5 \\ 3 & 10 \end{pmatrix}$

b) $\begin{pmatrix} x & y \\ z & 2 \end{pmatrix} + \begin{pmatrix} 2 & 3 \\ 4 & 5 \end{pmatrix} = \begin{pmatrix} 4 & 3 \\ 0 & 0 \end{pmatrix}$

c) $\begin{pmatrix} 2x & 3y \\ 5z & 3w \end{pmatrix} + \begin{pmatrix} 0 & 0 \\ 0 & 0 \end{pmatrix} = \begin{pmatrix} 0 & 1 \\ 5 & 0 \end{pmatrix}$

4. Given the matrix

$$\begin{pmatrix} 3 & 5 & 7 \\ 9 & 10 & 11 \\ 1 & 3 & 1 \end{pmatrix}$$

a) Describe its dimensions.
b) In what row is the element 11? In what column? How would you subscript it to indicate its position in the matrix?

5. Jane goes shopping for her three room mates and makes the following purchases:

   Mary: 1 bottle aspirin, 2 pencils, 1 notebook.
   Amy: 2 bottles aspirin, 2 notebooks.
   Lulu: 3 pencils, 4 notebooks.

   Prepare a matrix to indicate what Jane will purchase for each roommate.

6. At the store, Jane finds that the price of a bottle of aspirin is 50 cents, pencils are 10 cents each, and notebooks 25 cents each. How could the prices be written as a matrix? Is there more than one way to write this matrix?

It is likely that you found little, if anything, new in the definition of matrix addition. Matrix multiplication, however, is a new concept which has no analog in the system of real numbers.

Definition 4.8 (Multiplication of Matrices).

If $M = \begin{pmatrix} a & b \\ c & e \end{pmatrix}$ and $N = \begin{pmatrix} e & f \\ g & h \end{pmatrix}$, then

$$M \cdot N = \begin{pmatrix} a & b \\ c & d \end{pmatrix} \cdot \begin{pmatrix} e & f \\ g & h \end{pmatrix} = \begin{pmatrix} ae + bg & af + bh \\ ce + dg & cf + dh \end{pmatrix}$$

The entries in the *product matrix*, MN, are determined by following three basic steps:

1. The entry in the product matrix MN in position 11—that is, row 1, column 1— is found by multiplying the elements in the first row of M by the corresponding elements in the first column of N. The sum of these products is the entry in MN.

$$\text{Row 1} \quad \begin{pmatrix} a & b \\ - & - \end{pmatrix} \cdot \begin{pmatrix} e & - \\ g & - \end{pmatrix} = \begin{pmatrix} ae + bg & - \\ - & - \end{pmatrix}$$
$$\text{Column 1}$$

2. The entry in MN in position 21—that is, row 2, column 1—is found by multiplying the elements in the second row of M by the corresponding elements in the first column of N. The sum of these products is the entry in MN.

$$\text{Row 2} \quad \begin{pmatrix} - & - \\ c & d \end{pmatrix} \cdot \begin{pmatrix} e & - \\ g & - \end{pmatrix} = \begin{pmatrix} - & - \\ ce + dg & - \end{pmatrix}$$
$$\text{Column 1}$$

3. The entry in position 12 and the entry in position 22—that is, row 1, column 2 and row 2, column 2, respectively—are found in a similar way. In general, for all square matrices, the entry in the position MN is the sum of the products of the elements in row M multiplied by the corresponding elements in column N. Thus

$$\begin{pmatrix} 2 & 3 \\ 4 & 7 \end{pmatrix} \cdot \begin{pmatrix} 1 & 2 \\ 4 & 3 \end{pmatrix} = \begin{pmatrix} 2 \cdot 1 + 3 \cdot 4 & 2 \cdot 2 + 3 \cdot 3 \\ 4 \cdot 1 + 7 \cdot 4 & 4 \cdot 2 + 7 \cdot 3 \end{pmatrix} = \begin{pmatrix} 14 & 13 \\ 32 & 29 \end{pmatrix}$$

Or

$$\begin{pmatrix} -3 & 5 \\ 2 & -4 \end{pmatrix} \begin{pmatrix} -5 & 1 \\ 2 & -3 \end{pmatrix} = \begin{pmatrix} -3 \cdot -5 + 5 \cdot 2 & -3 \cdot 1 + 5 \cdot -3 \\ 2 \cdot -5 + -4 \cdot 2 & 2 \cdot 1 + -4 \cdot -3 \end{pmatrix}$$
$$= \begin{pmatrix} 25 & -18 \\ -18 & 14 \end{pmatrix}$$

The operation of multiplication for (2 × 2) matrices follows the same postulates as multiplication of real numbers—with one important exception. In general, *matrix multiplication* is *not* commutative. Consider the following matrices and their product.

$$\begin{pmatrix} 2 & 3 \\ 5 & 6 \end{pmatrix} \cdot \begin{pmatrix} 1 & 2 \\ 2 & 5 \end{pmatrix} = \begin{pmatrix} 8 & 21 \\ 17 & 45 \end{pmatrix}$$

We now commute these matrices and multiply.
$$\begin{pmatrix} 1 & 3 \\ 2 & 5 \end{pmatrix} \cdot \begin{pmatrix} 2 & 3 \\ 5 & 6 \end{pmatrix} = \begin{pmatrix} 17 & 21 \\ 29 & 36 \end{pmatrix}$$

By the definition of equality, the matrix $\begin{pmatrix} 8 & 21 \\ 17 & 45 \end{pmatrix}$ is not equal to $\begin{pmatrix} 17 & 21 \\ 26 & 36 \end{pmatrix}$.

Using this counterexample, we have proved that matrix multiplication is not commutative.

The *identity matrix* for multiplication of (2 × 2) matrices is

$$1 = \begin{pmatrix} 1 & 0 \\ 0 & 1 \end{pmatrix}$$

Every (2 × 2) matrix, $A = \begin{pmatrix} a & b \\ c & d \end{pmatrix}$, has an *inverse* for multiplication, unless $as - bc = 0$. If a matrix, A', is the inverse of A, then

$$A'A = AA' = 1 \quad \text{or} \quad A' \begin{pmatrix} a & b \\ c & d \end{pmatrix} = \begin{pmatrix} a & b \\ c & d \end{pmatrix} A' = \begin{pmatrix} 1 & 0 \\ 0 & 1 \end{pmatrix}$$

We shall now show you how the matrix

$$A' = \begin{pmatrix} \dfrac{d}{ad-bc} & \dfrac{-b}{ad-bc} \\ \dfrac{-c}{ad-bc} & \dfrac{a}{ad-bc} \end{pmatrix}$$

is the inverse of A.

$$\begin{pmatrix} \dfrac{d}{ad-bc} & \dfrac{-b}{ad-bc} \\ \dfrac{-c}{ad-bc} & \dfrac{a}{ad-bc} \end{pmatrix} \cdot \begin{pmatrix} a & b \\ c & d \end{pmatrix} = \begin{pmatrix} \dfrac{ad-bc}{ad-bc} & \dfrac{db-bd}{ad-bc} \\ \dfrac{-ca+ca}{ad-bc} & \dfrac{-bc+ad}{ad-bc} \end{pmatrix}$$

$$= \begin{pmatrix} 1 & 0 \\ 0 & 1 \end{pmatrix}$$

And

$$\begin{pmatrix} a & b \\ c & d \end{pmatrix} \cdot \begin{pmatrix} \dfrac{d}{ad-bc} & \dfrac{-b}{ad-bc} \\ \dfrac{-c}{ad-bc} & \dfrac{a}{ad-bc} \end{pmatrix} = \begin{pmatrix} \dfrac{ad-bc}{ad-bc} & \dfrac{-ab+ab}{ad-bc} \\ \dfrac{cd-cd}{ad-bc} & \dfrac{-bc+ad}{ad-bc} \end{pmatrix}$$

$$= \begin{pmatrix} 1 & 0 \\ 0 & 1 \end{pmatrix}$$

If you inspect this inverse matrix, you will see that an inverse cannot exist when $ad - bc = 0$, since each element would then have *zero* in the denominator.

Theorems for Matrices

Theorems for matrices would be developed in a course called "Matrix Algebra." In such a course, methods of solving equations consisting of many unknowns would be studied, and we would learn that the elements of a matrix would not be restricted to real numbers. Since matrix algebra is an important course in the undergraduate mathematics, a few simple problems will be solved in Chapter 7.

EXERCISE 4.5

1. Find the products AB and BA.

   a) $A = \begin{pmatrix} 1 & 5 \\ 7 & 1 \end{pmatrix}$, $B = \begin{pmatrix} 2 & 3 \\ 1 & 2 \end{pmatrix}$ b) $A = \begin{pmatrix} x & y \\ z & w \end{pmatrix}$, $B = \begin{pmatrix} 2 & 6 \\ 1 & 5 \end{pmatrix}$

   c) $A = \begin{pmatrix} 1 & 0 \\ 0 & 1 \end{pmatrix}$, $B = \begin{pmatrix} 5 & 6 \\ 1 & 2 \end{pmatrix}$ d) $A = \begin{pmatrix} 6 & 7 \\ 5 & 3 \end{pmatrix}$, $B = \begin{pmatrix} 1 & 1 \\ 1 & 1 \end{pmatrix}$

2. Given the matrices

   $$A = \begin{pmatrix} 2 & 3 \\ 1 & 2 \end{pmatrix}, \quad B = \begin{pmatrix} 6 & 7 \\ 2 & 4 \end{pmatrix}, \quad C = \begin{pmatrix} 1 & 9 \\ 4 & 1 \end{pmatrix}$$

   find

   a) $(A \cdot B) \cdot C$ b) $A \cdot (B \cdot C)$
   c) $(A \cdot C) \cdot B$ d) $A \cdot (C \cdot B)$

3. Find the multiplicative inverse for each of the following matrices.

   a) $A = \begin{pmatrix} 1 & 4 \\ 3 & 2 \end{pmatrix}$ b) $B = \begin{pmatrix} 2 & 3 \\ 5 & 6 \end{pmatrix}$

   c) $C = \begin{pmatrix} 3 & -2 \\ -2 & 1 \end{pmatrix}$ d) $D = \begin{pmatrix} 3 & 6 \\ 4 & 2 \end{pmatrix}$

4. Determine whether multiplicative inverses exist for the following matrices.

   a) $A = \begin{pmatrix} 2 & 1 \\ 1 & 3 \end{pmatrix}$ b) $B = \begin{pmatrix} 1 & 1 \\ 1 & 1 \end{pmatrix}$

   c) $C = \begin{pmatrix} 6 & 4 \\ 3 & 2 \end{pmatrix}$ d) $D = \begin{pmatrix} \frac{1}{2} & 1 \\ 3 & 6 \end{pmatrix}$

5. The distributive property for real numbers is $a(b + c) = ab + ac$.
   a) Does the distributive property hold for matrices, that is, is the following statement true? $A \cdot (B + C) = A \cdot B + A \cdot C$.
   b) Is the following true? $(B + C)A = BA + CA$.

6. Is it necessary to find the entire product of two matrices to show that multiplication is noncommutative?

4.5 THE SYSTEM OF VECTORS

In studying complex numbers, we found that every point in the plane could be represented by an ordered pair of real numbers (a, b). This concept of an *ordered pair of real numbers* will now be utilized in our study of vectors. As we

4.5 The System of Vectors

develop the system of vectors, we shall see that a complex number and a vector in the plane have many common characteristics and behave, mathematically, in the same way.

The *system of vectors*, like matrices, is a relatively recent addition to mathematics. No one person is entirely responsible for conceiving this system; however an American scientist J. Willard Gibbs (1839–1903), is credited with major contributions in its development.

Just as the computer increased the use of matrices, the space age greatly influenced the importance of vectors as a mathematical tool. However the system of vectors is also used widely in many scientific fields not directly related to space technology.

We shall first present the mathematical definition of a vector in the plane and then develop the notation for its use.

Definition 4.9 A *vector* is a directed-line segment in the plane. The directed-line segment from a point, A, in the plane to another point, B, is denoted by $\overrightarrow{AB}$ (read "vector AB"), as shown in Figure 4.4. The arrow tells us the *direction of the vector*, and the length of the line segment, $\overline{AB}$, gives us its *magnitude*.

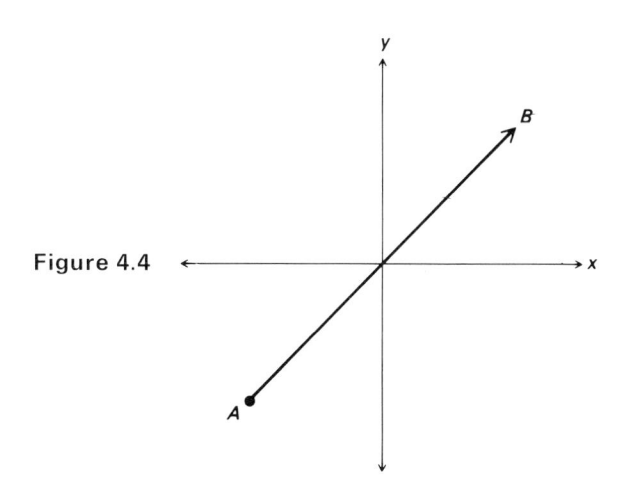

Figure 4.4

Since A and B represent two points in the plane, we can identify A as the point whose coordinates are (x_1, y_1), and B as the point whose coordinates are (x_2, y_2), as shown in Figure 4.5.

We shall now use the coordinates of A and B (Figure 4.5) to develop a better method for denoting a vector. A plane vector has two components: an x component and a y component. The two components may be found by subtracting the coordinates of the tail of the vector (A in Figure 4.5) from the corresponding coordinates of the head of the vector (B in Figure 4.5). The x component of the vector AB is $x_2 - x_1$; the y component is $y_2 - y_1$. To

Figure 4.5

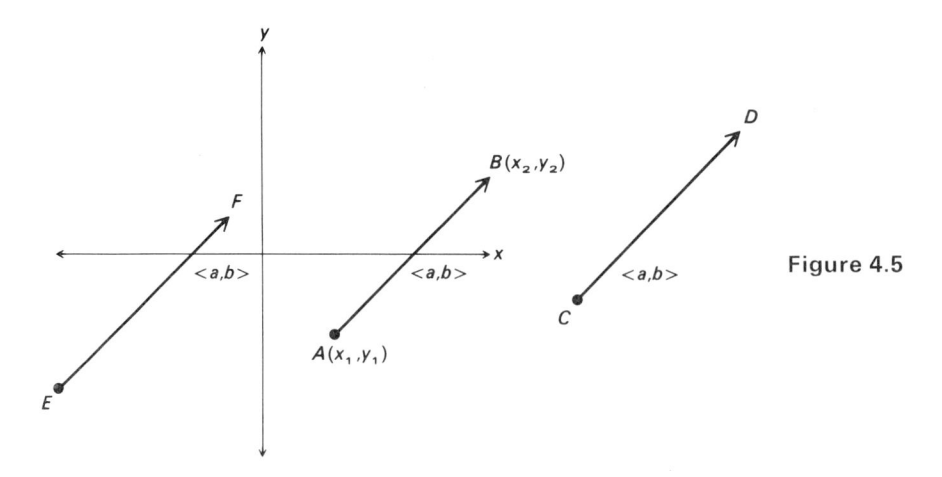

illustrate, assume that the coordinate of A in Figure 4.5 is $(2, -2)$ and the coordinate of B is $(5, 2)$. The x component of $\overline{AB}$ is $(5 - 2)$ or 3, and the y component is $[(2 - (2-2)]$ or 4. Any vector of the same magnitude and direction as $\overline{AB}$ can be represented by the pair $(3, 4)$. All of the vectors in Figure 4.5 can be represented by this pair, since each has the *same* direction and magnitude as $\overline{AB}$. In general, a plane vector may be represented by (a, b), where a and b are real numbers indicating the x and y components. To distinguish the vector from the complex number (a, b), we shall denote a vector by the symbol $\langle a, b \rangle$. Vectors utilizing this notation are shown in Figure 4.6.

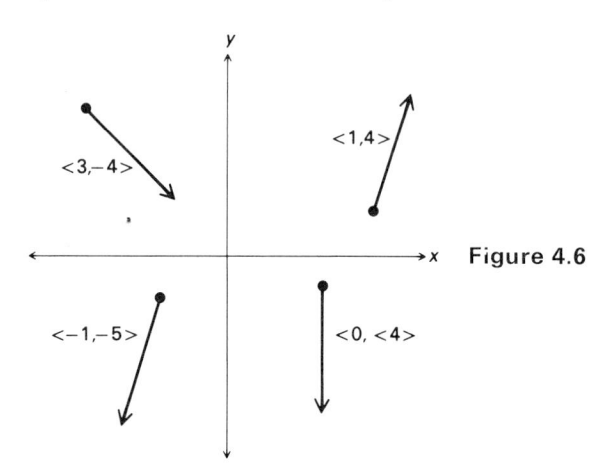

Figure 4.6

Vector Addition

Definition 4.10 The *sum of two vectors* is defined to be a vector. Thus

$$\langle a, b \rangle + \langle c, d \rangle = \langle a + c, b + d \rangle$$

We may represent this sum geometrically, as we have in Figure 4.7.

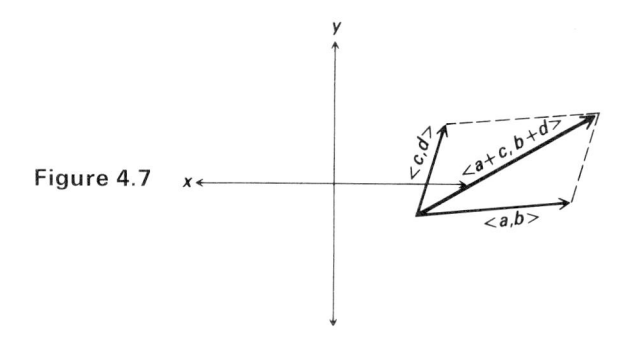

Figure 4.7

The following examples will serve as illustrations.

Example 1. $\langle 2, 3 \rangle + \langle 5, 7 \rangle = \langle 7, 10 \rangle$

Example 2. $\langle -3, -5 \rangle + \langle -7, 2 \rangle = \langle -10, -3 \rangle$

Example 3. $\langle 2, 0 \rangle + \langle 0, 2 \rangle = \langle 2, 2 \rangle$

Vector Products

We shall now consider *products* involving vectors. There are five possible types of products in vector multiplication. We shall study two of these types.

This is our first encounter with a mathematical system involving *several* products. Previously, each of our systems was concerned with only one product, although more than one may be found in a further study of matrices. The necessity for so many products arises because we are no longer concerned solely with a number representing a point in the plane. We must now consider the geometric properties of a directed-line segment as well as the usual properties of magnitude.

First, we shall examine the product affecting magnitude. The operation for finding this product is called *scalar multiplication*. When discussing vectors, a real number is called a *scalar*.

Definition 4.11 If $\langle a, b \rangle$ is a vector and k is a scalar, then $k\langle a, b \rangle$ is defined to be the vector $\langle ka, kb \rangle$.

Example 1. $2\langle 4, 3 \rangle = \langle 2 \cdot 4, 2 \cdot 3 \rangle = \langle 8, 6 \rangle$.

Example 2. $-3\langle 4, -2 \rangle = \langle -3 \cdot 4, -3 \cdot -2 \rangle = \langle -12, 6 \rangle$.

When k is a positive scalar, only the magnitude of the vector is affected, as in Example 1 where the magnitude of the resultant vector $\langle 8, 6 \rangle$ is twice that of the original vector $\langle 4, 3 \rangle$. Figure 4.8 represents the vector $\langle 4, 3 \rangle$ before multiplication, and Figure 4.9 shows the vector after it has been multiplied by the scalar 2.

90   Other Mathematical Systems   **4.5**

When k is a *negative scalar*, both the magnitude and the direction of the vector are altered. The magnitude is increased according to the value of the scalar, but the direction is reversed. Thus, in Example 2, the magnitude is increased threefold, but the direction of the resultant vector $\langle -12, 6 \rangle$ is the opposite of the original vector $\langle 4, -2 \rangle$. Figure 4.10 represents the vector before multiplication and Figure 4.11 represents the same vector after multiplication by the scalar -3.

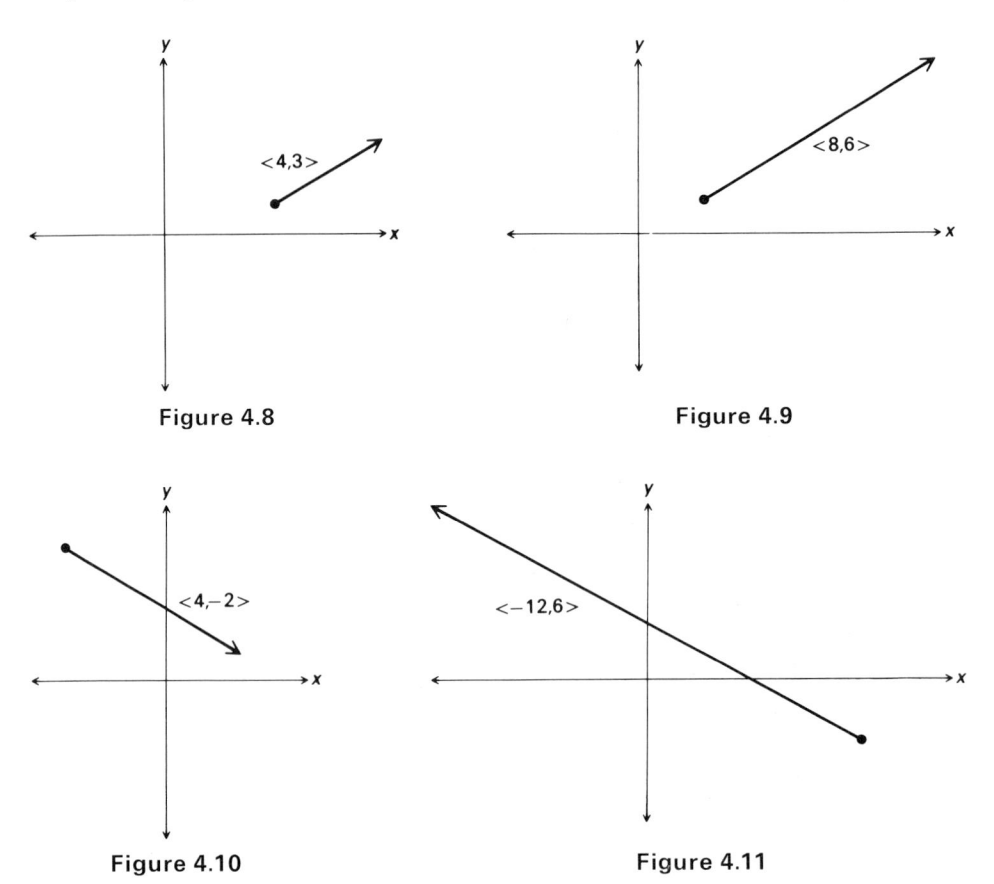

Figure 4.8

Figure 4.9

Figure 4.10

Figure 4.11

Scalar multiplication has several interesting features not previously encountered in our study of mathematical systems.

1. The two elements involved are from *different* mathematical systems; that is, the scalar is an element of the system of real numbers and the vector is from the system of vectors.
2. The *commutative property* has no meaning. A scalar multiplies a vector, but a vector does not multiply a scalar.
3. The *associative property* must include *two* scalars and *one* vector. Thus

$$k(1\langle a, b \rangle) = k1\langle a, b \rangle = \langle k1a, k1b \rangle$$

4. The *distributive property* assumes two forms.
   a) A vector can be multiplied by the *sum of two scalars*.
   $$(k + 1) \langle a, b \rangle = \langle (k + 1 \cdot a), (k + 1 \cdot b) \rangle$$
   b) The *sum of two vectors* can be multiplied by a scalar.
   $$k(\langle a, b \rangle + \langle c, d \rangle) = \langle ka, kb \rangle + \langle kc, kd \rangle$$

We may now summarize the properties of vector addition and scalar multiplication.

	Addition	Scalar Multiplication
Closure	Yes	Does not apply
Associative	Yes $\langle a, b \rangle + (\langle c, d \rangle + \langle e, f \rangle)$ $= (\langle a, b \rangle + \langle c, d \rangle) + \langle e, f \rangle$	Yes $k(1\langle a, b \rangle) = k1\langle a, b \rangle$
Commutative	Yes $\langle a, b \rangle + \langle c, d \rangle$ $= \langle c, d \rangle + \langle a, b \rangle$	Does not apply
Identity	Yes $\langle 0, 0 \rangle$	Yes 1
Inverse	Yes $\langle a, b \rangle + \langle -a, -b \rangle = \langle 0, 0 \rangle$	Does not apply
Distributive	Does not apply	Yes $(k + 1) \langle a, b \rangle$ $= \langle (k + 1)a, (k + 1)b \rangle$

	Both Operations
Distributive	Yes $k(\langle a, b \rangle + \langle c, d \rangle)$ $= \langle ka, kb \rangle + \langle kc, kd \rangle$

A mathematical system with these properties is called a *vector space*. The vector space we have developed is a two-dimensional system. Each vector $\langle a, b \rangle$ has two components, a and b, and lies in a plane that has two dimensions.

A vector space may be three dimensional; in which case, each vector would be written $\langle a, b, c \rangle$. It is possible to construct an abstract vector space in any number of "dimensions." Such a space is called an *n*-space. While this may sound very complicated, abstract vectors can have quite ordinary applications.

A vector space of two dimensions has the *same number of elements* and the *same properties* as the complex number system. When two mathematical systems behave in this manner, they are said to be *isomorphic*.

The Dot Product of Vectors

We have already mentioned that several types of products exist in vector multiplication, due to the dual nature of a vector. In this section, we shall discuss one of these new products—the *dot product* (also called the *inner product*).

> **Definition 4.12** The *dot product* of two vectors, $\langle a, b \rangle$ and $\langle c, d \rangle$, is the scalar $(ac + bd)$.

The product is denoted by a big dot imprinted more heavily than the multiplication dot symbol.

Example 1. $\langle 2, 3 \rangle \bullet \langle -2, 5 \rangle = 2(-2) + 3 \cdot 5 = 11$.

Example 2. $\langle 3, 0 \rangle \bullet \langle -1, -5 \rangle = 3(-1) + 0 \cdot -5 = -3$.

Example 3. $\langle 3, 4 \rangle \bullet \langle -4, 3 \rangle = 3(-4) + 4 \cdot 3 = 0$.

Example 4. $\langle 1, 0 \rangle \bullet \langle 0, 1 \rangle = 1 \cdot 0 + 0 \cdot 1 = 0$.

One of the uses of the dot product is to define the *length* of a vector.

> **Definition 4.13** The *length of the vector* $\langle a, b \rangle$ is defined as the square root of the dot product $\langle a, b \rangle \bullet \langle a, b \rangle$.

Thus the length of the vector $\langle a, b \rangle$ is $\sqrt{\langle a, b \rangle \bullet \langle a, b \rangle} = \sqrt{a^2 + b^2}$.

Example 1. The length of the vector $\langle 3, 4 \rangle$ is $\sqrt{3^2 + 4^2} = \sqrt{9 + 16} = \sqrt{25} = 5$.

Example 2. The length of the vector $\langle -3, -4 \rangle$ is $\sqrt{(-3)^2 + (-4)^2} = 5$.

Obviously, the direction of a vector does not affect its length.

The dot product is also used to determine the angle between two vectors, but we shall leave this application for later study, since certain knowledge of trigonometry is needed.

EXERCISE 4.6

1. Find the sum of the following vectors.
    a) $\langle 3, 5 \rangle + \langle 2, 7 \rangle$
    b) $\langle -2, 1 \rangle + \langle 3, -1 \rangle$
    c) $\langle -5, 6 \rangle + \langle 1, 4 \rangle$
    d) $\langle 0, 1 \rangle + \langle 1, -1 \rangle$

2. Find the magnitude of the following vectors.
    a) $\langle 2, 3 \rangle$
    b) $\langle 7, 9 \rangle$
    c) $\langle 2, 0 \rangle$
    d) $\langle -2, 0 \rangle$
    e) $\langle 0, 2 \rangle$
    f) $\langle 0, -2 \rangle$

3. Assume that each of the vectors in Problem 2 originates at the origin of the Cartesian coordinate system. Sketch each vector on the coordinate system. Vectors that originate at the origin are called *position vectors*.

4. Find the vector that originates in the first coordinate and terminates in the second coordinate. Sketch each vector.
   a) (2, 3), (5, 7)   b) (−4, −2), (−6, −5)
   c) (−1, 1), (0, 0)   d) (0, 0), (−4, −3)

5. Perform the indicated scalar multiplication.
   a) $2\langle 3, 4\rangle$ b) $a\langle c, d\rangle$
   c) $3(\langle 4, 5\rangle + \langle 3, 2\rangle)$ d) $3(4\langle 5, 6\rangle)$
   e) $(3 \cdot 4)\langle 5, 6\rangle$

6. Find the dot product.
   a) $\langle 2, 3\rangle \bullet \langle 7, 1\rangle$ b) $\langle 0, 1\rangle \bullet \langle 1, -1\rangle$
   c) $\langle 6, 2\rangle \bullet \langle -3, 1\rangle$ d) $\langle -1, -2\rangle \bullet \langle -3, -5\rangle$

7. Determine whether the following postulates apply to the dot product.
   a) closure   b) associative
   c) commutative

8. Solve for the unknown vector or scalar.
   a) $\langle x, y\rangle + \langle 2, 3\rangle = \langle 4, 5\rangle$ b) $2\langle x, y\rangle = \langle 4, 8\rangle$
   c) $-3\langle x, y\rangle = \langle -2, -3\rangle$ d) $k\langle 3, 7\rangle = \langle 0, 0\rangle$
   e) $k\langle 4, 5\rangle \bullet \langle 2, 2\rangle = 9$

9. Assume that we define a new product of vectors, symbolized by x (called the vector product).

$$\langle a, b\rangle \times \langle c, d\rangle = \langle ac - bd, ad + bc\rangle$$

   Use this definition to find
   a) $\langle 2, 3\rangle \times \langle 1, 3\rangle$
   b) Find the product of the complex numbers (2, 3) and (1, 3).

   [*Note:* The answers to a) and b) are the same except for the symbols. With a definition for the product of vectors, we can show that a vector and a complex number have the same structure.]

10. Considering Problem 9, conjecture a geometric interpretation of the product of two complex numbers.

4.6 APPLICATION OF VECTORS

Applications of the mathematical system of vectors are numerous. Although many scientific applications require an extensive study of vectors, there are several that we can appreciate with the knowledge we have gained so far.

Everyday physical concepts such as *velocity*, *acceleration*, and *force* are vector quantities. The theories behind electric currents and magnetism has been developed vectorially, and the subject of geometry can be studied with the use of vectors. In this text, however, we shall confine our discussion to an examination of velocity and force vectors.

94 Other Mathematical Systems   4.6

Consider a rope tug-of-war between two boys. If the tug-of-war is a tie, this means that the two boys have pulled on the rope with a force of the same magnitude but in opposite directions.

Let us assume that each boy pulled on the rope with a force of 100 pounds. We can then represent the tug-of-war as shown in Figure 4.12.

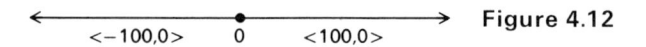

Figure 4.12

When we add the two vectors $\langle -100, 0 \rangle + \langle 100, 0 \rangle$, the sum is the vector $\langle 0, 0 \rangle$. This vector $\langle 0, 0 \rangle$ is called the *resultant force*.

Let us modify the tug-of-war somewhat. We will not change the magnitude but will alter the direction. Instead of the same forces acting in opposite directions, we will let them act at right angles to each other as shown in Figure 4.13.

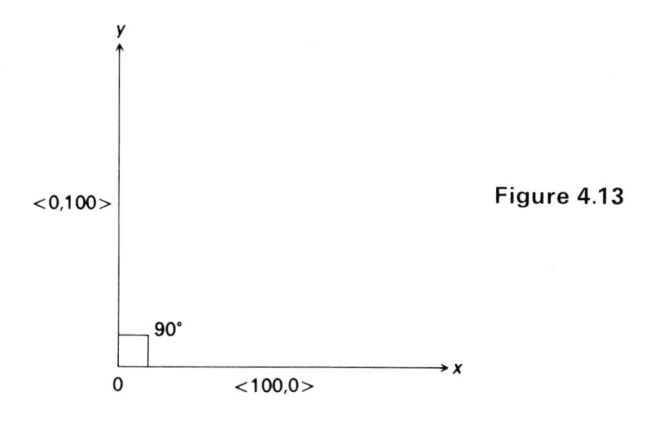

Figure 4.13

Notice that the components of the left vector have been changed. The basis for making this change is the representation of vectors in the coordinate plane.

If we consider the horizontal vector to be along the *x*-axis and the vertical vector to lie along the *y*-axis, then the horizontal vector becomes $\langle 100, 0 \rangle$ and the vertical vector $\langle 0, 100 \rangle$. (We have merely made a slight change in the notation to indicate that in each case, we wish to consider the directed-line segment instead of the two points.)

Let us again add the vectors, $\langle 100, 0 \rangle + \langle 0, 100 \rangle = \langle 100, 100 \rangle$. The resultant vector is no longer $\langle 0, 0 \rangle$ but a vector with a component of 100 in the horizontal position and 100 in the vertical position. This is illustrated in Figure 4.14.

We may now generalize the concept of a force vector. If the vector is $\langle a, b \rangle$, then *a* represents the horizontal component and *b* represents the vertical component*. The magnitude of the vector is the scalar $\sqrt{a^2 + b^2}$. Thus the magnitude of the resultant vector in Figure 4.14 is $100\sqrt{2}$. The following examples are illustrations of force vectors.

---

*See page 88 for the meaning of *a* and *b*.

4.6 Application of Vectors

Figure 4.14

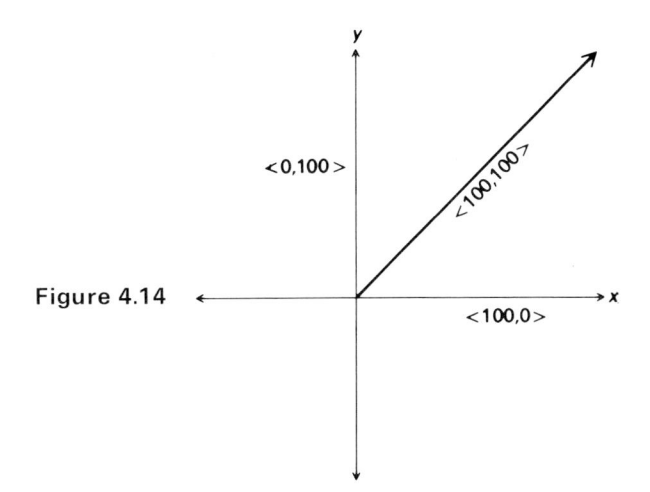

Example 1. A force of 3 pounds acting horizontally to the right and a force of 4 pounds acting vertically upward.

Magnitude: $\sqrt{3^2 + 4^2} = 5$.

Direction: As shown in Figure 4.15.

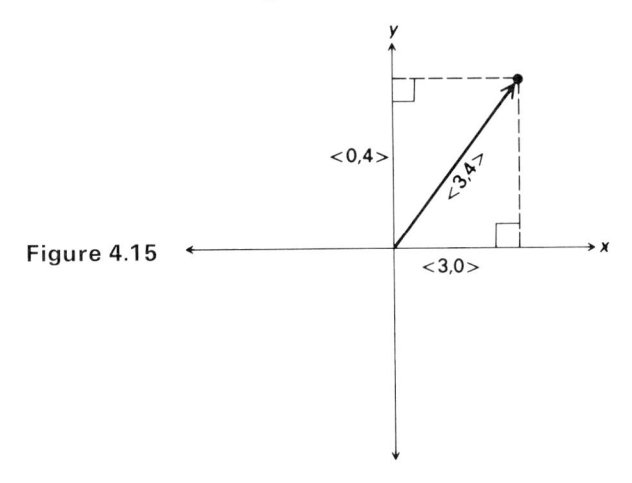

Figure 4.15

Example 2. A force of 3 pounds acting horizontally to the left and a force of 4 pounds acting vertically downward.

Magnitude: $\sqrt{(-3)^2 + (-4)^2} = 5$.
Direction: As shown in Figure 4.16.

The direction of the resultant vector would normally be indicated in terms of an angle, as illustrated in Figure 4.17.

Obviously, the two components of the resultant force determine both the magnitude and direction of the force.

96 Other Mathematical Systems   4.6

Figure 4.16

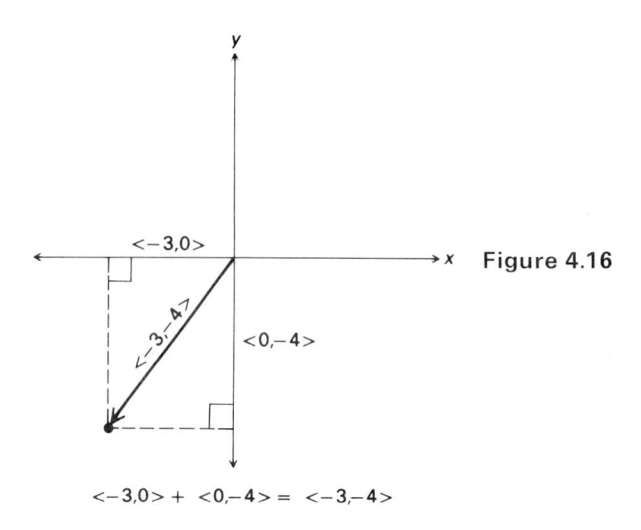

$\langle-3,0\rangle + \langle 0,-4\rangle = \langle-3,-4\rangle$

We shall now consider the velocity vector. In everyday usage, we regard velocity and speed as synonymous. But, as used in mathematics and physics, speed is the magnitude of the velocity vector. *Speed* is a scalar, and *velocity* is a vector quantity—that is, it has both direction and magnitude. The concept of velocity is illustrated in the following examples.

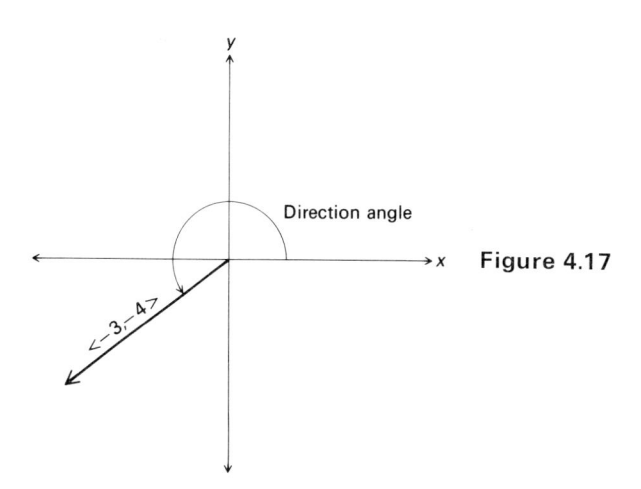

Figure 4.17

Example 1. A river has a current of 10 miles per hour. An outboard motor can propel a boat at 15 miles per hour in still water. When the boat proceeds against the current, the resultant is 5 miles per hour upstream. If we let the x-axis have the same direction as the stream, we can represent the velocity vectors for the current and the boat, as shown in Figure 4.18.

Resultant velocity vector: $\langle 15, 0\rangle + \langle -10, 0\rangle = \langle 5, 0\rangle$.
Speed: $\sqrt{5^2 + 0^2} = 5$ mph.

4.6 Application of Vectors

Figure 4.18

```
          <-10,0>           <15,0>
River <----------•---------> x-axis
      Current    0   Boat
```

Example 2. When the boat in Example 1 proceeds downstream (with the current), the velocity is

$$\text{Current} \qquad \text{Boat}$$
$$\langle -10, 0 \rangle + \langle -15, 0 \rangle = \langle -25, 0 \rangle$$

Speed: $\sqrt{(-25)^2 + (0)^2} = 25$ mph.

Example 3. A boy decides to swim across a river that is 2 miles wide. He can swim in still water at a rate of 4 miles per hour. The river has a current of 3 miles per hour. What is the velocity vector? If we again let the x-axis lie in the direction of the river, we can represent the velocity vectors for the boy and the river current, as shown in Figure 4.19.

Resultant velocity vector: $\langle -3, 0 \rangle + \langle 0, 4 \rangle = \langle -3, 4 \rangle$.
Speed: $\sqrt{(-3^2) + 4^2} = 25 = 5$ mph.

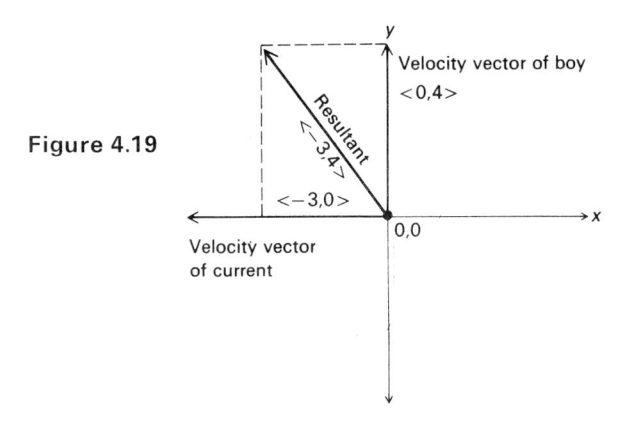

Figure 4.19

Example 4. An airplane can fly at 400 miles per hour in still air. When the plane flies north, there is a 50-mile per hour wind from the west. What is the velocity vector and the speed of the airplane? We let the x-axis be in the east-west direction and sketch the velocity vectors, as shown in Figure 4.20.

Resultant velocity vector: $\langle 50, 0 \rangle = \langle 0, 400 \rangle = \langle 50, 400 \rangle$.
Speed: $\sqrt{(50)^2 + (400)^2} = \sqrt{162,500} = 403$ mph (approximately).

Figure 4.20

Airplane still-air velocity <0,400>
Resultant velocity vector <50,400>
Wind <50,0>

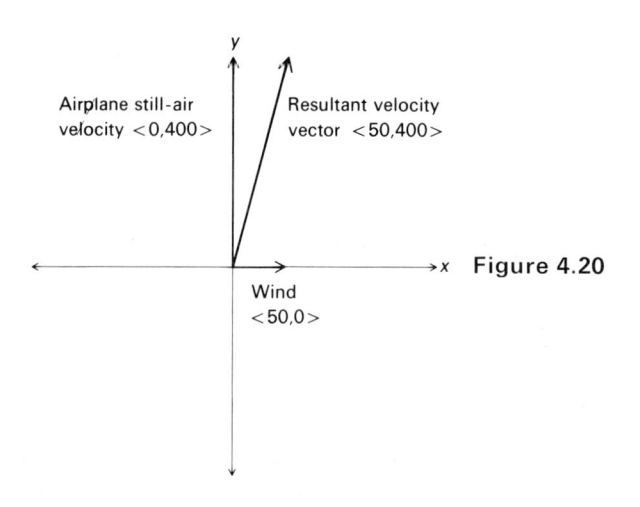

EXERCISE 4.7

1. Distinguish between speed and velocity. Under what conditions is the speed of an object equal to one of the components of the velocity vector?

2. A force of 300 pounds is applied to an object in the east direction. Another force of 400 pounds is applied to the object in the south direction. Represent these force vectors geometrically.

3. What is the resultant force vector in problem 2? Represent these vectors geometrically.

4. Three forces are applied to an object—one east, one north, and one northeast. What is the resultant force vector?
Represent it geometrically.

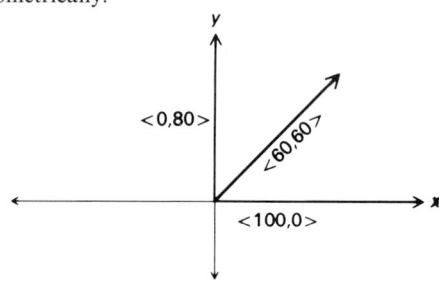

<0,80> <60,60> <100,0>

5. An airplane is flying northeast at the rate of 400 miles per hour. At what rate is the plane moving east? At what rate is it moving north?

REFERENCES

Byrne, J. Richard. *Number Systems: An Elementary Approach.* New York: McGraw-Hill, 1967.

Haag, Vincent H. and Donald W. Western. *Introduction to College Mathematics.* New York: Holt, Rinehart and Winston, 1968.

Hamilton, Norman and Joseph Laudin. *Set Theory and the Structure of Arithmetic.* Boston: Allyn and Bacon, 1961.

Hohn, Franz E. *Elementary Matrix Algebra,* 2d ed. New York: Macmillan, 1964.

Stanton, R. G. and K. D. Fryer. *Topics in Modern Mathematics.* Englewood Cliffs, N. J.: Prentice-Hall, 1964.

Concepts of Algebra 5

5.1 INTRODUCTION TO ALGEBRA

The earliest treatment of algebra is found in an Egyptian manuscript, dated 1700 B.C., in which this simple equation appears: "Hau (heap), its seventh, its whole, it makes 19." Today, we would write this equation as $x/7 + x = 19$. Egyptian algebra was rudimentary, but even the Greeks were capable of solving equations only by using geometric forms. The oldest written text in the Western world on algebra is by Diophantus of Alexandria, who lived in the fourth century A.D. In his work, *Arithmetica*, he presents methods of simplifying equations that are still used today.

The development of algebra among the Hindus and Arabs seems to have preceded further advances in European countries. The first notable Arabian algebraist was Mohammed Ben Musa al-Khowarizmi, whose studies in algebra in the ninth century A.D. bore the name *Ilm al-Jebrwa'l-Mugabola*. Presumably, the name "algebra" is derived from this title.

Italian mathematicians led the renaissance of mathematics in Europe. For example, Lucas Paciolus published an important work on the subject in 1494. Scipio Ferro discovered the solution of one case of the cubic equation in 1505. Two others, Tartaglia of Buscia and Cardano of Milan, both extended a solution that came to be known as Cardan's rule.

During the fifteenth and sixteenth centuries, the French mathematicians Vieta and Descartes introduced the practice of representing an unknown quantity in an equation with a letter of the alphabet.

Historically, the concept of algebra was limited to solutions of equations in the system of real numbers and, as such, was a mathematical system itself. Today, the *concept of algebra* has been generalized to become *the study of mathematical systems involving operations.*

5.2 ALGEBRAIC EXPRESSIONS

In preceding chapters, we have made statements with general application by using a letter of the alphabet to represent members of a set. This enabled us to make a statement that would hold for all members of the set. For example, if our set N is the set of even natural numbers, then we know that $2 \in N$, $4 \in N$, etc., but the futility of listing all elements of the set N is apparent. Instead, we may write $2n \in N (n \in N)$ and refer to any one of the elements of set N. The term $2n$ is an example of an algebraic expression.

Since n has no specific value and may be assigned to represent any element of the set N, n is called a *variable*, and the set N is the *replacement set* or *domain of the variable*. The individual numbers of the replacement set $\{1, 2, 3, \ldots\}$ are the values of the variable. When the variable can be assigned to only one value of the replacement set, it is called a *constant*.

An expression that contains a variable, such as $2n$, is called an *open expression* because the value of n is not known. That is, we do not know the value of $2n$ until the value of n has been specified. By letting the variable assume particular values from the replacement set, the numerical value of an expression can be found. This process is called *evaluating the expression*.

An algebraic expression that is written as a product or quotient of constants or variables or both is called a *term*. In an expression that contains more than one term, the individual terms are joined by addition or subtraction. To illustrate, the expressions,

$$3x, \quad 9xy, \quad \frac{(x+2)}{3}, \quad \frac{2(x-1)}{3xy}$$

each contain one term, while each of the expressions,

$$2x + y, \quad 3x + 2y + 1, \quad \frac{x}{2} + \frac{y}{2} - \frac{4}{xy}$$

have more than one term.

Example. Evaluate $\dfrac{3x}{y}$, when $x = 4$ and $y = 6$.

Solution. By substituting the values for x and y, we have

$$\frac{3x}{y} = \frac{3 \cdot 4}{6} = \frac{12}{6} = 2.$$

EXERCISE 5.1
Evaulate the following expressions.

1. $\dfrac{x+y}{x-y}$, where $x = 3$ and $y = 2$.

2. $2x(x+3) - y(y+2) + \dfrac{3y}{x}$, where $x = 6$ and $y = 10$.

3. $\dfrac{3x+4y}{x-y} + 2x$, where $x = 2$ and $y = -1$.

4. $(2n+1)(3m-1) + 2n$, where $n = 6$ and $m = 4$.

5. $\dfrac{2n(m+3)}{3m(n+2)} - \dfrac{3n(m-3)}{2m(m-2)}$, where $n = 4$ and $m = 5$.

6. $\dfrac{1}{2}bh$, where $b = 10$ and $h = 7$ (Area of a triangle).

7. $2(l+w)$, where $l = 48$ and $w = 32$ (Perimeter of a rectangle).

8. $E = IR$, where $I = 1$, $E = 110$ (Ohm's law).

9. $W = IV$, where $W = 300$, $V = 110$ (watts = amps × volts).

10. πd, where $\pi = 3.1416$, $d = 12$ (Circumference of a circle).
11. $\dfrac{h(b_1 + b_2)}{2}$, where $b_1 = 10$, $b_2 = 16$, and $h = 6$ (Area of a trapezoid).
12. $\dfrac{9C}{5} + 32$, where $C = 35$ (degrees centigrade to degrees fahrenheit).
13. Sum of the first *n-positive* integers, $1 + 2, +3, + \cdots + n$; $\dfrac{n(n + 1)}{2}$ where $n = 10$,
14. P·r·t, where $P = 1000$, $r = .06$, and $t = 5$ (simple interest).

5.3 ALGEBRAIC SENTENCES

Recall that *a proposition is a sentence that can be meaningfully called true or false*. Consider the following sentence.

The city of a is in Tennessee.

The sentence as written, is neither true nor false. If the replacement set of a is the cities in the United States, then the sentence is true if a is replaced by *Memphis*. However, if a is replaced by *Atlanta*, then the sentence is false. The sentence becomes true or false as the variable a is replaced by one of the elements in the replacement set. Thus a sentence that contains a variable is *neither* true nor false, since the value of the variable is left open. A sentence that contains a variable is called an *open sentence*.

A sentence that is composed of algebraic expressions related by one of the symbols $=$ (equal), $\neq$ (not equal), $<$ (less than), $>$ (greater than), $\leq$ (less than or equal), $\geq$ (greater than or equal) is called an *algebraic sentence*. An algebraic sentence in which the expressions are related by the symbol $=$ is called an *equation*. For example,

$$2x + 1 = 9$$

is an equation that states that the expression $2x + 1$, on the left side of the equal sign, has the same value as the expression 9, on the right side. Suppose we let the replacement set be (3, 4), then it would be possible to determine which values of x makes the equation true.

$$\begin{array}{ll} 2x + 1 = 9 & \quad 2x + 1 = 9 \\ 2(3) + 1 = 9 & \quad 2(4) + 1 = 9 \\ 6 + 1 = 9 & \quad 8 + 1 = 9 \\ 7 = 9 \ \text{(False)} & \quad 9 = 9 \ \text{(True)} \end{array}$$

The subset of the replacement set that makes the equation true is called the *solution set*. The solution set of $2x + 1 = 9$ is $\{4\}$. When the solution set has been found, the equation has been solved, and each member of the solution set is thus a *root* of the equation.

When one of the symbols $\neq$, $<$, $\leq$, $>$, $\geq$ is used to show the relation between expressions, the sentence is called an *inequality*. That is,

$$2x + 1 < 9$$

is an inequality that states that the value of the expression on the left side of the equality sign is less than the value of the expression on the right side. Again, using (3, 4) as the replacement set, it is possible to determine which values of x make the inequality true.

$$2x + 1 < 9 \qquad\qquad 2x + 1 < 9$$
$$2(3) + 1 < 9 \qquad\qquad 2(4) + 1 < 9$$
$$6 + 1 < 9 \qquad\qquad 8 + 1 < 9$$
$$7 < 9 \text{ (True)} \qquad\qquad 9 < 9 \text{ (False)}$$

The solution set is $\{3\}$.

The solution set of an algebraic sentence may be illustrated by a graph. The graph of an algebraic sentence that contains only one variable is usually a point on the horizontal number line.

Example 1. Solve the equation $3x - 1 = 5$, where the replacement set is the set $\{1, 2, 3\}$, and locate its graph on the number line.

Solution.

$$3x - 1 = 5 \qquad\qquad 3x - 1 = 5 \qquad\qquad 3x - 1 = 5$$
$$3(1) - 1 = 5 \qquad\qquad 3(2) - 1 = 5 \qquad\qquad 3(3) - 1 = 5$$
$$3 - 1 = 5 \qquad\qquad 6 - 1 = 5 \qquad\qquad 9 - 1 = 5$$
$$2 = 5 \text{ (False)} \qquad 5 = 5 \text{ (True)} \qquad 8 = 5 \text{ (False)}$$

The truth set is $\{2\}$.

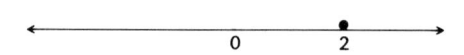

Example 2. Solve the inequality $3x + 2 \leqslant 11$, where the replacement set is $\{1, 3\}$, and locate its graph on the number line.

Solution.
$$3x + 2 \leqslant 11 \qquad\qquad 3x + 2 \leqslant 11$$
$$3(1) + 2 \leqslant 11 \qquad\qquad 3(3) + 2 \leqslant 11$$
$$3 + 2 \leqslant 11 \qquad\qquad 9 + 2 \leqslant 11$$
$$5 \leqslant 11 \text{ (True)} \qquad\qquad 11 \leqslant 11 \text{ (True)}$$

The truth set is $\{1, 3\}$.

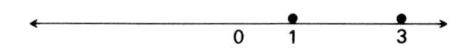

Example 3. Solve the inequality $3x - 1 \neq 5$, where the replacement set is $\{2, 3, 4, 5\}$, and locate its graph on the number line.

Solution. The inequality $2x - 1 \neq 5$ can be restated as $2x - 1 < 5$ or $2x - 1 > 5$. The solution set will contain the values of x that make either of the two inequalities true.

5.3 Algebraic Sentences

By substitution we find that

$2(2) - 1 < 5$ (True)	$2(2) - 1 > 5$ (False)
$2(4) - 1 < 5$ (False)	$2(4) - 1 > 5$ (True)
$2(5) - 1 < 5$ (False)	$2(5) - 1 > 5$ (True)

The solution set is $\{2, 4, 5\}$.

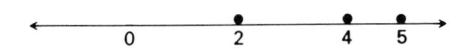

$$\longleftarrow\underset{0}{\quad}\underset{2}{\bullet}\quad\underset{4}{\bullet}\underset{5}{\bullet}\longrightarrow$$

Example 4. Solve the inequality $1 < x < 5$, where the replacement set is $\{1, 2, 3, 4, 5\}$, and locate its graph on the number line.

Solution. $1 < x < 5$

$1 < 1 < 5$ (False) $1 < 3 < 5$ (True)
$1 < 2 < 5$ (True) $1 < 4 < 5$ (True)
                         $1 < 5 < 5$ (False)

The solution set is $\{2, 3, 4\}$.

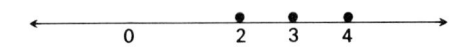

$$\longleftarrow\underset{0}{\quad}\underset{2}{\bullet}\underset{3}{\bullet}\underset{4}{\bullet}\longrightarrow$$

EXERCISE 5.2

Determine the solution set for the algebraic statements from the given replacement sets and show each graph on number lines.

1. $x - 3 = 4$, $x \in \{1, 3, 5, 7\}$
2. $2x + 1 = 9$, $x \in \{0, 1, 4\}$
3. $x + 2 = 5$, $x \in \{1, 3, 5\}$
4. $2x + 1 \geqslant x + 7$, $x \in \{4, 5, 6, 7\}$
5. $x + 3 = 2x - 4$, $x \in \{3, 5, 7, 9\}$
6. $5x - 2 \leqslant 2x + 4$, $x \in \{0, 1, 2, 3\}$
7. $8 \neq 3y + 2$, $x \in \{1, 2, 3\}$
8. $\dfrac{x}{2} + 1 \geqslant x - 3$, $x \in \{5, 6, 7\}$
9. $\dfrac{x}{2} < x + 2$, $x \in \{2, 4, 6\}$
10. $2(x + 3) = 2x + 3$, $x \in \{1, 2, 3\}$
11. $2x + 1 = x - 2$, $x \in N$
12. $x - 3 \leqslant 3x - 4$, $x \in N$
13. $x \leqslant x \leqslant 6$, $x \in N$
14. $-2 \geqslant 2x \geqslant -5$, $x \in (-1, -2, -3\}$
15. $2x \geqslant 5$ or $\leqslant -2$, $x \in \{-3, -2, 0, 1, 2, 3\}$

In the following statements, substitute the values from the given replacement sets and tell whether the resulting equations are true or false.

16. $3x + 27 = 6xy$, $x \in \{1, 2\}, y \in \{1, 2\}$
17. $2(2x - 7) = (4x(-y))$, $x \in \{0, 1\}, y \in \{0, 2\}$
18. $3x + 2 < 5x + 2y$, $x \in \{4, 7, 0\}, y \in \{0, 1\}$
19. $10 + 8x - 2 < 2x + 12 + 4x$, $x \in \{2, 1\}$
20. $x + yz = (x + y)z$, $x \in \{0, 1\}, y \in \{0, 3\}, z \in \{2\}$
21. $\dfrac{x \cdot x - y \cdot y}{x - y} = x + y$, $x \in \{2, 4\}, y \in \{2, 4\}$
22. $5x + 3y - 2 > 2x + 3y + 6$, $x \in \{2, 3\}, y \in \{3\}$
23. $x(y + z) \neq xy + z$, where (a) $x = 4, y = 2, z = 3$ and (b) $x = 2, y = 1, z = 2$

24. $\dfrac{xy + y}{y} \leqslant xy$, where (a) $x = 1, y = 2$ and (b) $x = 3, y = 1$

25. $(x - y)(x + y) \leqslant x \cdot x - y \cdot y \leqslant (x + y)(x + y)$ where (a) $x = 2, y = 3$ and (b) $x = -3, y = -2$.

5.4 SOLUTIONS FOR EQUATIONS WITH ONE VARIABLE

Suppose that we are given the equation

$$2x + 1 = 5$$

whose domain is the set of real numbers and are asked to find the solution set. The solution is found by writing a series of equivalent equations—based on the axioms of equality and real numbers—that result in a simple statement that gives the value of the variables.

Example 1. Solve the equation $2x + 1 = 5$ and locate it on the solution number line.

Solution. $2x + 1 = 5$ [Given equation]
$2x + 1 + -1 = 5 + -1$ [Add (-1)]
$2x + 0 = 4$ [$1 + (-1) = 0$]
$2x = 4$ [$2x + 0 = 2x$]
$\frac{1}{2}(2x) = \frac{1}{2}(4)$ [Multiply by $\frac{1}{2}$]
$x = 2$

The solution set is $\{2\}$.

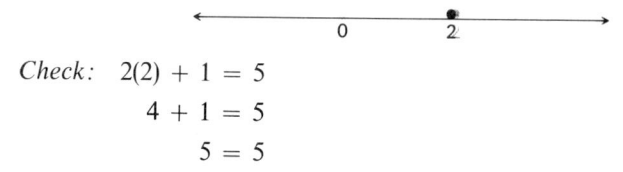

Check: $2(2) + 1 = 5$
$4 + 1 = 5$
$5 = 5$

Example 2. Solve the equation $3x - 2 = x - 6$, whose domain is the set of real numbers, and locate the solution on the number line.

Solution. $3x - 2 = x - 6$ [Given equation]
$3x + -x - 2 + 2 = x + -x - 6 + 2$ [Add $-x, 2$]
$2x = -4$
$\frac{1}{2}(2x) = \frac{1}{2}(-4)$ [Multiply by $\frac{1}{2}$]
$x = -2$

The solution set is (-2).

Check: $3(-2) - 2 = -2 - 6$
$-6 - 2 = -2 - 6$
$-6 = -6$

The equation for solving an applied problem is always based on information contained within the problem.

Example 3. Susie bought a hamburger and a coke for 45 cents. The hamburger costs twice as much as the coke. What was the price of each?

Solution. Let x represent the cost of the coke. Then $2x$ represents the cost of the hamburger. The total cost is 45 cents. Thus

$$x + 2x = 45 ¢$$
$$3x = 45 ¢$$
$$x = 15 ¢ \quad [\text{Cost of coke}]$$
$$2x = 30 ¢ \quad [\text{Cost of hamburger}]$$

Check: $15 ¢ + 2(15 ¢) = 45 ¢$
$45 ¢ = 45 ¢$

Example 4. A pound of ground chuck costs 12 cents a pound more than regular beef. If Mrs. Jones bought 2 pounds of ground chuck and 3 pounds of ground beef and her total bill was $4.09, what was the price per pound of each?

Solution. Let x represent the cost of a pound of ground beef. Then $x + .12$ represents the cost of a pound of ground chuck. Thus

$$3(x) + 2(x + .12) = 4.09$$
$$3x + 2x + .24 = 4.09$$
$$5x = 3.85$$
$$x = .77 \quad [\text{Cost of a pound of ground beef}]$$
$$x + .12 = .77 + .12 = .89 \quad [\text{Cost of a pound of ground chuck}]$$

EXERCISE 5.3

Solve the following equations and check the solution. (The domain is the set of real numbers.)

1. $2x + 3x = 40 - 15$
2. $5x - 2x = 6 + 9$
3. $14 = 9x - 2x$
4. $x + \frac{1}{2}x = 6$
5. $24 = 3x - 6 - x$
6. $\frac{3x}{2} - x = 4$
7. $72 = 9x + 36$
8. $2a + 5 = \frac{3a}{2}$
9. $\frac{2x}{3} + \frac{x}{2} = 7$
10. $4y + 3y = 5y - 16$
11. $1.5x + .75 = 3$
12. $\frac{3b}{4} - \frac{b}{8} = \frac{5}{2}$

13. $\frac{3}{4}z + \frac{1}{3}z = 13$

14. $\frac{13}{6}x - \left(-\frac{1}{3}x\right) = 17$

15. $\frac{3b}{5} - \frac{b}{2} = \frac{1}{5}$

16. $\frac{1}{4}x + \frac{1}{4}x = \frac{1}{4}$

17. $\frac{1}{3}y - \frac{2}{3}y = 2$

18. $2(x + 2) = 6$

19. $3(2x - 1) = 2x + 7$

20. $.5x - .2 = .3$

21. $5x + 6(x - 1) = 3(2x) + 4$

22. $25 + (5a + 7) = 32 - a$

23. $10x - 5 + 5x - 10 = 0$

24. $2t + 3 - t + 1 = -t$

Solve the following formulas for the letter indicated.

25. $A = \frac{1}{2}bh$, solve for h. (Area of a triangle)
26. $P = 2(1 + w)$, solve for 1. (Perimeter of a rectangle)
27. $C = 2\pi r$, solve for π. (Circumference of a circle)
28. $S = \frac{a}{1 - r}$, solve for a. (Sum of an infinite series)

29. John is twice as old as Mary, and the sum of their ages is 21 years. How old is each?

30. A flower garden is rectangular in shape; its length is 3 feet less than twice its width; and its perimeter is 30 feet. What are its dimensions?

31. Mr. and Mrs. Camp have three children, and the sum of their ages is 36 years. The ages are such that the oldest child is 3 years less than twice the age of the youngest child, who is 3 years less than the next older. What are the ages of the three children?

32. The sum of two numbers is 24. If three times the smaller number is increased by twice the larger number, the sum is 54. What are the two numbers?

33. Mr. Brown buys 324 feet of fencing to enclose a rectangular plot of ground that is 18 feet longer than it is wide. What are the dimensions of the lot?

34. Tom is twice as old as John, but in 6 years John will be $\frac{3}{4}$ as old as Tom. Find their present ages.

35. If the difference between a certain number and 5 is multiplied by 6, the product is 24. What is the number?

36. Two planes leave the airport at the same time but fly in opposite directions. One plane flies 40 miles per hour faster than the other, and in 2 hours they are 1520 miles apart. Find the speed for each plane.

37. A man invests $5000 in stocks and bonds. The stocks pay an annual interest rate of $5\frac{1}{2}\%$, and the bonds pay 6%. In one year, he receives $280 in interest. How much did he invest in each?

38. A woman purchases a dress, purse, and shoes; the total cost is $74. The shoes cost $2 more than the purse, and the dress twice as much as the purse. What is the cost of each item?

39. The perimeter of a triangle is 102 inches. The longest side is twice the length of the shortest side, and the other side is 6 inches less than 1.5 times shorter than the side. Find the dimensions of the triangle.

40. Company A sells $\frac{1}{2}$ as many insurance policies as Company B, while Company C sells sells 50% more than Company B. In one month, the total sales of the three companies was 120 policies. How many policies did each company sell?

5.5 SOLUTION FOR INEQUALITIES WITH ONE VARIABLE

For any real numbers, a and b, exactly one of the following relationships is true:

$$a = b, \quad a > b, \quad \text{or} \quad a < b$$

These relationships are called the *trichotomy axiom*. The equality $a = b$ is true if and only if $a - b = 0$. The inequality $a > b$ is true if and only if $a - b > 0$. Also, the inequality $a < b$ is true if and only if $a - b < 0$.

In addition to the axioms for real numbers given in Chapter 3, we must include the following *order axioms*, if we are to solve statements of inequality.

1. If a, b and c are real numbers such that $a > b$, then $a + c > b + c$ (*Additive axiom for inequality*).
2. If a and b are real numbers, $a > b$, and c is a real number greater than 0, then $ac > bc$ (*Multiplication axiom for inequality*).
3. If a, b, and c are real numbers such that $a > b$ and $b > c$, then $a > c$ (*Transitive axiom for inequality*).

The multiplication axiom for inequality requires that c be a positive number. If c is a negative number, then when multiplication is performed, the direction of the inequality is reversed. To illustrate: suppose that we have the inequality

$$4 > 2$$

If we multiply by a negative number, say -1, we have

$$-4 < -2$$

In general, if $a > b$ and $c < 0$, then

$$ac < bc \quad \text{and} \quad \frac{a}{c} < \frac{b}{c}$$

Example 1. Solve the inequality $2x + 1 > 5$, where the domain of x is the set of real numbers.

Solution. $2x + 1 > 5$

$2x + 1 + -1 > 5 + -1$

$2x > 4$

$x > 2$

The solution set is $x > 2$.

The open circle in the diagram indicates that the value 2 is not in the solution set. This is called *open interval* notation (2, ∞) and the parenthesis indicates that the value, 2, is not the solution set.

Example 2. Solve the inequality $3x - 2 \leqslant 7$.

Solution.
$$3x - 2 \leqslant 7$$
$$3x - 2 + 2 \leqslant 7 + 2$$
$$3x \leqslant 9$$
$$x \leqslant 3$$

The solution set is $x \leqslant 3$.

The closed circle indicates that the value 3 is in the solution set. This is called *closed interval* notation $[-\infty, 3)$ and indicates that the value, 3, is included in the solution set. The values ∞ and −∞ are always left open, since such values are boundless.

EXERCISE 5.4

In each statement replace ? with one of the symbols, $<, \leqslant, >, \geqslant$ to obtain a true statement. All variables are real numbers.

1. If $x > y$, then $3x$? $3y$.
2. If $x < -y$, then $-x$? y.
3. If $x \leqslant y$ then, $x - 5$? $y - 5$.
4. If $5 + x \geqslant 5 + y$, then x ? y.
5. If $x \geqslant y$ and $y > z - 2$, then x ? $z - 2$.
6. If $x = -6, y = 12$, and $z = -2$, then xz ? yz.
7. If $2(x + 6) = y + 12$ then, x ? y.

Answer each statement as true or false. If false, give a counter example.

8. If $x < y$ and $y < 0$, then $xy < 0$.
9. If $x < y$ and $y > 0$, then $x + y > 0$.
10. If $x > y$ and $y < 0$, then $xy < 0$.
11. If $x < y$ and $x > 0$, then $x - y < 0$.
12. If $x < y$ and $y < 0$, then $x - y < 0$.

Solve the inequalities and locate the solution set on the number line.

13. $3x > -6$
14. $2x + 1 < 5$
15. $\dfrac{x+1}{2} > 3$
16. $\dfrac{2x-1}{3} < 0$
17. $\dfrac{x}{2} + 1 < \dfrac{x}{3}$
18. $\dfrac{3x+1}{2} > x - \dfrac{1}{2}$
19. $3(x - 2) \leqslant 2(x + 2)$
20. $\dfrac{5(x-1)}{2} \geqslant 2x + 1$

5.6   Absolute Value

21. $2x \geq 6$ or $3x \leq -6$ 22. $x - 1 \leq 5$ and $-2x < 10$
23. A student has test grades of 84 and 93. What must his score be on the third test to have an average of 90?
24. Carley Brown and her sister, Sue, plan to buy a used compact car. The salesman tells them that he has such a car and that it will cost no more than $1200. Carley agrees that she should pay $300 more on the purchase price than Sue. What is the maximum amount that Sue should pay?
25. Lula has two assignments to prepare—one in math and one in science. She estimates that the math assignment will require 15 minutes more than twice the time for science. If she has at most 3 hours of study time, how much should she devote to the assignment in science?
26. A slice of chocolate cake contains 60 calories more than three times the calories in a glass of milk. Together they contain at least 220 calories. Find the smallest amount of calories in a glass of milk.
27. Kathy goes shopping for a new purse and dress and plans to spend at most $35 on the items. If she plans to spend $5 less than 3 times as much for the dress as for the purse, what is the maximum price she can pay for the purse?
28. Richard plans to purchase a portable radio, camera, and projector; he plans to spend at least $240. If the camera costs twice as much as the radio and the projector costs $10 less than the camera, what is the minimum price he should spend on each item?
29. A florist charges at most $15 for a mixed bouquet of two dozen flowers made up of roses and carnations. If the roses cost $10 per dozen more than the carnations, what is the maximum number of carnations that should be in the bouquet?
30. A man owns two apartments that he rents; he must receive at least $3060 in rent to break even on his investment. One apartment rents for $25 per month more than the other, but it is vacant for 3 months during the year. What is the minimum amount that should be charged for the less expensive apartment?
31. A company wants to produce a commercial brand of rubbing alcohol that is at least 84% alcohol by combining a liquid that is 74% alcohol with 5 ounces of a liquid that is 90% alcohol. What is the maximum number of ounces of the 74% alcohol that should be used?

5.6   ABSOLUTE VALUE

The distance from 0 for *any pair of numbers* that are *additive inverses of each other* is the same. That is, the distance from 0 to 5 is 5 units in the positive direction, while the distance from 0 to (−5) is 5 units in the negative direction (see the drawing).

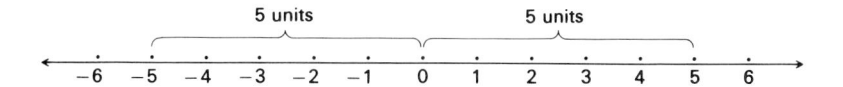

If a number is 0 or to the *right* of 0, then its distance from 0 is the number itself. On the other hand, if a number is to the *left* of 0, then its distance from 0 is its *additive inverse*. The distance from 0 of any number is its *absolute value*.

The absolute value of a number is denoted by placing the number between two vertical bars | |. Thus

$$|2| = 2$$
$$|-3| = 3$$
$$|0| = 0$$
$$|a| = a, \quad a \geq 0$$
$$|a| = -a, \quad a \leq 0.$$

Example 1. Solve the equation $|x| = 2$.

Solution. By definition, if $x \geq 0$, then $|x| = x$, and $x = 2$. If $x < 0$, then $|x| = -x$ and $-x = 2$, which gives $x = -2$.

The solution set is $\{2, -2\}$.

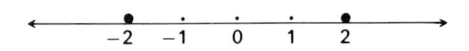

Example 2. Solve the equation $|x - 1| = 5$.

Solution. By definition, if $(x - 1) > 0$, then we have $x - 1 = 5 \Rightarrow x = 6$. If $(x - 1) < 0$, then we have

$$-(x - 1) = 5$$
$$-x + 1 = 5$$
$$-x = 4$$
$$x = -4$$

The solution set is $\{6, -4\}$.

Example 3. Solve the inequality $|x| < 2$.

Solution. If $x \geq 0$, then $|x| = x$, and we have $x < 2$. If $x < 0$, then $|x| = -x$, and we have $-x < 2$, which reduces to $x > -2$.

The solution set is $-2 < x < 2$.

The open circle around 2 and -2 indicates that these values are not in the solution set.

Example 4. Solve the inequality $|x + 1| \geq 5$.

Solution. If $(x + 1) \geq 0$, then $|x + 1| = (x + 1)$, and we have $x + 1 \geq 5$, which reduces to $x \geq 4$. If $(x + 1) < 0$, then $|x + 1| = -(x + 1)$, and we have $-(x + 1) \geq 5$, which reduces to

$$-x - 1 \geq 5$$
$$-x \geq 6$$
$$x \leq -6$$

The solution set is $x \geq 4$ or $x \leq -6$.

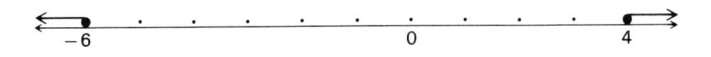

The solid circle around -6 and 4 indicates that these values are in the solution set.

Example 5. Solve $|2x| \geq 6$.

Solution. If $x \geq 0$, then $|2x| = 2x$, and we have $2x \geq 6$, which reduces to $x \geq 3$. If $x < 0$ then $|2x| = -2x$ and we have $-2x \geq 6$, which reduces to $2x \leq -6$ or $x \leq -3$. The solution set is $x \leq -3$ or $x \geq 3$.

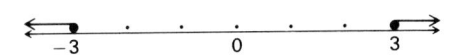

The solid circle around -3 and 3 indicates that these values are in the solution set.

EXERCISE 5.5

Evaluate the following expressions.

1. $|x| + |-2| =$
2. $|3| - |-4| =$
3. $-|2| - |10| =$
4. $|-3| + |-5| =$
5. $-2|2| + 4|-2| =$
6. $-|10| + |-10| =$
7. $-|2| - |-3| =$
8. $4(|5| + |-2|) =$
9. $x(|2| + |4|) =$
10. $-3(|-3| + |-3|) =$

Find the solution set and show it on the number line.

11. $|x| = 5$
12. $|3x| = 6$
13. $|x| + |-2| = 5$
14. $|2x| - |3| = 5$
15. $|x| < 4$
16. $|x| > 6$
17. $|2x| \leq 10$
18. $|x + 1| = 5$
19. $|x - 1| \leq 6$
20. $|2x + 3| = 15$
21. $|3x + 2| = 7$
22. $|2x - 1| \geq 5$
23. $|5x - 4| \leq 6$
24. $-2 < |x + 1|$
25. $1 < |x| < 3$

5.7 ALGEBRAIC SENTENCES FOR TWO VARIABLES

Suppose that a coin purse contains 50 cents in nickels and dimes. If we let

x = the number of nickels

and y = the number of dimes

then $5x$ = the amount of money in nickels

and $10y$ = the amount of money in dimes.

So the total amount of money in the purse can be expressed by the equation

$$5x + 10y = 50$$

Since the purse contains only 50 cents, the replacement set for x (nickels) is $A = \{0, 1, 2, 3, \ldots, 10\}$, and the replacement set for y (dimes) is $B = {0, 1, 2, \ldots, 5}$. If 8 is selected from the replacement set for x and 1 is selected from the replacement set for y, then the pair (8, 1) makes the equation true. That is,

$$5(8) + 10(1) = 50$$

The first member of the pair of numbers is the *first coordinate* and represents the value of x. The second member is the *second coordinate* and represents the value of y. Each ordered pair of numbers that makes the equation true is a *root* of the equation. The set of ordered pairs that makes the equation true is called the *solution set*. The replacement set of the equation

$$5x + 10y = 50$$

is the Cartesian product set ($A \times B$). The solution set is

$$\{(0, 5), (2, 4), (4, 3), (6, 2), (8, 1), (10, 0)\}$$

To solve an equation for two variables, begin by replacing one of the variables with a member of its replacement set. This gives an equation with one variable that can be solved by the procedure, shown in Section 5.4. If the value of the second variable is a member of its replacement set, then the ordered pair is a root of the equation.

Example 1. Find the solution set of $2x + y = 5$, when the replacement set for both x and y is $R = \{0, 1, 2, 3, 4, 5\}$.

Solution. $2x + y = 5$

$y = 5 - 2x$

x	$y = 5 - 2x$	y	Ordered Pairs (replacement set)
0	$y = 5 - 2(0)$	5	(0, 5)
1	$y = 5 - 2(1)$	3	(1, 3)
2	$y = 5 - 2(2)$	1	(2, 1)
3	$y = 5 - 2(3)$	-1	$(3, -1)$
4	$y = 5 - 2(4)$	-3	$(4, -3)$
5	$y = 5 - 2(5)$	-5	$(5, -5)$

The solution set is $\{(0, 5), (1, 3), (2, 1)\}$.

5.7 Algebraic Sentences for Two Variables

Example 2. Find the solution set of $3x - y \leqslant 3$, when the replacement set for x is $\{0, 1, 2\}$ and the replacement set for y is $\{-3, -2, 0, 2\}$.

Solution.

$$3x - y \leqslant 3$$
$$-y \leqslant 3 - 3x$$
$$y \geqslant 3x - 3$$

x	$y \geqslant 3x - 3$	y	Ordered Pairs (replacement set)
0	$y \geqslant 3(0) - 3$	$-3, -2, 0, 2$	$(0, -3), (0, -2), (0, 0), (0, 2)$
1	$y \geqslant 3(1) - 3$	$0, 2$	$(1, 0), (1, 2)$
2	$y \geqslant 3(2) - 3$	3	$(2, 3)$

The solution set is $\{(0, -3), (0, -2), (0, 0), (0, 2), (1, 0), (1, 2)\}$.

EXERCISE 5.6

Find the solution set of each algebraic statement, when the replacement sets for x and y are those stated.

1. $x + y = 4$ $x \in \{2, 4, 5\}, y \in \{-1, 0, 1, 2\}$
2. $2x + 3y = 12$ $x \in \{1, 3, 4, 5, 6\}, y \in \{2, 4, 6\}$
3. $3x - 2y = 7$ $x \in \{2, -2, 3, -3\}, y \in \{1, -1, 3, -3\}$
4. $-x + 3y = 9$ $x \in \{-2, -3, -4\}, y \in \{1, 2, 3\}$
5. $x + 2y \geqslant 6$ $x \in \{-2, 3, 4\}, y \in \{1, 2, 3\}$
6. $2x - y \leqslant 5$ $x \in \{1, 2, 3\}, y \in \{-1, 0, 1\}$
7. $3x + 4y \geqslant 12$ $x \in \{0, 2, 4\}, y \in \{1, 2, 3\}$
8. $3x - 5y = 16$ $x \in \{1, 2, 3\}, y \in \{0, 2, 4\}$
9. $4x + 3y \leqslant 12$ $x \in \{-2, 0, 2\}, y \in 2, 3, 4\}$
10. $\dfrac{x-1}{2} \leqslant \dfrac{y-1}{3}$ $x \in \{-1, 0, 1\}, y \in \{0, 1, 2\}$
11. $y < -2x$ $x \in \{-1, 0, 1\}, y \in \{0, 2\}$
12. $\dfrac{x}{2} - \dfrac{y}{3} < 0$ $x \in \{4, 8\}, y \in \{6, 9\}$
13. $xy > 0$ $x \in \{1, 2, -1\}, y \in \{-1, 0, 1\}$
14. $3(x + y) > 2x$ $x \in \{4, 10\}, y \in \{-3, -4\}$
15. $4(x - 1) + 3(y + 1) > 10$ $x \in \{2, 3, 6\}, y \in \{1, 0, -5\}$
16. The cost of one pencil is 10 cents, and the cost of one tablet is 15 cents. If at least one of each is purchased, find the number that can be bought for $1.00. (List the solution set.)
17. A hamburger costs 35 cents and a soft drink costs 20 cents. John has $2.20. How many of each can he buy if he spends all of his money and buys at least one of each?
18. In Problem 17, how many can he buy if he must save 50 cents of his money to buy gasoline to get home?
19. A company has two machines, A and B, that produce 2 and 3 units, respectively, per hour of a certain product. If the daily output of both machines must be less than

20 units, how many hours can each machine be operated, assuming that each must produce at least one unit.

20. In Problem 19, if (to meet expenses) at least 15 units must be produced, how many hours should each machine be operated, assuming that each machine must produce at least one unit?

5.8 ALGEBRAIC STATEMENTS FOR TWO VARIABLES AND THE CARTESIAN PLAN

The *solution set of an algebraic statement* for *one variable* is found on *the number line*. If the algebraic statement is an equation, then the solution set is a point on the line. If the statement is an inequality, then the solution set is an interval on the line. The *solution set of an algebraic statement for two variables is a set of ordered pairs of real numbers in a plane.*

This *Cartesian plane*, although discussed previously, is reproduced here for the sake of convenience.

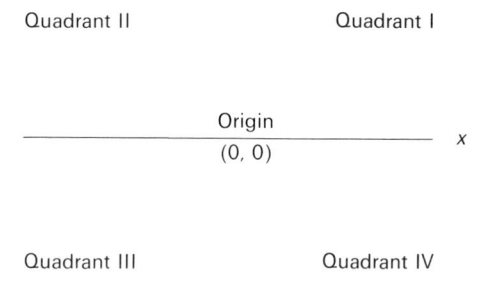

```
        Quadrant II              Quadrant I


                        Origin
        ─────────────────────────────────── x
                        (0, 0)


        Quadrant III             Quadrant IV
```

The horizontal number line or x-axis separates the y values in the plane into three disjoint sets of numbers: $y > 0$, $y = 0$, and $y < 0$. Similarly, the vertical number line or y-axis separates the x values into three disjoint sets of numbers: $x < 0$, $x = 0$, and $x > 0$. The x, y axes divide the plane into four quadrants as shown.

The signed values of x and y in each of the quadrants are:

Quadrant	(x, y)
I	(+, +)
II	(−, +)
III	(−, −)
IV	(+, −)

The plane is a set of points, and each point is associated with a particular pair of numbers. There exists a one-to-one correspondence between the set of points in the plane and the set of ordered pairs of real numbers. For this reason, the plane is also referred to as the *coordinate plane* or *plane of coordinates*.

The first member of an ordered pair of numbers representing a point in the plane is the x value or *abscissa*. The second member is the y value or *ordinate*.

5.8 Algebraic Statements for Two Variables and the Cartesian Plans

The replacement set for both x and y is the set of *real numbers*—unless otherwise specified, this will be true for the remainder of our algebraic concepts. To locate a point in the plane, draw a line parallel to the vertical axis through the abscissa on the horizontal axis and a line parallel to the horizontal axis through the ordinate on the vertical axis. The intersection of these two lines becomes the desired point. To illustrate, we shall locate the points P_1 and P_2, whose coordinates are $(3, -2)$ and $(-5, 4)$, respectively.

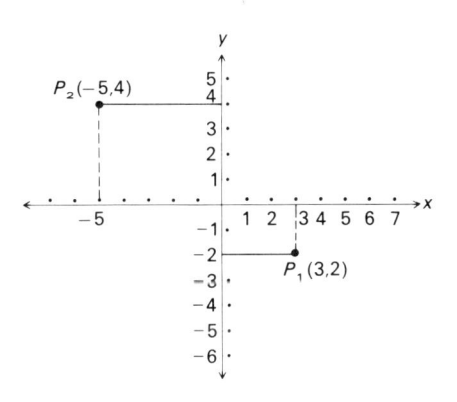

EXERCISE 5.7

On a coordinate plane, plot the graph of each of the following points.

1. $(4, 1)$
2. $(6, -2)$
3. $(-4, -4)$
4. $(3/2, -5/2)$
5. $(0, -3)$
6. $(-2, 0)$
7. $(-5, 3)$
8. $(7/2, 2/3)$
9. $(-3/5, -1)$
10. $(1/2, -1/2)$

On the coordinate plane shown below, write the coordinates of the point listed.

11. $A(\ ,\ )$
12. $B(\ ,\ )$
13. $C(\ ,\ )$
14. $D(\ ,\ )$
15. $E(\ ,\ )$
16. $F(\ ,\ )$
17. $G(\ ,\ )$
18. $H(\ ,\ )$
19. $I(\ ,\ )$
20. $J(\ ,\ )$

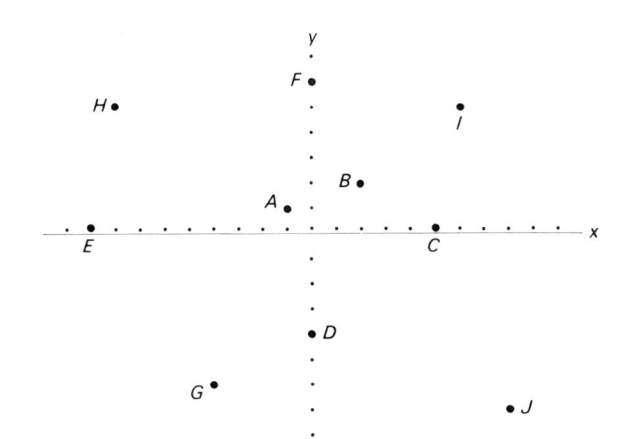

In which quadrant does the point corresponding to each of the ordered pair of numbers lie?

21. (5, 4) 22. (−4, −4) 25. (−6, 3) 26. (|5|, |3|)
23. (|−2|, |3|) 24. (0, 3) 27. (|½|, |−½|) 28. (5, 0)

True or false?
29. The equation $y = 0$ is the same set of points as the x-axis.
30. The y-axis separates the x values into three disjoint sets.
31. A point in the plane is represented by a complex number.
32. Each point in the plane is associated with a unique ordered pair of numbers.

5.9 GRAPHS OF ALGEBRAIC STATEMENTS FOR TWO VARIABLES

The solution set of the open equation $x + y = 3$ is the set of all ordered pairs, represented by (x, y), that makes the equation true. To find a root, write the equation in the form $y = 3 - x$, substitute values of x from its replacement set, and evaluate y.

x	$y = 3 - x$	y	Root
3	$y = 3 - 3$	0	(3, 0)
1	$y = 3 - 1$	2	(1, 2)
⋮	⋮	⋮	⋮
0	$y = 3 - 0$	3	(0, 3)

The plotting on the coordinate plane of the points representing the roots strongly suggests that the solution set will lie on a *straight line*.

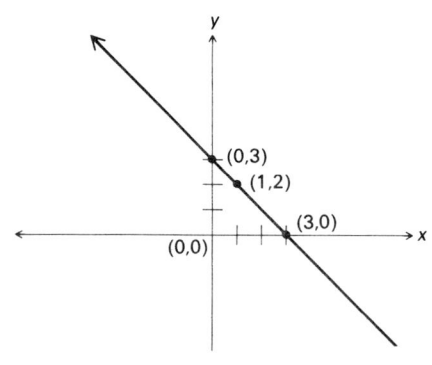

Since the plane is an infinite set of points (x, y), the replacement set for both variables, x and y, is the set of real numbers. Each root of the equation gives a point on the line, and the coordinates of each point on the line make the equation true. The line is called the *graph of the equation*, and $y = 3 - x$ is the *equation of the line*.

The graph of the equation $y = 3 - x$ is a straight line. Thus $y = 3 - x$ is a *linear equation for two variables*. In a linear equation, each term is a constant or a variable raised to the first power; i.e., $y = 2x - 3$ is linear, while the equations $xy = 2$ and $y = x^2$ are not.

5.9 Graphs of Algebraic Statements for Two Variables 117

In sketching the graph of a linear equation, only *two points* are needed; however it is good practice to plot a third point as a check against error. Usually, the two points plotted are the points where the line crosses the x-axis, called the *x-intercept*, and the y-axis, called the *y-intercept*. The x-intercept and the y-intercept are convenient points for plotting, since at each intercept, one of the variables is always zero.

Example 1. Sketch the graph of the equation $3x - y = 6$.

Solution. $3x - y = 6$
$$-y = 6 - 3x$$
$$y = 3x - 6$$

Substituting 0, 2, 1 for x and evaluating y, results in the points (0, 2), (2, 0), and (1, −3).

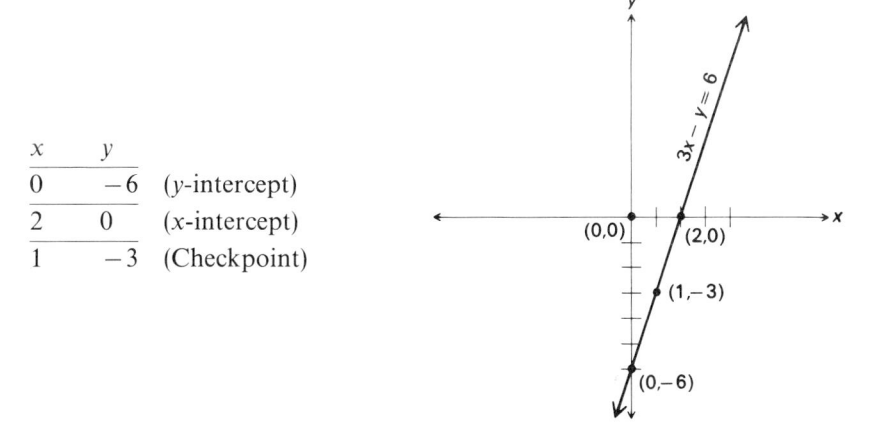

x	y	
0	−6	(y-intercept)
2	0	(x-intercept)
1	−3	(Checkpoint)

Example 2. Sketch the graph of the equation $3x + 4y = 12$.

Solution. $3x + 4y = 12$
$$4y = 12 - 3x$$
$$y = 3 - \tfrac{3}{4}x$$

Substituting 0, 4, 2 for x and evaluating y, results in the points (0, 3), (4, 0) and (2, 3/2).

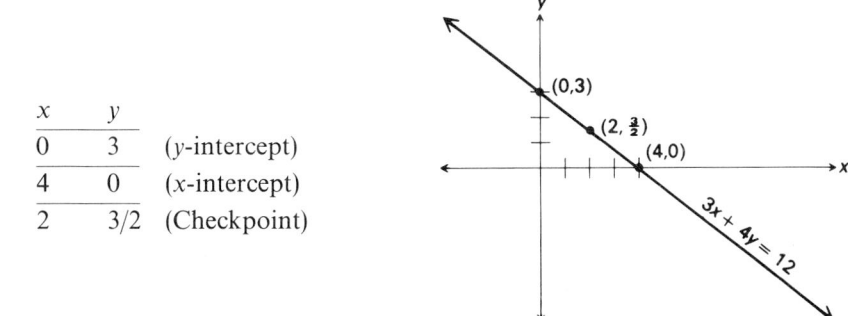

x	y	
0	3	(y-intercept)
4	0	(x-intercept)
2	3/2	(Checkpoint)

Example 3. Sketch the graph of the equation $y = 2$.

Solution. Since no restriction is placed on x, all the points whose second number is 2 make the equation true. Thus the graph is a line parallel to the x-axis, 2 units above.

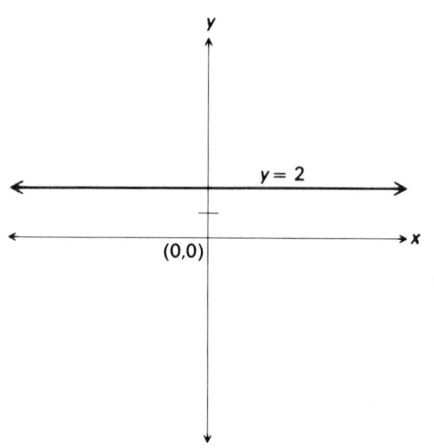

Example 4. Sketch the graph of the equation $x = y$.

Solution. $x - y = 0$.

Since the constant term is zero, the graph of the equation will pass through the origin, and the x-intercept is the same point as the y-intercept. Substituting 0, 2, -3 for x and evaluating y, results in the points $(0, 0)$, $(2, 2)$ and $(-3, -3)$.

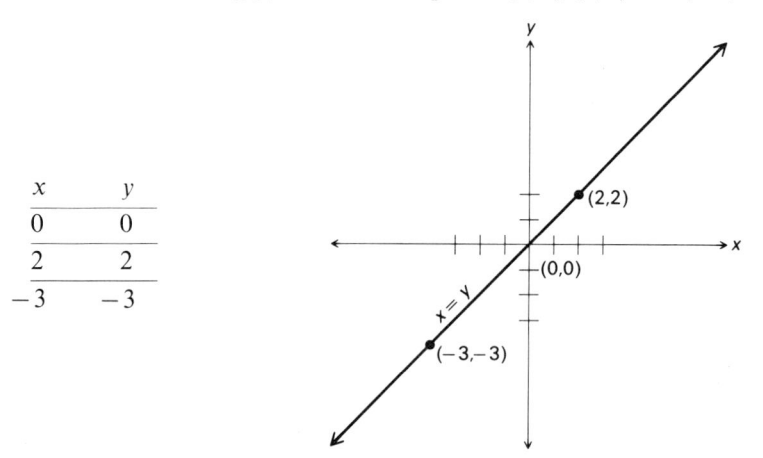

x	y
0	0
2	2
-3	-3

The graph of each of the equations in the preceding examples could have been found by what is called the *slope-intercept method*.

The *slope* (steepness) of a line is the amount of its *vertical change*, called *rise*, in relation to its *horizontal change*, called *run*. That is, the slope of a line, denoted by m, is

$$m = \frac{\text{Vertical change}}{\text{Horizontal change}} = \frac{\text{Rise}}{\text{Run}}$$

5.9 Graphs of Algebraic Statements for Two Variables   119

The slope-intercept form of an equation with two variables is $y = mx + b$. The slope of the line is m and the y-intercept is 1.
The solutions to the preceding Examples, using the slope-intercept method, are now described.

Example 5. Sketch the graph of the equation $3x - y = 6$.

Solution. $3x - y = 6$
$$y = 3x - 6$$

The slope m is 3, which means that for each 1 unit of change in a horizontal direction there will be 3 units of change in the vertical direction. The y-intercept b is the point $(0, -6)$. The y-intercept gives one point. A second point is found by moving 1 unit to the right from the point $(0, -6)$ and three units vertically. This gives a second point $(1, -3)$. The line can now be drawn.

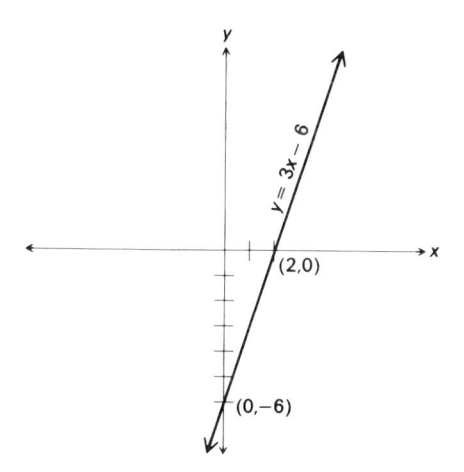

Example 6. Sketch the graph of the equation $3x + 4y = 12$.

Solution. $3x + 4y = 12$
$$4y = 12 - 3x$$
$$y = -\tfrac{3}{4}x + 3$$

The slope m is $-3/4$; the y intercept b is the point $(0, 3)$.

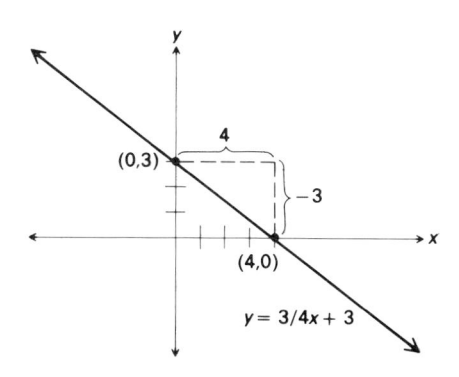

Example 7. Sketch the graph of the equation $y = 2$.

Solution. Since x has no restrictions, the slope $m = 0$. The y-intercept b is the point $(0, 2)$.

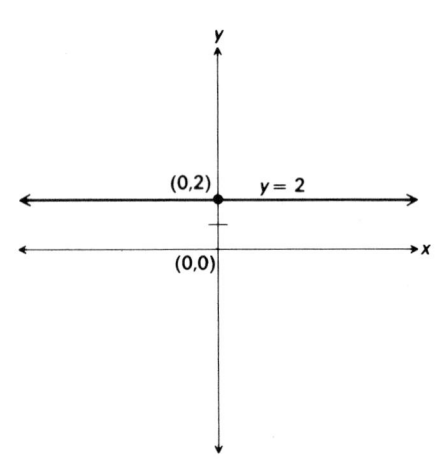

Example 8. Sketch the graph of the equation $x - y = 0$.

Solution. $x - y = 0$
$y = x + 0$

The slope m is 1. The y-intercept b is the point $(0, 0)$.

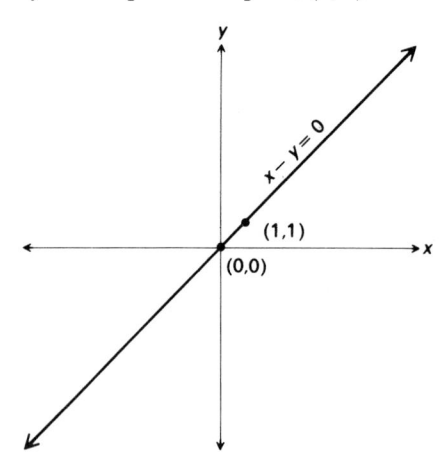

The graph of an inequality with two variables is a half-plane. The solution set is the set of points in the half-plane represented by (x, y) that makes the inequality true. For example, suppose that we have the inequality

$$y \geqslant mx + b$$

and want to sketch the graph of the solution set in the coordinate plane. The solution set or half-plane is bounded on one side by the line $y = mx + b$. The boundary line can be found by either of the two methods previously discussed,

5.9 Graphs of Algebraic Statements for Two Variables

and the solution set is then shown by *shading the half-plane whose points make the inequality statement true*. If one point in a half-plane makes the statement true, then *all* points in that half-plane are in the solution set. If one point makes the statement false, then *no* point in that half-plane is the solution set. The point (0, 0) is convenient for checking, unless the boundary goes through the origin. If the boundary goes through the origin, then another point—preferably a point on one of the axes—is used to check the statement.

Example 1. Sketch the graph of $y > 2x + 4$.

Solution. The boundary line is the equation $y = 2x + 4$, whose intercepts are $(-2, 0)$ and $(0, 4)$.

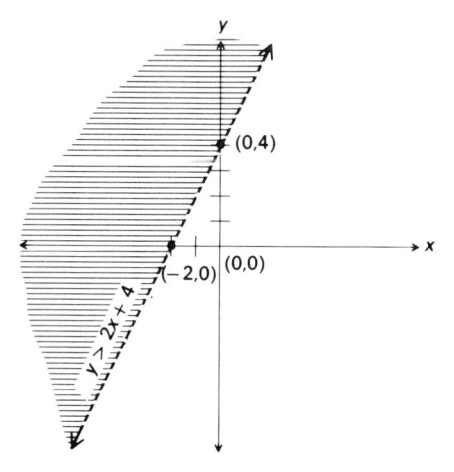

The coordinates of the point (0, 0) do not make the inequality true, and the solution set is the shaded half-plane. The dotted line indicates that the boundary is not the solution set.

Example 2. Sketch the graph of $y > 3x$.

Solution. The boundary is the equation $y = 3x$, which goes through the points (0, 0) and (1, 3).

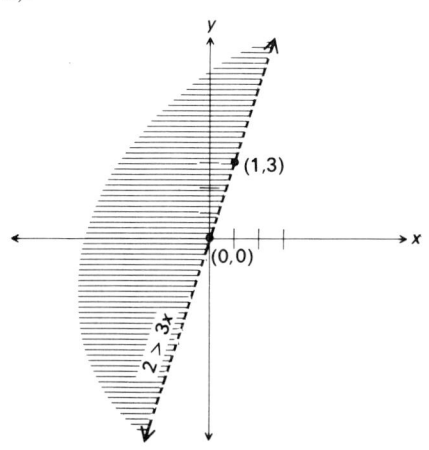

The coordinates of the point (1, 0) make the statement false. The solution set is the half-plane that does *not* contain the point (1, 0).

Example 3. Sketch the graph of $y \leqslant 2x - 2$.

Solution. The boundary is the equation $y = 2x - 2$, whose intercepts are $(0, -2)$ and $(1, 0)$.

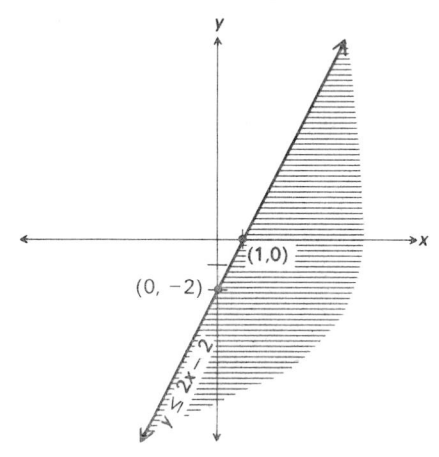

The coordinates of the point (0, 0) make the statement false. The solid line indicates that the line as well as the shaded half-plane is the solution set, since our statement specified "less than or equal to."

EXERCISE 5.8

Sketch the graph of the following equations using the x and y intercept method.

1. $2x - 3y = 6$
2. $4x - y = 8$
3. $3x - 2y = -12$
4. $5x - 3y = 10$
5. $2x = 6$ (y is unrestricted)
6. $3x = 4y$
7. $4(x + 2) = 2(3x - 2y)$
8. $-2x + \tfrac{1}{2}y = 1$

Sketch the graph of the following equations using the slope-intercept method.

9. $2x - y = 3$
10. $\tfrac{1}{2}x + y = 2$
11. $\dfrac{x + y}{2} = 0$
12. $3x - 2y = 0$
13. $3y = -6$ (x is unrestricted)
14. $\tfrac{1}{3}x - \tfrac{1}{2}y = 1$
15. $2(3x - 2y) = 4x + 2$
16. $3(x - 1) = \tfrac{1}{2}(y = 2)$

Sketch the graph of the following inequalities.

17. $2x - 3y > 6$
18. $4(x - 1) + 3(y + 1) \geqslant -2$
19. $3(x - y) < 2x - 3$
20. $\tfrac{1}{2}x - \tfrac{1}{3}y \leqslant 0$
21. $y < -2x$
22. $x > 0$ and $y > 0$
23. $3(x + y) - 2x \geqslant 0$
24. $x > 0$ or $y > 0$

5.9　Graphs of Algebraic Statements for Two Variables　　123

25. $\dfrac{x-1}{2} \leq \dfrac{y-1}{3}$　　　　26.　$x < 0$ and $y > 0$

Using the slope-intercept form of a line, $y = mx + b$, write the equation of the line when:

27.　$m = 2, \quad b = 2$　　　　　　28.　$m = -3, \quad b = 5$

29.　$m = \tfrac{2}{3}, \quad b = 4$　　　　　30.　$m = \dfrac{-5}{2}, \quad b = 3$

31.　$m = \tfrac{7}{3}, \quad b = \tfrac{9}{2}$

REVIEW EXERCISE 5.1

Determine the solution set for the algebraic statements from the given replacement set and show its graph on the number line.

1. $2x - 3 = 5, \quad x \in \{2, 4, 6\}$
2. $x + 1 = 2x - 1, \quad x \in \{0, 1, 2\}$
3. $2x + 3 \neq 7, \quad x \in \{1, 2, 3, 4\}$
4. $x + 1 > \dfrac{x}{2} + 2, \quad x \in \{1, 2, 3, 4\}$
5. $2x - 3 < x + 4, \quad x \in \{0, 5, 10, 15\}$
6. $4 < x < 7, \quad x \in \{1, 2, 3, \ldots, 10\}$
7. $3x > 6 \text{ or } x < 0, \quad x \in \{-2, -1, 0, 1, 2, 3\}$

In each of the following algebraic statements, substitute the values from the given replacement sets and state whether the resulting statement is true or false.

8. $3(2x + 2) = 6y, \quad x \in \{0, 1, 2\}, y \in \{0, 1, 2\}$
9. $\dfrac{x \cdot x + y \cdot y}{x + y} = x - y, \quad x \in \{0, 2\}, y \in \{0, 2\}$
10. $xy > \dfrac{xy + y}{y},$ (a) when $x = 4, y = 2$; (b) when $x = 3, y = 1$

Solve the following equations and check the solution. (The domain is the set of real numbers.)

11.　$3x - 6 = 12$　　　　　　　12.　$2x - 1 = 3x - 4$

13.　$\tfrac{1}{2}x - 2 = 1$　　　　　　　14.　$2(x - 3) = 4$

15.　$2x + 3(x - 4) = 3(2x - 2)$

Solve the following inequalities and locate the solution set on the number line.

16.　$2x > -8$　　　　　17.　$\dfrac{x-1}{3} < 3$

18.　$3(x - 2) \geq 5x$　　19.　$\dfrac{2x+1}{3} \geq x - 1$

20.　$\dfrac{x}{3} - 1 < \dfrac{x}{2}$

Find the solution set and locate its graph on the number line.

21. $|x| = 10$ 22. $|2x| + 1 = 7$
23. $|3x| \geqslant 12$ 24. $|2x| \leqslant 6$
25. $|2x + 1| \leqslant 9$
26. Sue is three times as old as her brother Sam, but in three years she will be only twice as old. What are their present ages?
27. How much distilled water must a nurse add to 1 pint of 95% alcohol to make a mixture that is 50% alcohol.
28. If a dress cost $18.75, for what must it be sold so that the profit margin will be 25% of the selling price?
29. Joe and Don together have $20.00, but Joe has $3.00 more than Don. How much money has each?
30. The total proceeds from the sale of 2000 tickets for a football game was $1900. Students tickets were sold for $0.75 and adult tickets cost $1.25. How many tickets of each kind were sold?
31. Sharon is taking a course in humanities; the instructor gives four tests and the final grade is the average of the scores. Sharon's grades on the first three tests were 91, 87, and 89. What is the minimum grade she can receive on the fourth test and have an average of at least 90?

SELF QUIZ 5.1

Determine the solution set for the algebraic statements from the given replacement sets and show each graph on a number line.

1. $5x + 3 = 3x + 9$, $x \in \{1, 2, 3, 4, 5\}$
2. $5x - 2 \geqslant 3x + 2$, $x \in \{0, 2, 4, 6\}$
3. $64 = 8x + 40$, $x \in N$
4. $3x - 2 \leqslant 5x + 4$, $x \in N$
5. $|x - 1| \leqslant 4$, $x \in N$
6. $\frac{x}{3} - 1 < \frac{x}{2}$, $x \in N$
7. A man invests $10,000 in stocks and bonds. The stock pays an annual rate of 6%, and the bonds pay 8%. In one year, he received $720 in interest. How much did he invest in each?
8. Dana plans to buy a new outfit consisting of shoes, purse and dress; she plans to spend at most $100. If the purse cost $6 less than the shoes and the dress cost as much as the purse and shoes combined, what is the maximum price she should pay for each?
9. If the cost of a sandwich and milkshake is $1.00 and the sandwich costs 5 cents less than twice the milkshake, what is the cost of each?
10. If Esther has grades of 93, 95 and 91, what is the lowest score she can make on a fourth test to maintain an average of 90?

5.10 SIMULTANEOUS SOLUTION OF A SYSTEM OF EQUATIONS

The graph of an equation for two variables is a straight line. When two such equations are sketched in the same coordinate plane, the results are known by three categories:

a) *intersecting lines*

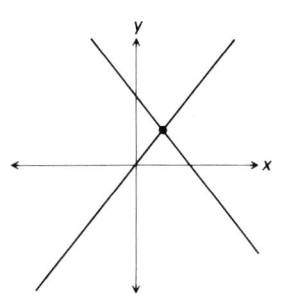

b) *colinear lines*

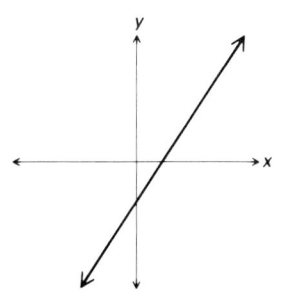

c) *parallel lines.*

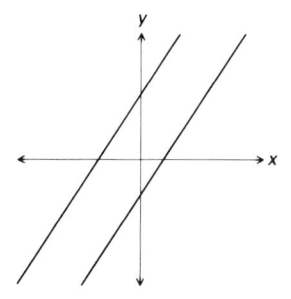

Two equations impose *two conditions* on each of the variables, and form what is called a *system of simultaneous equations.* The solution set of a system of simultaneous equations is the set of ordered pairs of numbers that make both equations true at the same time.

When the slopes of two equations are the same and the y-intercepts are not the same, the graphs are a pair of parallel lines that have no point in common.

No ordered pair will make both true, and the solution set is empty. The system

$$y = 2x - 3$$
$$y = 2x + 4$$

has no point in common, and the solution is ∅.

The graphs of the system

$$y = 3x - 2$$
$$2y = 6x - 4$$

are the same line; i.e., the slopes and *y*-intercepts are the same. The solution set is infinite, since any ordered pair that makes one equation true also makes the other true.

The graphs of the system

$$y = 2x - 2$$
$$y = x + 1$$

intersect in one point in the coordinate plane. The coordinates of the point (3, 4) meet both conditions imposed on the variables in the two equations and therefore become the solution set.

When a system of equations is graphed on the same coordinate plane, it is possible to estimate the solution set.

Example 1. Sketch the graphs of the system $y = 2x - 2$, $y = x + 1$ and estimate the solution set.

Solution. $y = 2x - 2$ $y = x + 1$

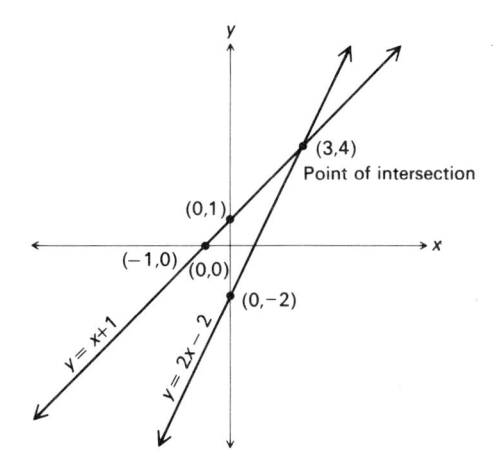

x	y
0	-2
1	0

x	y
0	1
-1	0

The estimated solution set is {(3, 4)}.

5.10 Simultaneous Solution of a System of Equations 127

Example 2. Sketch the graphs of the system $y = 2x - 3$, $y = 2x + 4$ and estimate the solution set.

Solution. $y = 2x - 3 \qquad y = 2x + 4$

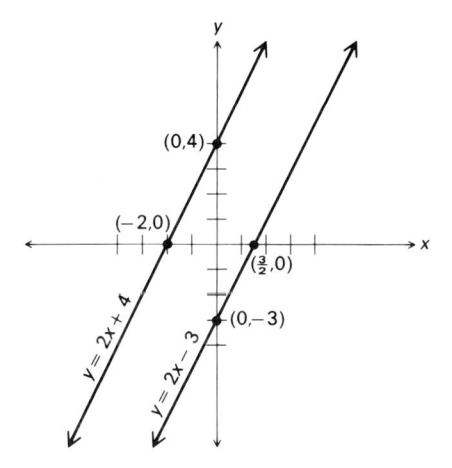

x	y
0	-3
$\frac{3}{2}$	0

x	y
0	4
-2	0

The lines are parallel, so the solution set is empty.

Example 3. Sketch the graphs of the system $y = 3x - 2$, $2y = 6x - 4$ and estimate the solution set.

Solution. $y = 3x - 2 \qquad 2y = 6x - 4$

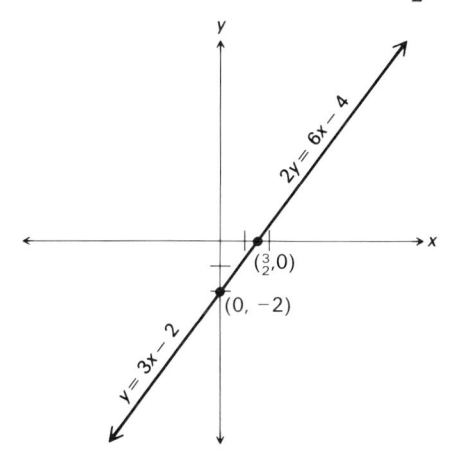

x	y
0	-2
$\frac{3}{2}$	0

x	y
0	-2
$\frac{3}{2}$	0

The two lines are the same, so the solution set is infinite.

EXERCISE 5.9

Solve graphically and estimate the solution set.

1. $x + y = 4$
   $2x - 3y = -2$
2. $2x - y = 6$
   $x + 3y = 10$
3. $2x - y = 7$
   $x + 3y = 2$
4. $x + 2y = 6$
   $y = 2x + 5$
5. $x + 4y = 27$
   $x = 21 - 2y$
6. $5x + 2y = 20$
   $3x - 2y = 4$
7. $3x + 2y = 5$
   $-6y = 7 + 9x$
8. $x + 2y = 3$
   $2x = 6 - 4y$
9. $2x - 3y = 6$
   $x = \frac{3}{2}y + 4$
10. $x = 3y$
    $2(x + 1) = y + 2$

Solution by Addition or Subtraction

The solution set of the system

$$y = 2x - 2$$
$$y = x + 1$$

can be found by writing the system in the form

$$2x - y = 2$$
$$x - y = -1$$

and eliminating one of the variables by addition or subtraction. The resulting equation will have one variable, which can be solved in the usual way.

Example 1. Solve the system

$$\begin{array}{r} 2x - y = 2 \\ x - y = -1 \\ \hline x + 0 = 3 \end{array} \text{(subtract)}$$
$$x = 3$$

Then substitute 3 for x in either of the original equations.

$$3 - y = -1$$
$$-y = -1 - 3$$
$$y = 4$$

The solution set is (3, 4).

Check: $2x - y = 2$ $x - y = -1$

$$2(3) - 4 = 2 \qquad 3 - 4 = -1$$
$$6 - 4 = 2 \qquad -1 = -1$$
$$2 = 2$$

Example 2. Solve the system
$$2x - 3y = 5$$
$$x + 2y = 6$$

Solution.
$$2x - 3y = 5$$
$$\underline{-2x - 4y = -12} \quad (x + 2y = 6 \text{ multiplied by } -2)$$
$$-7y = -7 \quad \text{(addition)}$$
$$y = 1$$
$$2x - 3(1) = 5$$
$$2x - 3 = 5$$
$$2x = 8$$
$$x = 4$$

The solution set is (4, 1).

Check:
$$2(4) - 3(1) = 5 \qquad 4 + 2(1) = 6$$
$$8 - 3 = 5 \qquad 4 + 2 = 6$$
$$5 = 5 \qquad 6 = 6$$

The algebraic solution of a system of equations with two variables can also be found by what is called the *substitution method*. Here *either of the two equations* can be solved for *one variable in terms of the other variable*. The substitution is then used to obtain a third equation with one variable. As an illustration, the preceding Examples will be solved using this method.

Example 3. Solve the system
$$2x - y = 2$$
$$x - y = -1$$

Solution. Solve for x in the equation $x - y = -1$; $x = y - 1$. Then substitute $y - 1$ for x in the equation $2x - y = 2$.

$$2(y - 1) - y = 2$$
$$2y - 2 - y = 2$$
$$y = 4$$
$$x - 4 = -1 \quad \text{(substitution: 4 for } y\text{)}$$
$$x = 3$$

The solution set is (3, 4).

Example 4. Solve the system

$$2x - 3y = 5$$
$$x + 2y = 6$$

Solution. Solve for x in $x + 2y = 6$:

$$x = 6 - 2y$$

Then substitute $6 - 2y$ for x in the equation $2x - 3y = 5$.

$$2(6 - 2y) - 3y = 5 \qquad 2x - 3(1) = 5$$
$$12 - 4y - 3y = 5 \qquad 2x = 8$$
$$-7 = -7 \qquad x = 4$$
$$y = 1$$

The solution set is (4, 1).

EXERCISE 5.10

Solve the system of equations by the addition or subtraction method.

1. $x + y = 4$
   $2x - y = 2$

2. $y = 2x - 3$
   $4x + 3 = 11y$

3. $2x = 6 - 3y$
   $3y - 6 = -2x$

4. $\frac{1}{3}x = \frac{1}{2}y$
   $2x - 3y = 6$

5. $3x - 4y = 12$
   $5x + 3y = 49$

6. $2x + 5y = -11$
   $5x - 3y = 19$

7. $\dfrac{2(x + 1)}{3} = 2y$
   $5x = 3(y + 2) + 1$

8. $.5x + 2 = 1.5y$
   $.1x - .1y = 0$

Solve the system of equations by the substitution method.

9. $x + y = 10$
   $2x + 3y = 25$

10. $2x - y = 6$
    $x + 2y = 8$

11. $3x - 4y = -1$
    $2x + y = 3$

12. $\frac{1}{2}x + \frac{2}{3}y = \frac{5}{6}$
    $3x - 2y = 1$

13. $2x + 3y = -1$
    $4x + 6y = -2$

14. $3x + 5y = 13$
    $6x + 10y = 0$

15. $\dfrac{2(x + 2)}{2} = y$
    $x = \dfrac{3y - 6}{3}$

16. $.4x + .5y = 9$
    $2x + y = 15$

Solve the applied problems by either method.

17. Three hamburgers and five sodas cost $2.11. Seven sodas and five hamburgers cost $3.29. Find the cost of each.
18. The sum of two numbers is 71, and the difference is -25. What are the two numbers?
19. The living room of a new house is 8 feet longer than it is wide; its perimeter is 80 feet. What are the dimensions of the room?
20. A neighborhood grocer pays $22.50 for a weeks supply of eggs. He paid $2.50 more for the medium size eggs that sell for 40 cents per dozen than he did for the large size eggs that sell for 50 cents per dozen. How many dozen of each size did he buy?
21. Professor Brown's house payment and car payments each month total $200. The house payment is $25 less than twice the car payment. How much does he pay monthly on each?
22. The combined ages of John and Mary is 36 years. Three times Mary's age exceeds John's age by 8 years. Find the age of each.
23. Kathy and Joan go shopping. Kathy buys 2 pounds of bacon and a dozen eggs for $2.21. Joan buys the same priced bacon and eggs but pays $1.99 for one pound of bacon and two dozen eggs. Find the cost of one unit of each item.
24. A fish fry was attended by 375 people, who paid a total of $431.25. The children under 12 years of age paid $0.75 for the dinner, and everyone else paid $1.35. How many children and how many others were served?
25. A mixture that is 86 percent alcohol is to be combined with a mixture that is 60 percent alcohol to yield 2 quarts that is 75 percent alcohol. How much of each mixture should be used?
26. Richard has $10,000 invested in stocks and bonds. The stock pays a yearly dividend of $4\frac{1}{2}\%$ and the bonds yield $5\frac{1}{4}\%$. In one year his total dividends were $490. How much did he have invested in each?

Cramer's Rule

A system of equations can also be solved by a procedure known as *Cramer's rule*. The solution of the system (written in general terms)

$$a_1 x + b_1 y = c_1$$
$$a_2 x + b_2 y = c_2$$

is found by solving the equations for *one variable in terms of the other variable and the constants*. That is,

$$x = \frac{b_2 c_1 - b_1 c_2}{a_1 b_2 - a_2 b_1} \quad \text{and} \quad y = \frac{a_1 c_2 - a_2 c_1}{a_1 b_2 - a_2 b_1}$$

The solution set is

$$\left\{ \frac{b_2 c_1 - b_1 c_2}{a_1 b_2 - a_2 b_1}, \frac{a_1 c_2 - a_2 c_1}{a_1 b_2 - a_2 b_1} \right\}$$

The x and y values in the solution set can be written as the ratio of two matrices. That is,

$$x = \frac{b_2 c_1 - b_1 c_2}{a_1 b_2 - a_2 b_1} = \frac{\begin{pmatrix} c_1 & b_1 \\ c_2 & b_2 \end{pmatrix}}{\begin{pmatrix} a_1 & b_1 \\ a_2 & b_2 \end{pmatrix}}$$

and

$$y = \frac{a_1 c_2 - a_2 c_1}{a_1 b_2 - a_2 b_1} = \frac{\begin{pmatrix} a_1 & c_1 \\ a_2 & c_2 \end{pmatrix}}{\begin{pmatrix} a_1 & b_1 \\ a_2 & b_2 \end{pmatrix}}$$

Each of the matrices is a *square matrix*. As such, there is a number, called a *determinant*, that is associated with each. The *value of the determinants* is found by multiplying along the diagonals—from upper left to lower right and from lower left to upper right, and then subtracting the second product from the first. To illustrate: the determinant of the matrix, $\begin{pmatrix} 2 & 1 \\ 3 & 4 \end{pmatrix}$, is denoted by $\begin{vmatrix} 2 & 1 \\ 3 & 4 \end{vmatrix}$ and is equal to $2 \cdot 4 - 3 \cdot 1 = 5$.

Returning to the solution of the general equations, we have

$$x = \frac{\begin{vmatrix} c_1 & b_1 \\ c_2 & b_2 \end{vmatrix}}{\begin{vmatrix} a_1 & b_1 \\ a_2 & b_2 \end{vmatrix}} \quad \text{and} \quad y = \frac{\begin{vmatrix} a_1 & c_1 \\ a_2 & c_2 \end{vmatrix}}{\begin{vmatrix} a_1 & b_1 \\ a_2 & b_2 \end{vmatrix}}$$

This solution is known as Cramer's rule.

Example 1. Solve the system by Cramer's rule.

$$x + 2y = 5$$
$$2x - y = 5$$

Solution. $a_1 = 1, b_1 = 2, c_1 = 5, a_2 = 2, b_2 = -1, c_2 = 5.$

$$x = \frac{\begin{vmatrix} 5 & 2 \\ 5 & -1 \end{vmatrix}}{\begin{vmatrix} 1 & 2 \\ 2 & -1 \end{vmatrix}} = \frac{5 \cdot (-1) - 5(2)}{1(-1) - 2(2)} = \frac{-5 - 10}{-1 - 4} = \frac{-15}{-5} = 3$$

$$y = \frac{\begin{vmatrix} 1 & 5 \\ 2 & 5 \end{vmatrix}}{\begin{vmatrix} 1 & 2 \\ 2 & -1 \end{vmatrix}} = \frac{1(5) - 2(5)}{1(-1) - 2(2)} = \frac{5 - 10}{-1 - 4} = \frac{-5}{-5} = 1$$

The solution set is (3, 1).

EXERCISE 5.11

Solve the following systems by using Cramer's rule.

1. $2x + 3y = 5$
   $x - 5y = -4$

2. $4x + 2y = 8$
   $5x - y = 3$

3. $2x = 3y$
   $3x - y = 3$

4. $2x = y + 4$
   $x + 3 = 3y$

5. $x + y = 9$
   $x - \frac{1}{3}y = 5$

6. $3x - 2y = 11$
   $2x - y = 8$

7. $2s - 3t = 0$
   $3s + 3t = 33$

8. $2s - 3t = 5$
   $3s - t = 18$

9. $2m + 2n = 22$
   $m - 2n = -6$

10. $\frac{1}{3}(r - t) = 2$
    $\frac{1}{4}(r + t) = 2$

Solve the applied problems using Cramer's rule.

11. Cathy and Dick traveled toward each other from cities 900 miles apart. When they met, Cathy had traveled 50 miles more than twice as far as Dick. How many miles had each traveled?

12. A tobacco shopowner wishes to mix a blend of tobacco for a customer that is 80% burly with a blend that is 65% burly to produce 8 ounces of tobacco that contains 70% burly. How many ounces of each should he use?

13. A father left $10,000 to be divided between his son and daughter. The daughter received 1.5 times as much as the son. How much did each receive?

14. A little league baseball team purchased 12 bats and 18 baseballs for $58.50. Later in the season, they purchased 5 additional bats and 12 balls for $30. What was the price of each?

15. Tea worth $1.20 per pound is mixed with tea worth $1.75 a pound to produce a tea that can be sold for $1.60 per pound. How many pounds of each of the teas should be used if 8 pounds of the mixture is to be made?

5.11 GRAPHING SOLUTIONS TO SYSTEMS OF LINEAR INEQUALITIES

The solution set of a system of linear inequalities, which is an infinite set, is usually more meaningful when depicted *graphically*. To do this, each inequality is sketched on the same coordinate plane; thus the solution set is that region of the plane whose points make all statements *simultaneously* true. In the following examples, the solution set is represented by the cross-hatched area.

Example 1. Sketch the system

$$y > 2x + 1$$
$$y < -x + 3$$

and shade the solution set.

134 Concepts of Algebra 5.11

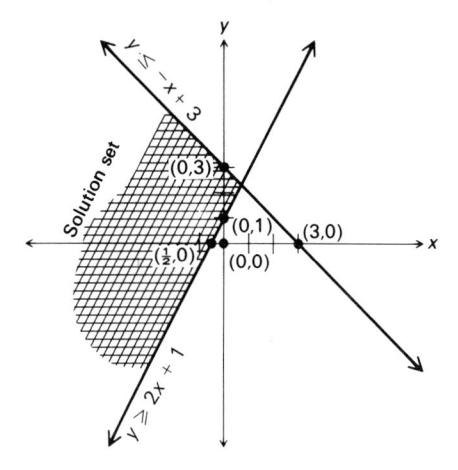

Solution. $y \geq 2x + 1$ $\qquad$ $y \leq -x + 3$
$\qquad y = 2x + 1$ (boundary) $\qquad y = -x + 3$ (boundary)

x	y
0	1
$-\frac{1}{2}$	0

x	y
0	3
3	0

Example 2. Sketch the system
$$y \geq 2x$$
$$y \geq -x$$
$$y \leq 4$$
and shade the solution set.

Solution. $y \geq 2x$ $\qquad$ $y \geq -x$ $\qquad$ $y \leq 4$
$\qquad y = 2x$ (boundary) $\qquad y = -x$ (boundary) $\qquad y = 4$ (boundary)

x	y
0	0
1	2

x	y
0	0
1	-1

5.11 Graphing Solutions to Systems of Linear Inequalities

In problems dealing with inequalities, there is seldom only one solution. However, in applied problems, some of the solutions may be superior to others.

Example 3. A man has a small orchard in which he has space for no more than 10 trees. He plans to have only apple and peach trees, and there must be at least 4 apple trees and 3 peach trees. He estimates that his profit will be $25 per apple tree and $30 per peach tree. How many of each will yield the most profit?

Solution. Let

$$x = \text{the number of apple trees.}$$
$$y = \text{the number of peach trees.}$$

Then the conditions on the number of trees are

$$x + y \leq 10$$
$$x \geq 4$$
$$y \geq 3$$

The profit is represented by

$$P = \$25x + \$30y$$

The graph of the system of inequalities is shown in the figure here, where the solution set is the enclosed triangle.

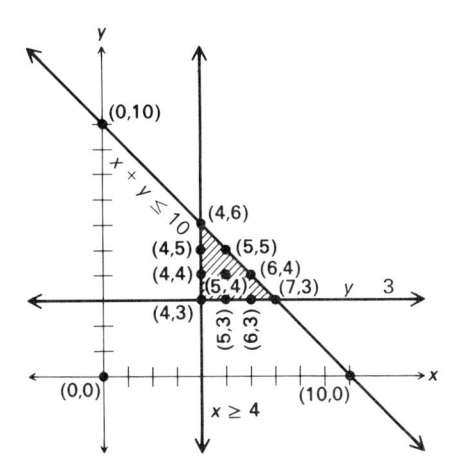

Since the variables x and y are elements of the natural numbers, there are only 10 ordered pairs in the solution set, (4, 3), (4, 4), (4, 5), (4, 6), (5, 3), (5, 4), (5, 5), (6, 3), (6, 4), (7, 3). Thus the profit is

$$P(4, 3) = \$25(4) + \$30(3) = \$190$$
$$P(4, 4) = \$25(4) + \$30(4) = \$220$$
$$P(4, 5) = \$25(4) + \$30(5) = \$250$$
$$P(4, 6) = \$25(4) + \$30(6) = \$280$$

$$P(5, 3) = \$25(5) + \$30(3) = \$215$$
$$P(5, 4) = \$25(5) + \$30(4) = \$245$$
$$P(5, 5) = \$25(5) + \$30(5) = \$275$$
$$P(6, 3) = \$25(6) + \$30(3) = \$240$$
$$P(6, 4) = \$25(6) + \$30(4) = \$270$$
$$P(7, 3) = \$25(7) + \$30(3) = \$265$$

So, we can now see that the highest estimated profit, $280, will occur at the vertex (4, 6) of the triangle.

Note that the *lowest estimated profit* will occur at another vertex (4, 3) of the triangle. This is not just a coincidence, since in problems of this type (i.e., extreme values), *maximum* and *minimum* will always occur at a *vertex* of the enclosed polygon. That is, if the set of conditions between two variable quantities whose conditions can be expressed as a system of linear inequalities whose solution set is a closed polygon—provided another set of conditions can be expressed as a linear equation—then both the maximum and minimum value of the equation will occur at a vertex. This branch of applied mathematics is called *linear programming*.

Example 4. What is the maximum and minimum value of $P = 6x + 8y$ subject to the conditions

$$2x + 3y \leq 12$$
$$x \geq 2$$
$$y \geq 1$$
$$2x + y \geq 8$$

Solution. $2x + y \geq 8$

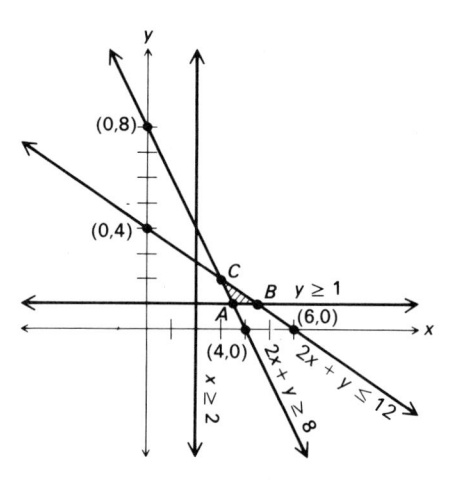

The vertices of the closed polygon are found by finding the intersection of the appropriate equations. Thus vertex A represents the intersection of $y = 1$ and $2x + y = 8$, and the coordinates are (7/2, 1); vertex B represents the intersection of $y = 1$ and $2x + 3y = 12$, and the coordinates are $(9/2, 1)$; vertex C represents the intersection of $2x + y = 8$ and $2x + 3y = 12$, and the coordinates are $(3, 2)$.

Vertex	$P = 6x + 8y$
$A(7/2, 1)$	29 (minimum)
$B(9/2, 1)$	35 (maximum)
$C(3, 2)$	34

EXERCISE 5.12

Sketch the graphs of the systems and shade each solution set.

1. $x - 2y > 4$
   $2x + 3y < 6$

2. $x + y > 8$
   $2x \quad y > 4$

3. $5x - y < 10$
   $2x + 3y \geqslant 6$

4. $3x + y > 3$
   $2x - 3y < 6$

5. $\frac{1}{2}x + \frac{1}{3}y > 6$
   $\frac{2}{5}x + \frac{3}{2}y < 1$

6. $x - 2y > -1$
   $x < y$
   $3x + 4y < 12$

7. $2x - 3y \leqslant -12$
   $y \leqslant 4$
   $x \geqslant -2$

8. $3x - 2y \geqslant -6$
   $x \leqslant 2$
   $x + 3y \geqslant 6$

9. $x \geqslant y$
   $x \geqslant 0$
   $y \leqslant 4$
   $y \geqslant 0$

10. $y < 2x + 1$
    $x + y < 3$
    $x + 3y > 3$
    $x < 2$

Sketch the graphs of the following system of inequalities; find the coordinates of the vertices of the enclosed polygon and evaluate the given equations.

11. $3x + 4y \leqslant 12$
    $5x + y \geqslant 10$
    $x \geqslant 1$
    $y \geqslant 0$
    $P = 4x + y$

12. $x \geqslant 1$
    $y \geqslant 2$
    $x \geqslant y$
    $x + y \geqslant 5$
    $3x + 2y \leqslant 18$
    $P = 5x + 2y$

13. $x \geqslant 1$
    $3x - 2y \leqslant 0$
    $x \leqslant 5$
    $y \leqslant 4$
    $3x + 4y \geqslant 12$
    $P = 6x - 5y$

14. $x + y \leqslant 4$
    $x - y + 2 \leqslant 0$
    $x + 2y \geqslant 2$
    $x - y \leqslant 1$
    $P = 10x + 12y$

15. $3x - y \geq -3$
    $x + y \geq 4$
    $2x + y \geq 6$
    $x + y \leq 8$
    $y \geq 2$
    $x \leq 6$
    $P = 2x - y$

16. A service station owner has found that to meet his customers' demands, he should have at least 3 heavy duty batteries and 4 regular batteries on hand. He has space for no more than 10 batteries. If his profit is $5 on the heavy duty and $4 on the regular, how many of each should he stock to yield maximum profit, assuming he sells his entire stock before it is replenished?

17. In arranging a tour, an agency has found that it can provide accommodations for at most 100 people. The agency has decided that there should be at least 40 women and at least 30 men on the tour. The agency makes a profit of $35 for each woman and $45 for each man. How many of each sex should be included to yield maximum profit?

18. An investment broker has two types of income investments that pay 5 and 8 percent, respectively. The broker's fee is 2 percent of the income of the 5 percent investment and 1 percent of the income of the 8 percent investment. A customer has $150,000 to invest and must have a yearly income of at least $9,600. He also insists that no more than $100,000 be invested at 8 percent. How much should the broker invest at each rate to receive a maximum fee?

19. A company has two machines that make identical products. Machine A can produce at least 2 units of the product in one hour, and machine B can produce at least 3 units per hour. The company knows that to avoid overproduction the two machines must not produce more than 30 units per day, but to make a profit, the two machines must produce at least 20 units. The union contract specified that each must operate for at least one hour per day. Since machine B costs more to operate, the profit on each unit produced by machine B is $35, while the profit for each unit produced by machine A is $40. How many units should be produced by each machine to yield maximum profit?

20. Cathy is having company and plans to serve meatloaf as a main dish. She estimates that she should have at least 3 but not more than 5 pounds of meat. Her recipe calls for at least 2 pounds of beef to each pound of pork, and at least one pound of pork must be used. If pork costs $80 per pound and beef costs $1.40 per pound, how much of each should she use to keep the cost to a minimum?

5.12 RELATIONS

The solution set of a linear equation with two variables is the set of ordered pairs of numbers whose coordinates make the equation true. A pairing of two sets of numbers in this way is called a relation.

A *relation* is *any set of ordered pairs* and may be described in one of three ways.

a) The *roster method*: {(−1, −1), (0, 0), (1, 1), (2, 2), ... }
b) A *graph*:

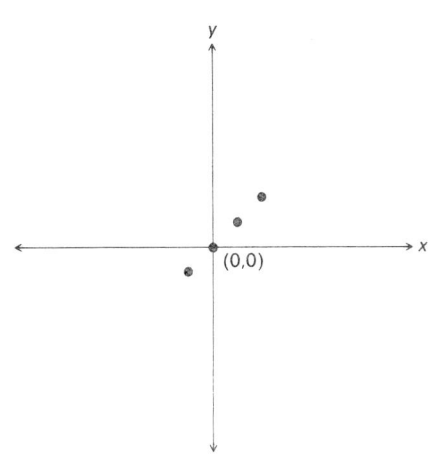

c) A *rule or formula*: $y = x + 1$

The two sets of numbers that are paired are called the *domain* and the *range*. When the roster method is used to describe a relation, the set of *first members* is the domain, and the set of *second members* is the range. If the equation is sketched on the coordinate plane, values corresponding to points along the horizontal axis represent members of the domain, and values corresponding to points along the vertical axis represent members of the range. When the relation is described by a rule or formula such as $y = x$, the domain is the replacement set for x, and the range is the replacement set for y. If the domain and range are not specified, assume that they are the largest subset for which there is meaning. (x and y are not always real numbers—in fact, they may not even be numbers.)

Example 1. State the domain and range of the relation

$$\{(2, 4), (6, 2), (5, 0), (6, 10)\}$$

Solution. Domain, $D = \{2, 6, 5\}$
Range, $R = \{4, 2, 0, 10\}$

Example 2. Give a formula that expresses the relationship of distance to rate and time.

r	20	30	60	75
t	2	4	5	3

State the elements in the domain and range and plot them on a coordinate plane.

Solution. The formula is $d = rt$. The domain is the set $D = \{20, 30, 60, 75\}$, and the range is the set $R = \{2, 4, 5, 3\}$.

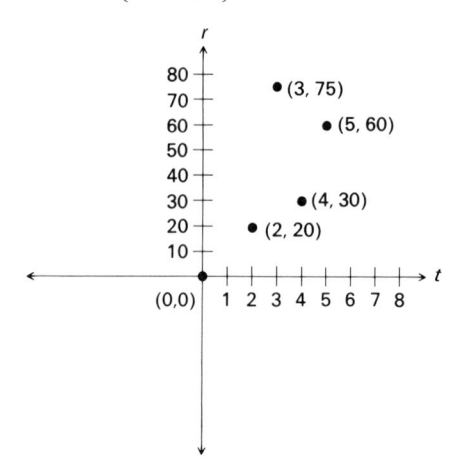

Example 3. Sketch the graph of $y = x + 1$, where both the domain and range is the set of real numbers.

Solution. $y = x + 1$

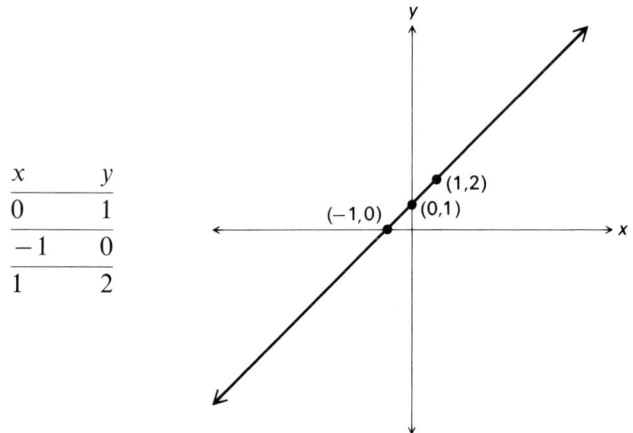

x	y
0	1
-1	0
1	2

Domain: The set of real numbers.

Range: The set of real numbers.

EXERCISE 5.13

Plot the graphs of the following relations on a coordinate plane and state the domain and range of each.

1. $\{(0, 0), (2, 3), (5, 8), (7, 11)\}$
2. $\{(1, 1), (\frac{1}{2}, 2), (\frac{1}{4}, 4), (\frac{1}{8}, 8)\}$
3. $\{(-3, 1), (-2, 2), (-1, 3), (0, 4), (1, 5)\}$
4. $\{(3, -2), (4, -3), (5, 4), (6, 5)\}$

Graph the following relations for the domain $D = \{2, -1, 0, 3\}$.

5. $y = x + 1$
6. $y = x^2 + 2x$
7. $y = |x|$
8. $y = x^2 - 1$

Write a formula that expresses the relationship of the ordered pairs in each roster.

9. Length of a rectangle:

Area	40	60	96	160
Width	8	10	16	40

10. Cost of steaks:

Lbs.	2	3	5	6
Price per lb.	1.90	1.60	2.25	1.50

11. $y = :$

x	2	5	8	10
y	4	10	16	20

12. $y = :$

x	1	3	5	9	0
y	2	4	6	10	1

Plot the graph of each of the relations where the replacement set for x is D, and the replacement set for y is R.

13. $y \leqslant x$, $D = \{0, 1, 2, 3, 4, 5\}$; $R = \{0, 1, 2, 3, 4, 5\}$
14. $y \geqslant x$, $D = \{0, 1, 2, 3, 4, 5\}$; $R = \{0, 1, 2, 3, 4, 5\}$
15. $y \geqslant 2x - 1$, D = set of real numbers; R = set of real numbers
16. $y \geqslant |x|$, D = set of real numbers; R = set of real numbers

5.13 FUNCTIONS

Each of the following examples is a special kind of relation, called a function. A function is a relation that assigns to each element of the domain one and only one element of the range.

The relationship between the area of a square and the length of one side is given by the formula

$$A = x^2$$

Thus, for each value of x, there is a unique value of A. For example:

If $x = 2$, then $A = 4$.
If $x = 10$, then $A = 100$.

Similarly, the relationship between the diameter of a circle and its circumference is

$$C = \pi d$$

If $D = 10$, then $C = 10\pi$.
If $D = 25$, then $C = 25\pi$.

If a function is described by the roster method, then no two ordered pairs will have the same first member. If a function is described by a graph on the coordinate plane, then for each x value there is only one associated y value.

It is common practice to designate a function by a letter, such as *f*, *g*, or *h*. If *x* is an element of the domain of a function, *f*, then the element of the range that is associated with *x* is denoted by $f(x)$. The symbol $f(x)$ is read as "*f* at *x*" and means the value of the function at a particular value of *x*. Suppose we have the relation

$$y = x + 1$$

Since *y* is a function of *x*, we may write the equation in *functional notation*; that is,

$$f(x) = x + 1$$

Its graph is the same as the graph of $y = x + 1$.

Example 1. Sketch the graph of the function $f(x) = x - 2$, whose domain is the set of real numbers.

Solution. $f(x) = x - 2$

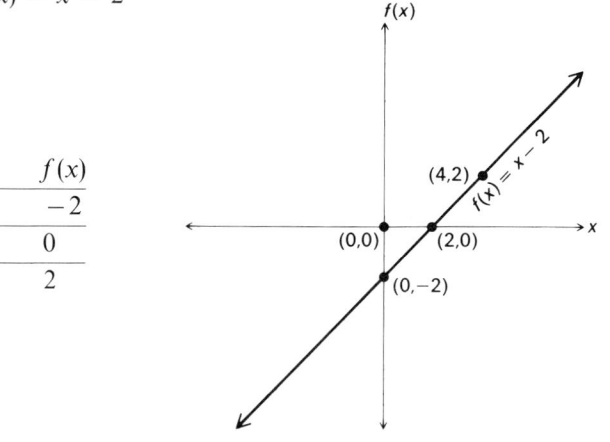

x	f(x)
0	−2
2	0
4	2

Example 2. Sketch the graph of the function $f(x) = |x|$, whose domain is the set of real numbers.

Solution. $f(x) = |x|$

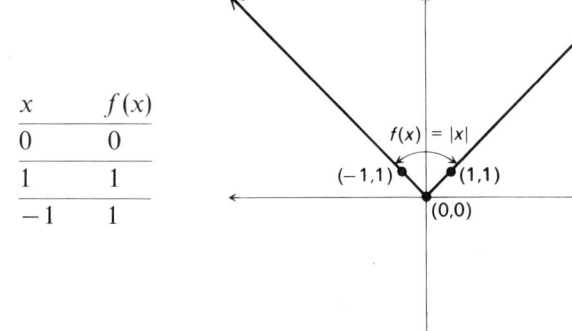

x	f(x)
0	0
1	1
−1	1

EXERCISE 5.14

In each of the following equations: if y is a function of x, write the equation using functional notation. The domain of x is the set of real numbers.

1. $y = 2x + 3$
2. $y = 6 - x$
3. $y = .5x$
4. $y \geqslant x$
5. $y + 1 \leqslant x$

Write a formula stating the domain and range and graph each function defined by the following statements.

6. The number of inches in x feet.
7. The number of ounces in x pounds.
8. The distance traveled in 10 hours at x miles per hour.
9. The cost of n ice-cream cones at 15 cents each.
10. The cost of renting a car for one day and driving n miles at $5.00 plus $1.00 for each 10 miles or part of 10 miles.
11. The pressure of water on the bottom of a tank is 62.5 times the depth in feet.
12. The volume of a cube is the third power of its edge, e.
13. A trip of D miles requires t hours at 65 miles per hour.
14. The perimeter of a square is four times the length of the side, y.
15. The charge for renting a TV set at $5.00 plus $2.00 per day for n days.

REVIEW EXERCISES 5.2

Find the solution set of each algebraic statement when the replacement set for x and y are stated.

1. $2x + y = 5$, $x \in \{0, 1, 2\}$, $y \in \{1, 3, 5\}$
2. $3x + 6 = 2y$, $x \in \{-2, 0, 2\}$, $y \in \{0, 3, 6\}$
3. $2y > -x$, $x \in \{-1, 0, 3\}$, $y \in \{5, 3, 0\}$
4. $xy < 0$, $x \in \{-1, 0, 1\}$, $y \in \{-1, 0, 1\}$

On a coordinate plane, sketch the graph of the following equations or inequalities, when the replacement set for both variables is the set of real numbers.

5. $2x - 3y = -6$
6. $5x - 3y = 15$
7. $4x + y = 2$
8. $3x - 2y = 2$
9. $2(x - 1) > 3x$
10. $x > -1$ or $x < -2$
11. $x > -2$ and $x < 5$

Write the equation of the line when:

12. $m = \frac{3}{2}$, $b = -2$
13. $m = -2$, $b = \frac{1}{2}$
14. $m = 1$, $b = 0$

Solve each system graphically and estimate the solution set.

15. $2x - 3y = 12$
    $x + y = 0$
16. $2x + y = 6$
    $3x - y = 14$
17. $3x + y = 3$
    $x - 2y = 8$

Solve each system algebraically.

18. $5x = 3y$
    $2x - y = 1$
19. $2x + 3 = -3y$
    $3x + 2 = -4y$
20. $6x + 5 = y$
    $\frac{1}{4}x = 4y$
21. $x + y = 2$
    $4x + 7y = -1$
22. $12x + y = 1$
    $3y + 10x = -10$

Sketch the graphs of the systems of inequalities and shade the solution set.

23. $x + y \geq 4$
    $x - 2y \leq 6$
24. $x - y \geq -2$
    $2x + y \leq -4$
    $y \geq -2$

Sketch the graphs of each function on a coordinate plane.

25. $y = 2x + 3$
26. $y = 3x - 4$
27. John has $1.50 to spend for school supplies. If tablets cost 12 cents each and pencils cost 7 cents each and he must purchase at least 5 of each item, how many of each can he buy if he spends all of his money?
28. Sam and Tom each work 8 hours on a job; together they earn $35.20. If Tom earns 25 cents per hour less than twice as much as Sam, how much does each earn per hour?
29. The total cost of 10 quarts of milk and ice cream is $4.10. How many quarts of each did Mrs. Brown buy if the milk cost 25 cents a quart and the ice-cream 65 cents?
30. A nursery wants to mix grass seed worth 75 cents a pound with grass seed worth 95 cents a pound to make a mixture of 10 pounds to sell at 84 cents a pound. How many pounds of each should be used?

SELF QUIZ 5.2

Find the solution set of each statement, when the replacement set for x and y are as stated.

1. $2x + y = 6$, $x \in \{0, 3, 6\}$, $y \in \{0, 1, 2, 3\}$
2. $3x - 2y = 12$, $x \in \{0, 2, 4, 6\}$, $y \in \{-4, -2, 0\}$
3. $x - 2y \leq 6$, $x \in \{0, 6, 12\}$, $y \in \{0, 2, 4\}$

Sketch the graph of the statement using the method indicated.

4. $3x - 4y = 12$ (x, y-intercept form)
5. $y = 2x - 3$ (point-slope form)
6. $3x - 2y \geq -6$ (establish boundary by either form)

Find the algebraic solution of the system by the method indicated.

7. $\begin{cases} x + 2y = 5 \\ 2x - 3y = 3 \end{cases}$ (addition or substitution)

8. $\begin{cases} 2x - y = 5 \\ x + 2y = 5 \end{cases}$ (Cramer's rule)

9. Shade the solution set determined by the system.
$$2x + y \geqslant 2$$
$$4x - y \leqslant 4$$
$$x \geqslant y$$

10. Find the vertices of the solution set (polygon) in Problem 9.
11. At a candy store, the owner advertises a special price of 71 cents a pound in 5 pound bags. To make the special, he mixed candy worth 85 cents a pound with candy worth 50 cents a pound. How many pounds of each did he use?

6 Exponents, Radicals and Quadratic Equations

6.1 INTRODUCTION TO EXPONENTS

When two numbers are multiplied the result is called a *product*, and each of the numbers is called a *factor* of that product. In this example,

$$15 = 3 \cdot 5$$

15 is the product, and the factors are 3 and 5. Some other products and their factors are:

Product	Factors
6	2, 3, or 1, 6
8	2, 4 or 1, 8
24	3, 8 or 2, 12 or 4, 6 or 1, 24.

This is also true of numbers of the form $3x$. The product is $3x$, and the factors are 3 and x. It is customary to refer to each of the factors as the *coefficient* of the other. That is, 3 is the coefficient of x, and x is the coefficient of 3. The factor 3 indicates that x is to be multiplied by the number 3.

Products that contain more than one variable may be expressed in factored form. Thus

$$2xy = 2 \cdot x \cdot y$$

Each factor of the product is the coefficient of the product of the other factors. In the term $2xy$, $2x$ is the coefficient of y, $2y$ is the coefficient of x, and 2 is the coefficient of xy.

The *constant* (numerical part) *of a term* is usually called the *numerical coefficient*. In the term $2xy$, the numerical coefficient is 2. A coefficient of 1 is usually deleted, since 1 times a number is the number; i.e., $1 \cdot 2 = 2$, $1 \cdot a = a$.

Often, a number appears more than once as a factor in a product. In such cases, the product may be written in a simpler form; that is, the product $x \cdot x$ is commonly written as x^2. The term x^2 is read "x squared," "x square," or "x raised to the second power." The small, superscripted number is called an *exponent*. It shows that x, called the *base*, is to be used twice as a factor.

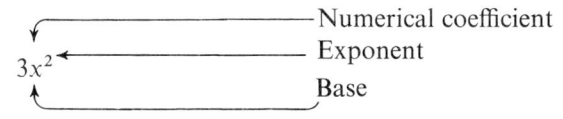

$3x^2$ — Numerical coefficient, Exponent, Base

Thus an exponent *indicates the number of times a base is to be used as a factor*.

6.1 Introduction to Exponents 147

The difference in meaning between the coefficient and exponent is illustrated in the following, where x has been replaced by 7.

$$x^2 = x \cdot x \qquad 2x = 2 \cdot x$$
$$x^2 = 7 \cdot 7 \qquad 2x = 2 \cdot 7$$
$$x^2 = 49 \qquad 2x = 14$$
$$2x^2 = 2 \cdot x^2 = 2 \cdot 49 = 98 \qquad (2x)^2 = (2 \cdot 7) \cdot (2 \cdot 7) = 14 \cdot 14 = 196$$

When a number is expressed by using a base and an exponent, it is called a *power*.

First power: $x^1 = x$ (an exponent of 1 is usually deleted)
Second power: $x^2 = x \cdot x$ (read "x square")
Third power: $x^3 = x \cdot x \cdot x$ (read "x cube")
Fourth power: $x^4 = x \cdot x \cdot x \cdot x$ (read "x fourth")
nth power: $x^n = x \cdot x \cdot x \cdot x \ldots x$ (read "x nth").
n times ($n \in$ natural numbers)

EXERCISE 6.1

In Problems 1–12, write each of the following terms as a product.

1. $2x$
2. $3s$
3. $5y$
4. $\frac{1}{2}x$
5. $\frac{2}{3}y$
6. $.3x$
7. xy
8. $3xy$
9. $.7ab$
10. $2(x + y)$
11. $3(x + 1)^2$
12. $3a(x + y)^2$

In Problems 13–20, list the factors of the given term.

13. 11
14. 12
15. $2x^2$
16. $6xy^2$
17. $3x^3y^2$
18. $\dfrac{ab}{2}$
19. $\dfrac{6a^2b^3}{2}$
20. $\dfrac{2abc^2}{2}$

In Problems 21–28, what is the coefficient of x?

21. $6x$
22. x
23. $\frac{1}{2}x$
24. $2xy$
25. $x(y + 2)$
26. $3x - 1$
27. $3 - 1(x + 2)$
28. $a + xy$

148 Exponents, Radicals and Quadratic Equations   6.1

In Problems 29–37, rewrite each expression in a shorter form.

29. $a \cdot a \cdot a$
30. b cubed
31. y used as a factor 5 times
32. s used as a factor n times
33. four times the cube of b
34. three times the cube of b
35. six times the fourth power of xy
36. the square of the sum; x plus 1
37. Two times the cube of the difference; $s - 1$

In problems 38–48, let $x = 2, y = 3, z = 4$ and evaluate the expressions.

38. $x + y - 2$
39. $2x + 3y - z$
40. $2x^2 + 3x - 2z$
41. $2x^2 + y^2 - z^2$
42. $\dfrac{3x^2 + xy}{z}$
43. $\dfrac{x^2 + 2z^2}{y^2}$
44. $\dfrac{x^3 - 2z}{y^2}$
45. $\dfrac{3x^2}{2y - z}$
46. $(xy)^2 + (xz)^2 - (xyz)$
47. $(x + y)^2 + 2(z + 3)^2$
48. $\dfrac{2(x + z)^2 + y^3}{3(x + y - z)^3}$

49. The area of a square is found by using the formula $A = s^2$. Find the area of a square when
   a) $s = 6$ inches
   b) $s = 1.5$ feet
   c) $s = 14$ yards
   d) $s = 2r$

50. The circumference of a circle is found by using the formula, $C = \pi d$. Find the circumference of a circle when
   a) $d = 1$ foot
   b) $d = 10$ feet
   c) $d = \dfrac{5}{2}$ feet

51. Simple interest is computed by the formula $I = Prt$. Find the interest when
   a) $P = \$100, r = .06, t = 2$
   b) $P = \$400, r = .055, t = 6$
   c) $P = \$250, r = .05, t = \tfrac{1}{2}$

52. The volume of a sphere is found by the formula $V = \dfrac{4\pi r^3}{3}$.
   Find the volume of a cube when (leave answer in terms of π)
   a) $r = 2$ b) $r = 4$
   c) $r = \tfrac{1}{2}$ d) $r = 2s$

6.2 THE PRODUCT OF POWERS

Frequently, our problem involves the *multiplication of two powers*. In the multiplication of two powers of the same base, the base is retained and the exponents are added. For example

$$x^3 \cdot x^2 = \underbrace{(x \cdot x \cdot x)}_{3 \text{ factors}} \cdot \underbrace{(x \cdot x)}_{2 \text{ factors}} = \overbrace{x^3 + x^2}^{5 \text{ factors}} = x^{3+2} = x^5$$

In general, for positive integral exponents, m and n and base b,

$$b^m \cdot b^n = b^{m+n}$$

This relation is called the *theorem of exponents for multiplication*.

The theorem of exponents for multiplication, along with the associative and commutative properties, enables us to determine the *numerical coefficient* and the *variable factors* of a term.

$$(2x^2y^3)(-3x^3y^2) = (2 \cdot -3)(x^2 \cdot x^3)(y^3 \cdot y^2) = -6 \cdot x^5 \cdot y^5 = -6x^5y^5$$

Or

$$(3ab^2)(2a^2b)(2) = (3 \cdot 2 \cdot 2)(a \cdot a^2)(b^2 \cdot b) = 12a^3b^3$$

This theorem applies only if the bases of the powers are the same. It cannot be used to simplify such problems as $x^3 \cdot y^2$ because the bases are not the same.

EXERCISE 6.2

Find each of the following products.

1. $(5rs)(4r^2s)$
2. $(-2a^2b)(-3ab^2)b^3$
3. $(2x)(-2x)(-2)$
4. $(-a)(2a)(3ab)$
5. $(5x)(3y)(-2z)$
6. $(3s^2)(2s^3)(24s^4)$
7. $(.5x^2y^3z)(4xyz^2)(xyz)$
8. $\frac{1}{2}gt^2(\frac{1}{2}gt)$
9. $(-5a)(-5c)(-5b)abc$
10. $(.2x)^2(.2x)^3$
11. $(\frac{1}{4}xy)(8xy^2y)(\frac{1}{2}y)$
12. $(.2a^2)(.3b^2)(-b)$
13. $(2a)^3(ab)(.3b)^3$
14. $(.4b)(.8b^2)(-2ab)$

Simplify by finding the indicated product and then combining terms.

15. $(-5x^2)(2y)(-2xy) + (8xy)(-2x^2y)$
16. $(5a^2)(3b)(2ab^2) - (3ab)(3ab)(3ab)$
17. $(4x^2wz^3)(-2xw^2z) + (-3z^2)(-6x^3w^2)(wz^2)$
18. $-(2^2a^5b^3)(5ab^7)(-5c^2) + (3^2b^6a^3c) \cdot (-b^2ca^2)(ab^2)$
19. $(3^2x^3y^3z)(-2x^4y^4z^5) - (-z^3x^2y^3) \cdot (8^2x^5y^4z^3)$
20. $x^5(2x + 1) + 4x^2(x^2 + x)$
21. $3a^2(2a^2 - a) - a^3(2a - 1)$
22. $a^m(a^n + b^m) + b^m(a^m + b^n)$

23. John has two rectangular lawns to mow. The lots are the same width but have different lengths. One lawn is 20 feet longer than it is wide, while the other lawn is 30 feet longer. Using the formula $A = lw$,
   a) What term represents the area of each lawn?
   b) What term represents the total area that John must mow?

24. An architect's plans for the design of a new building requires that two circles be drawn. The circles are such that the radius of the smaller is $\frac{1}{2}$ the radius of the larger. Using the formula for area, $A = \pi r^2$,
   a) What term represents the area of the large circle?
   b) What term represents the area of the small circle?
   c) What single term represents the difference between the areas of the two circles?

6.3 THE POWER OF A PRODUCT

Let us consider the two terms $2x^3$ and $(2x)^3$. Unless $x = 0$, the two terms are not equal. That is,

$$2x^3 = 2 \cdot x \cdot x \cdot x$$

and

$$(2x)^3 = (2x)(2x)(2x) = 2^3 \cdot x^3 = 8x^3$$

In general, for every positive integral exponent m, it is possible to write

$$(xy)^m \text{ as } \overbrace{(xy)(xy)(xy)\ldots(xy)}^{m \text{ factors}}$$

and

$$(xy) = \overbrace{(x \cdot x \cdot x \ldots \cdot x)}^{m \text{ factors}} \overbrace{(y \cdot y \cdot y \ldots \cdot y)}^{m \text{ factors}}$$

Therefore

$$(xy)^m = x^m y^m$$

This relation is known as the *theorem of exponents for a power of a product*.

$$(3x)^3 = 3^3 x^3 = 27x^3$$
$$(-2x)^4 = (-2)^4 (x)^4 = 16x^4$$

Often, the product whose power is to be found may itself be a power; that is,

$$(x^2)^3 = x^2 \cdot x^2 \cdot x^2 = x^{2+2+2} = x^6$$

and

$$(x^2 y^3)^2 = (x^2 y^3)(x^2 y^3) = x^2 \cdot x^2 \cdot y^3 \cdot y^3 = x^4 y^6$$

In general, for all positive integers m and n, it is possible to write

$$(x^m)^n \quad \text{as} \quad \overbrace{(x^m \cdot x^m \cdot x^m \ldots \cdot x^m)}^{n \text{ factors}}$$

Therefore
$$(x^m)^n = \overbrace{x^{m+m+m+\cdots+m}}^{n \text{ adders}} = x^{mn}$$

This relation is known as the *theorem of exponents for a power of a power.*
$$(2x^2)^3 = 2^3 \cdot (x^2)^3 = 8x^6$$
$$(-3x^2y^4)^5 = (-3)^5 (x^2)^5 (y^4)^5 = -243x^{10}y^{20}.$$

EXERCISE 6.3

Find each of the indicated products.

1. $(2x^3)^2$
2. $(-3x^3)^3$
3. $2x(2x^2)^2$
4. $2ab(2a^2b)^3$
5. $-2m(-5mn^2)^2$
6. $(-a)(-2a)^3$
7. $(4m)(3m^2n^2)^2$
8. $(4a)(-2a^3bc)^3$
9. $(-2m)(.5m^2n^3)^2$
10. $(-.5x^2y)^3(-2xy)^3$
11. $(.2a^2b)(-3c^3b^2a^2)^2$
12. $(3np^2q)(-3n^2pq^3)^2$

Simplify each of the following expressions.

13. $(3xy)^2 - (-2x)(-4xy)(-y)$
14. $(-2a)(3bc)^3 + (3a)^2(bc)^2(-5d)$
15. $m(-m)^2 + (2m^2)(-2m^2)^3$
16. $(-mn)^3(.6m^2n) + (m^2n)^2(.1m^3) + (m^2n)(m^2n)^2$
17. $(-ab)^5(.5ab^2) + (a^2b)^3(ab)^2 + (-a^3b)^2(-b)^4(b)$
18. $(-xy^2z)^2(-xyz)^3 - (-xz)^5(y)^7$
19. $(2abc)^3(bc) + (2a)^2(ab)(-4b)(2c)(abc)^3$
20. $(3x^2y^2z^2)(2xyz)^2 + (-2xyz)^3(xyz) - (2xyz)^2(x^2y^2z^2)$

6.4 THE PRODUCT OF TWO POLYNOMIALS

Expressions are classified by the *number of terms* that they contain. For example; $3x^2$ is a *monomial* because it contains one term; $x^2 - 2x$ is a *binomial* because it contains two terms; and $3x^2 + 2x - 1$ is a *trinomial* because it contains three terms. Each of these is an expression of the form $a_0x^n + a_1x^{n-1} + a_2x^{n-2} + \ldots a_nx^{n-n}$, where the coefficients are real numbers and n is a nonnegative integer called a *polynomial.*

We are able to find the product of any two polynomials by using the distributive property of real numbers and the theorems of exponents for multiplication.

152   Exponents, Radicals and Quadratic Equations   6.4

The product of two monomials is
$$2xy(3x^2y) = 6x^3y^2$$
The product of a monomial and a binomial is
$$2a(3a^2 + 2) = 2a(3a^2) + 2a(2) = 6a^3 + 4a$$
The product of two binomials is
$$(2a + b)(3a - b) = 2a(3a) + 2a(-b) + b(3a) + b(-b)$$
$$= 6a^2 - 2ab + 3ab - b^2$$
$$= 6a^2 + ab - b^2$$

EXERCISE 6.4

Write the expressions in their simplest form

1. $3x^2y^2z^3(-2x^3yz)$
2. $b^2(-a^2 + b - c)$
3. $-5(x^2 - 3x - 4)$
4. $(2 - 3x + 4x^2)(-2x^3)$
5. $2a(a^2 + 2ab + b^2)$
6. $(a - b)(a + b)$
7. $(2a + 3)(3a - 2)$
8. $(2x + 3y)(x - y^2)$
9. $-a^2(10 - a + a^2)$
10. $(5 - 2xy + y^2)(2x^2y)$
11. $(x - 5)(5 - 2x)$
12. $(2a - .3b)(4a + .36)$
13. $-2a^2b^2(a^2b - a^3b^2 + b^5)$
14. $(x - 2)(2x^2 + 3x - 4)$
15. $(x^2 - 5)(3x^2 - 5)$
16. $-3a^2b^2(a^5b + 4a^4b - 4a^2b^2 - 2b^5)(2ab)$
17. $(2x + 5y)(2x - 3y + 1)$
18. $(x + 2)(4x^3 + 3x + 4)$
19. $(2x^2 + x - 1)(3x^2 - x + 2)$
20. $(3x^2 - x - 2)(-2x^2 - 3x - 4)$
21. $(a + 1)(a^3 + 2a^2 + 3a - 1)$

Give each answer as a polynomial either in the simplest form or as a direct number.

22. The length of the living room in Sue's and John's new house is 5 feet less than twice its width. What polynomial represents its area?
23. The dimensions of a patio are such that the length is 3 feet longer than the square of its width. What polynomial represents the area?
24. The length of a sandlot football field is 20 feet less than twice its width. What polynomial represents its area?
25. A rectangular field is 40 feet longer than it is wide. For purposes of cultivation, a strip 10 feet wide on each of the shorter sides is left unplanted. What polynomial represents the area of the planted field?
26. The building codes of Garden City require that for a certain highrise apartment building, the foundation must have an area of 1800 square feet. The foundation of the rectangular building is 2 feet thick, and its inside length is twice its inside width. Let x equal the inside width and write following:

    a) The polynomial that represents the inside area;
    b) The polynomial that represents the total area;
    c) The equation that shows the total area is equal to the inside area plus the area of the foundation; and

d) The equation of part c) and then find the inside dimensions of the building.

27. A still life painting is one and one-half times as long as it is wide and is enclosed in a frame that is 3 inches wide. If the area of the picture frame is 336 square inches, what are the dimensions of the picture?

6.5 THE QUOTIENT OF POWERS

The fundamental principle of fractions, which we have already stated as

$$\frac{aa}{b} \cdot \frac{k}{k} = \frac{ak}{bk} \qquad b \neq 0, k \neq 0$$

is a helpful principle in simplifying quotients of powers. For example,

$$\frac{5^4}{5^2} = \frac{5^2 \cdot 5^2}{5^2} = 5^2$$

and

$$\frac{x^6}{x^4} = \frac{x^2 \cdot x^4}{x^4} = x^2$$

The results can also be found by the "reverse" operation of the product of powers; that is

$$\frac{5^4}{5^2} = 5^{4-2} = 5^2$$

or

$$\frac{x^6}{x^4} = x^{6-4} = x^2$$

When division is indicated, the quotient may be obtained by retaining the base and subtracting the exponents.

These are the *theorems of exponents for division.* For every positive integer m and n and for all nonzero denominators,

$$\text{If } m > n \text{ then } \frac{a^m}{a^n} = a^{m-n}$$

and

$$\text{if } m < n \text{ then } \frac{a^m}{a^n} = \frac{1}{a^{n-m}}$$

These theorems apply when m and n are unequal. But, if m and n are equal, then we have

$$\frac{a^m}{a^n} = a^{m-n} = a^0$$

or

$$\frac{a^m}{a^n} = \frac{1}{a^{n-m}} = \frac{1}{a^0}$$

By the transitive property, we have

$$a^0 = \frac{1}{a^0}$$

Thus a^0 is its own multiplicative inverse, and the only number with this property is 1. From this discussion, we define "$a^0 = 1$ for all nonzero a." No meaning is given to the term 0^0.

These theorems, together with the fundamental principle of fractions, provide a method for dividing monomials. Samples of steps in dividing monomials appear below.

$$\frac{24x^3y^2}{3x^2y} = \frac{24 \cdot x^3 \cdot y^2}{3x^2y} = 8 \cdot x^{3-2} \cdot y^{2-1} = 8xy$$

$$\frac{18x^2y^3}{6x^5y^7} = \frac{18}{6} \cdot \frac{x^2}{x^5} \cdot \frac{y^3}{y^7} = 3 \cdot \frac{1}{x^{5-2}} \cdot \frac{1}{y^{7-3}} = \frac{3}{x^3y^4}$$

$$\frac{10x^4y^5z}{15x^4y^3z^2} = \frac{10}{15} \cdot \frac{x^4}{x^4} \cdot \frac{y^5}{y^3} \cdot \frac{z}{z^2} = \frac{2 \cdot 5}{3 \cdot 5} \cdot x^{4-4} \cdot y^{5-3} \cdot \frac{1}{z^{2-1}} = \frac{2y^2}{z}$$

EXERCISE 6.5

Find each of the following quotients. (All variables in the denominators are nonzero.)

1. $\dfrac{49a^5b}{7a^4}$

2. $\dfrac{36a^3b^2}{9a^4b}$

3. $\dfrac{-20x^3b^4}{-4x^3b}$

4. $\dfrac{-72x^5y^3}{24x^7y^2}$

5. $\dfrac{18a^3b^4}{15a^5b^2}$

6. $\dfrac{27r^5s^{10}}{36rs^{12}}$

7. $\dfrac{-81p^0x^5}{-9x^5}$

8. $\dfrac{84x^2y}{7xy^2}$

9. $\dfrac{-56m^3n^5}{8m^3n^5}$

10. $\dfrac{78p^2q^3}{-3p^3q}$

11. $\dfrac{3x^2y^3}{5x^2y}$

12. $\dfrac{-6m^2n}{3(mn)^2}$

13. $\dfrac{4rs^7}{(2rs^2)^3}$

14. $\dfrac{-9abc}{(-3abc)^2}$

15. $\dfrac{(-3)^2 (xy)^3}{2(3xy)^2}$

16. $\dfrac{(2x^0)^3 (3y)^2}{72x^3 y}$

17. $\dfrac{6(a^2 b)^3}{(3ab)^0}$

18. $\dfrac{6a^m b^n}{3ab}$

19. $\dfrac{2x^a y^b}{2x^b y^a}$

20. $\dfrac{3a(xy)^m}{16x^m y^n}$

The procedure for dividing monomials together with the distributive property provides a method for *dividing any polynomial by a monomial*. This method is illustrated in the following examples.

Example 1. $\dfrac{45 + 60}{3}$

Solution. $\dfrac{45 + 60}{3} = \dfrac{1}{3}(45 + 60)$

$= \dfrac{1}{3}(45) + \dfrac{1}{3}(60)$

$= 15 + 20$

$= 35$

Example 2. $\dfrac{4a^3 + 10a^2 + 6a}{2a}$

Solution. $\dfrac{4a^3 + 10a^2 + 6a}{2a} = \dfrac{1}{2a}(4a^3 + 10a^2 + 6a)$

$= \dfrac{1}{2a}(4a^3) + \dfrac{1}{2a}(10a^2) + \dfrac{1}{2a}(6a)$

$= \dfrac{4a^3}{2a} + \dfrac{10a^2}{2a} + \dfrac{6a}{2a}$

$= 2a^2 + 5a + 3$

Example 3. $\dfrac{6a^4 b^3 + 18a^3 b^2 + 12ab}{6ab}$

Solution. $\dfrac{6a^4 b^3 + 18a^3 b^2 + 12ab}{6ab} = \dfrac{1}{6ab}(6a^4 b^3 + 18a^3 b^2 + 12ab)$

$= \dfrac{6a^4 b^3}{6ab} + \dfrac{18a^3 b^2}{6ab} + \dfrac{12ab}{6ab}$

$= a^3 b^2 + 3a^2 b + 2$

EXERCISE 6.6

Find each of the indicated quotients. (All variables in the denominator are nonzero.)

1. $\dfrac{3x + 6y}{3}$

2. $\dfrac{9x^2 + 12x}{3x}$

3. $\dfrac{2x + 5x}{x}$ 4. $\dfrac{8a - 4a}{4a}$

5. $\dfrac{3t^2 - 6t + 3}{3}$ 6. $\dfrac{8a^3 - 9a^2 + 7a}{a}$

7. $\dfrac{12x^3y^2 + 4x^2y^3 + 8x^2y^2}{4x^2y^2}$ 8. $\dfrac{18x^3y^3 - 6x^2y^2 + 24xy}{6xy}$

9. $\dfrac{24a^5b^4 + 18a^4b^3 - 36a^3b^2}{12a^2b^2}$ 10. $\dfrac{72m^7n^8 - 48m^{10}n^{13} + 96m^{12}n^{12}}{24m^7n^8}$

11. $\dfrac{30a^3b^3 + 45a^2b^2 + 15ab^4}{75ab^2}$ 12. $\dfrac{6a^2b^2 + 18a^2b^3 - 12a^3b^3}{21a^2b^4}$

6.6 DIVISION OF POLYNOMIAL EXPRESSIONS

Finding the factors of a polynomial is an *inverse* operation of finding a product of given factors. When a product is written as two factors—one of which is given—the other factor can be found by *division*.

When dividing polynomials, the dividend and divisor are written in the order of the *decreasing degree of the variable*; a pattern similar to that in the following examples develops.

Example 1. $x^2 - 5x + 4 \div x - 1$

Solution.

$$
\begin{array}{r}
x - 2 \\
x - 1 \overline{\smash{)}\,x^2 - 5x + 4} \\
\end{array}
$$

$x \leftarrow x^2 \div x$

$x(x - 1) \longrightarrow x^2 - x$ Subtract

$-4x + 4 \longleftarrow$ Difference

$x - 4 \longleftarrow -4x \div x$

$x - 1 \overline{\smash{)}\,x^2 - 5x + 4}$

$x^2 - x$

$-4(x - 1) \longrightarrow -4x + 4$ Subtract

$-4x + 4$

0

Check: $(x - 1)(x - 4) + 0 = x^2 - 5x + 4$

Example 2. $2x^2 - x - 6 \div 2x + 3$

Solution.

$$
\begin{array}{r}
x - 2 \\
2x + 3 \overline{\smash{)}\,2x^2 - x - 6} \\
2x^2 + 3x \\
\hline
-4x - 6 \\
-4x - 6 \\
\hline
0
\end{array}
$$

Check: $(2x + 3)(x - 2) + 0 = 2x^2 - x - 6$

6.6 Division of Polynomial Expressions

Example 3. $a^3 - 5a + 8 \div a - 2$

Solution.

$$\begin{array}{r} a^2 + 2a - 1 \\ a - 2 \overline{\smash{\big)}\, a^3 + 0a^2 - 5a + 8} \\ \underline{a^3 - 2a^2} \\ 2a^2 - 5a + 8 \\ \underline{2a^2 - 4a} \\ -a + 8 \\ \underline{-a + 2} \\ 6 \end{array}$$

[*Note*: The missing term is written with 0 coefficient]

Check: $(a - 2)(a^2 + 2a - 1) + 6 = a^3 + 5a + 8.$

EXERCISE 6.7

Do the indicated operation, express each as a complete quotient, and then check your answer. (All variables in the denominator are nonzero.)

1. $\dfrac{x^2 + 3x + 2}{x + 1}$

2. $\dfrac{a^2 + 5a + 6}{a + 2}$

3. $\dfrac{x^2 + 7x + 12}{x + 3}$

4. $\dfrac{x^2 - 6x + 8}{x - 4}$

5. $\dfrac{10a^2 + 7a - 12}{2a + 3}$

6. $\dfrac{n^2 - 11np - 102p^2}{n - 17p}$

7. $\dfrac{5a^2 - 13ab + 6b^2}{a - 2b}$

8. $\dfrac{6b^2 + 11b - 10}{2b + 5}$

9. $\dfrac{x^2 + 16}{4 + x}$

10. $\dfrac{-6ab + a^2 - 27b^2}{a - 9b}$

11. $\dfrac{x^3 + y^3}{x + y}$

12. $\dfrac{8a^3 - b^3}{2a - b}$

13. $\dfrac{64m^3 - 27n^3}{4m - 3n}$

14. $\dfrac{2m^2 + 11m - 18}{2m - 3}$

15. $\dfrac{12a^2 + 4a - 18}{2a + 3}$

16. $a + 3 \overline{\smash{\big)}\, 3a^3 + 11a^2 + 15}$

17. $a - 5 \overline{\smash{\big)}\, 2a^3 - 7a^2 - 17a - 10}$

18. $2n - 5 \overline{\smash{\big)}\, 6n^3 + n^2 - 18n - 80}$

19. $a^2 - a + 1 \overline{\smash{\big)}\, 3a^4 - 7a^3 + 12a^2 - 9a + 5}$

20. $n^2 + 2n - 1 \overline{\smash{\big)}\, 2n^5 + 7n^4 - 2n^3 - 10n^2 + 16n - 5}$

21. One factor of $x^2 - x - 12$ is $x + 3$. Find the other factor.
22. One factor of $6x^2 - x - 2$ is $2x + 1$. Find the other factor.
23. One factor of $x^3 - 8$ is $x - 2$. Find the other factor.
24. If 220 is divided by a certain number, the quotient is 29 and the remainder is 17. Find the number.
25. If 210 is divided by a certain number, the quotient is 17 and the remainder is 6. Find the number.

26. A flower bed in the shape of a rectangle is three times as long as it is wide. The flower bed is surrounded by a walk that is 3 feet wide and its area is 180 sq. ft. Find the dimensions of the flower bed.

6.7 NEGATIVE EXPONENTS

The theorem of exponents for division $a^m/a^n = a^{m-n}$ results in a negative exponent when $m < n$. For example,

$$\frac{a^3}{a^5} = a^{3-5} = a^{-2}$$

while

$$\frac{a^5}{a^3} = a^{5-3} = a^2$$

And, since a^3/a^5 and a^5/a^3 are multiplicative inverses, a^{-2} and a^2 are multiplicative inverses.

$$a^{-2} = \frac{1}{a^2} \quad \text{and} \quad \frac{1}{a^{-2}} = a^2$$

In general therefore,

$$a^{-n} = \frac{1}{a^n} \quad \text{and} \quad \frac{1}{a^{-n}} = a^n$$

So the theorems of exponents, which we discussed previously, may now be extended to include *negative exponents*.

The following examples, where all exponents are written as positive numbers, should be studied.

Example 1. $a^3 \cdot b^{-2} = a^3 \cdot \dfrac{1}{b^2} = \dfrac{a}{b^2}$

Example 2. $3x^{-1}y^4 = 3 \cdot \dfrac{1}{x} \cdot y^4 = \dfrac{3y^4}{x}$

Example 3. $(2x)^{-3} = \dfrac{1}{(2x)^3} = \dfrac{1}{8x^3}$

Example 4. $-2a^{-3} \cdot 4a^{-2} = -8a^{-3-2} = -8a^{-5} = \dfrac{-8}{a^5}$

Example 5. $\left(\dfrac{2a^2}{3b^3}\right)^{-2} = \dfrac{1}{\left(\dfrac{2a^2}{3b^3}\right)^2} = \left(\dfrac{3b^3}{2a^2}\right)^2 = \dfrac{9b^6}{4a^4}$

Example 6. $(-3a^2)^{-3} = \dfrac{1}{(-3a^2)^3} = \dfrac{1}{-27a^6}$

Example 7. $(\frac{2}{3}x^2)^{-2} = \dfrac{1}{(\frac{2}{3})^2 (x^2)^2} = \dfrac{1}{\frac{4}{9}x^4} = \dfrac{9}{4x^4}$

Example 8. $-5x^{-2} \cdot -4x^{-3} = 20x^{-5} = \dfrac{20}{x^5}$

Example 9. $a^{-2} + b^{-2} = \dfrac{1}{a^2} + \dfrac{1}{b^2} = \dfrac{b^2 + a^2}{a^2 b^2}$

Example 10. $-6a^5 \cdot (2a)^{-3} = -6a^5 \cdot \dfrac{1}{(2a)^3}$

$= -6a^5 \cdot \dfrac{1}{8a^3} = \dfrac{-6}{8} \cdot a^{5-3} = \dfrac{-3a^2}{4}$

6.8 RADICALS (FRACTIONAL EXPONENTS)

In section 6.2, we showed that the power of a number is the product of factors each of which is equal to the number. That is,

$$2^3 = 2 \cdot 2 \cdot 2$$

and

$$x^n = \overbrace{x \cdot x \cdot x \cdot \ldots x}^{n \text{ factors}}$$

When a number is expressed in this way, we call it *raising to a power*.

The inverse operation of raising to a power is called *extracting a root*. Thus, for any positive integer n, if $x^n = a$, then a is the nth root of x.

$$2^2 = 4 \quad (2 \text{ is a 2nd root of 4})$$

and

$$3^3 = 27 \quad (3 \text{ is a third root of 27})$$

The nth root of a is indicated by the expression $\sqrt[n]{a}$. The symbol $\sqrt{\ }$, called a *radical*, indicates that a root is to be taken; the root index n signifies the root to be taken. When no root-index number is given, $\sqrt{\ }$ indicates that the square root is to be taken. Thus

$$\sqrt{25} = 5$$
$$\sqrt[3]{64} = 4$$
$$\sqrt[5]{32} = 2$$

The square of either a positive or negative number is a positive number, that is, $3^2 = 9$ and $(-3)^2 = 9$. Every positive number has two square roots— one positive and one negative. However the expression $\sqrt{9}$ indicates "the positive root of 9," and is called the *principal root*. Thus $\sqrt{9} = 3$ and $-\sqrt{9} = -3$. In taking the square root of a variable, the root is written as absolute value to ensure that it is positive, e.g., $\sqrt{x^2} = |x|$. Since the square of every real number is either zero or a positive number, negative numbers do not have square roots in the set of real numbers.

The *square root of a number* may be extracted directly, using either an

160   Exponents, Radicals and Quadratic Equations   6.8

algorithm or *Newton's method of approximation*. In many cases, we can find the square root of a large number by determining its factors, expressing the factors as a product of powers, and then taking the root of the powers.

Example 1. Find the square root of 3136.

Solution. $\sqrt{3136} = \sqrt{49 \cdot 64} = \sqrt{7^2 \cdot 8^2} = \sqrt{7^2} \cdot \sqrt{8^2} = 7 \cdot 8 = 56$

Example 2. Find the cube root of 216.

Solution. $\sqrt[3]{216} = \sqrt[3]{8 \cdot 27} = \sqrt[3]{2^3 \cdot 3^3} = \sqrt[3]{2^3} \cdot \sqrt[3]{3^3} = 2 \cdot 3 = 6$

In general, the following assumptions hold true:

$$\text{If } a \geq 0 \text{ and } b \geq 0, \text{ then } \sqrt{ab} = \sqrt{a} \cdot \sqrt{b}$$

$$\text{If } a \geq 0 \text{ and } b \geq 0, \text{ then } \sqrt{\frac{a}{b}} = \frac{\sqrt{a}}{\sqrt{b}}$$

Example 3. Find the square root of $\frac{18}{25}$.

Solution. $\sqrt{\frac{18}{25}} = \frac{\sqrt{18}}{\sqrt{25}} = \frac{\sqrt{2 \cdot 3^2}}{\sqrt{5^2}} = \frac{3\sqrt{2}}{5}$

Example 4. Find the cube root of $\frac{1}{8}$.

Solution. $\sqrt[3]{\frac{1}{8}} = \frac{\sqrt[3]{1}}{\sqrt[3]{8}} = \frac{\sqrt[3]{1^3}}{\sqrt[3]{2^3}} = \frac{1}{2}$

If an expression contains a denominator with a radical, such as $1/\sqrt{2}$, it is customary to rewrite the expression and place the radical in the numerator. This is accomplished by multiplying the expression by a number that makes the denominator a *perfect square*. For the expression $1/\sqrt{2}$, the number that makes the denominator a perfect square is $\sqrt{2}/\sqrt{2}$. Thus

$$\frac{1}{\sqrt{2}} = \frac{1}{\sqrt{2}} \cdot \frac{\sqrt{2}}{\sqrt{2}} = \frac{\sqrt{2}}{\sqrt{2^2}} = \frac{\sqrt{2}}{2}$$

Example 5. Rationalize the denominator in the expression $1/\sqrt{3}$.

Solution. $\frac{1}{\sqrt{3}} = \frac{1}{\sqrt{3}} \cdot \frac{\sqrt{3}}{\sqrt{3}} = \frac{\sqrt{3}}{\sqrt{3} \cdot \sqrt{3}} = \frac{\sqrt{3}}{\sqrt{3^2}} = \frac{\sqrt{3}}{3}$

Example 6. Rationalize the expression $\sqrt{\frac{50}{75}}$.

Solution. $\sqrt{\frac{50}{75}} = \frac{\sqrt{2 \cdot 25}}{\sqrt{3 \cdot 25}} = \frac{\sqrt{2 \cdot 5^2}}{\sqrt{3 \cdot 5^2}}$

$= \frac{5\sqrt{2}}{5\sqrt{3}} = \frac{\sqrt{2}}{\sqrt{3}} = \frac{\sqrt{2}}{\sqrt{3}} \cdot \frac{\sqrt{3}}{\sqrt{3}} = \frac{\sqrt{6}}{\sqrt{3^2}} = \frac{\sqrt{6}}{3}$

The *n*th root of a number can also be expressed by using *fractional exponents*; that is, the *n*th root of a can be expressed as $a^{1/n}$. To signify that a square

6.8 Radicals (Fractional Exponents)

root is to be taken, the fractional exponent $\frac{1}{2}$ is used; to signify a cube root; the fractional exponent $\frac{1}{3}$ is used; and to signify the nth root, the fractional exponent $1/n$ is used. Thus,

$$9^{1/2} = 3$$
$$16^{1/2} = 4$$
$$27^{1/3} = 3$$
$$25^{1/5} = 2$$

The preceding Examples, involving radicals and their solutions, may also be written with fractional exponents.

Example 1. Find the square root of 3136.

Solution. $(3136)^{1/2} = (7^2 \cdot 8^2)^{1/2} = (7^2)^{1/2} (8^2)^{1/2} = 7^{2/2} \cdot 8^{2/2} = 7 \cdot 8 = 56$

Example 2. Find the square root of $\frac{18}{25}$.

Solution. $(\frac{18}{25})^{1/2} = \frac{18^{1/2}}{25^{1/2}} = \frac{(9 \cdot 2)^{1/2}}{(5 \cdot 5)^{1/2}} = \frac{(3^2)^{1/2}(2)^{1/2}}{(5^2)^{1/2}} = \frac{3^{1/2} \cdot 2^{1/2}}{5^{2/2}} = \frac{3 \cdot 2^{1/2}}{5}$

Example 3. Find the cube root of $\frac{1}{8}$.

Solution. $(\frac{1}{8})^{1/3} = \frac{(1)^{1/3}}{(8)^{1/3}} = \frac{(1^3)^{1/3}}{(2^3)^{1/3}} = \frac{1}{2^{3/3}} = \frac{1}{2}$.

Example 4. Rationalize the expression $(\frac{50}{75})^{1/2}$.

Solution. $(\frac{50}{75})^{1/2} = \frac{(50)^{1/2}}{(75)^{1/2}} = \frac{(5^2 \cdot 2)^{1/2}}{(5^2 \cdot 3)^{1/2}}$
$= \frac{5 \cdot 2^{1/2}}{5 \cdot 3^{1/2}} = \frac{2^{1/2}}{3^{1/2}} = \frac{2^{1/2}}{3^{1/2}} \cdot \frac{3^{1/2}}{3^{1/2}} = \frac{2^{1/2} \cdot 3^{1/2}}{3^{1/2} \cdot 3^{1/2}} = \frac{6^{1/2}}{3}$

EXERCISE 6.8

Write each expression in its simplest form, using the notation in which the expression is stated.

1. $\sqrt{121}$
2. $\sqrt{324}$
3. $256^{1/2}$
4. $484^{1/2}$
5. $\sqrt[3]{64}$
6. $\sqrt[4]{625}$
7. $(17^2)^{1/2}$
8. $\left(\frac{a^4}{100}\right)^{1/2}$
9. $((x+y)^2)^{1/2}$
10. $\sqrt{(+3)^2}$
11. $\left(\frac{2^6}{2^8}\right)^{1/2}$
12. $\left(\frac{49}{81}\right)^{1/2}$
13. $\left(\frac{9x^4}{y^8}\right)^{1/2}$
14. $\left(\frac{50a^4}{100}\right)^{1/2}$
15. $-\sqrt{\frac{1089}{841}}$
16. $(48m^4n^8)^{1/2}$

17. $(13^2 - 12^2)^{1/2}$ 18. $(3^3 + 4^2)^{1/2}$

19. $\dfrac{1}{\sqrt{2}}$ 20. $\left(\dfrac{1}{8x^3}\right)^{1/3}$

6.9 SPECIAL PRODUCTS AND FACTORING

In section 6.6, we used the operation of division to find the second factor, when the product *and* one factor were given. For special products, we can find the factors when only the *product* is given.

The process whereby a polynomial is written as a product of polynomials is called *factoring*. To illustrate: The polynomial $2x^2 + 4x$ has two terms, and each term has $2x$ as a factor. So using the distributive property, we have

$$2x^2 + 4x = 2x(x + 2)$$

The factor $2x$ in this polynomial is called the *greatest common factor* because it is the factor having the largest numerical coefficient or the highest degree of the variable—or both. For example,

$$4x^3 + x^2 = x^2(4x + 1) \quad \text{(Greatest common factor, } x^2\text{)}$$
$$18x^2 - 27 = 9(x^2 - 3) \quad \text{Greatest common factor, } 9\text{)}$$
$$6x^3 + 9x^2 + 12x = 3x(2x^2 + 3x + 4) \quad \text{(Greatest common factor, } 3x\text{)}$$
$$5x^4y^3 - 10x^3y^4 + 14x^2y^5 = 5x^2y^3(x^2 - 2xy + 3y^2) \quad \text{(Greatest common factor, } 5x^2y^3\text{)}$$

This type of factoring is called *factoring by removing the greatest common factor*.

EXERCISE 6.9

Write each polynomial in factorial form.

1. $3x^2 - 12$
2. $x^2y - xy^2$
3. $5x^2 + 10y^2$
4. $7x^3 - 21x^4$
5. $6a^2 + 9a^3$
6. $15a^2 - 5ac$
7. $12a^2 + 6a^2b$
8. $49x^2 - 98x$
9. $9b^3 - 27a^3b^2$
10. $3n^2 + 13n$
11. $x + 3xyz$
12. $13x^3y^4 - 17x^4y^5 + 25x^3y^3$
13. $6t^2 + 9r^2t^3$
14. $12x^3 + 13x^2 + 24x$
15. $8x^5y^3 + 12x^4y^2 - 16x^2y^4$
16. $5a^4b^2 - 10a^4b^5 + 20a^3b^3 - 25a^5b^6$
17. $25x - 50x^2$
18. $2x^4y^5 - 4x^3y^4 + 2x^4y^5$
19. $3x^4 + 15x^2$
20. $a^2b^2 + 14ab^2 + 6a^2b - 7ab^2$

Polynomials of the form $a^2 - b^2$ are often referred to as the *difference of two perfect squares*. Such polynomials can be factored by extracting the square root of each term and writing the factors as the sum and difference of the square

roots. Finding the difference of two perfect squares may be shown as follows:
$$a^2 - b^2 = (a - b)(a + b)$$
$$4x^2 - 9 = (2x - 3)(2x + 3)$$
$$25x^2 - 64y^2 = (5x - 8y)(4x + 8y)$$
$$9x^4y^2 - 4a^4b^6 = (3x^2y - 2a^2b^3)(3x^2y + 2a^2b^3)$$

EXERCISE 6.10

Factor each polynomial. Check by multiplication.

1. $x^2 - 16$
2. $4x^2 - 9$
3. $25 - 16x^2$
4. $4x^2 - z^2$
5. $1 - 9a^2$
6. $36m^2 - 1$
7. $-9 + t^2s^2$
8. $-4t^2 + 9s^2$
9. $.09a^2 - .16$
10. $.25a^2b^4 - .36c^6$
11. $.81 - t^2$
12. $x^2 - \frac{1}{4}$
13. $-4a^4 + 16a^2$
14. $3x^4 - 27x^2$
15. $2a^3b^4 - 72ab^2$
16. $x^6y - x^2y^3$
17. $a^{2n} - 1$
18. $a^2 - b^{2n}$
19. $(x + y)^2 - 1$
20. $(a + 2b)^2 = 4c^2$

Polynomials such as
$$a^2 + 2ab + b^2$$
or
$$a^2 - 2ab + b^2$$
are referred to as *trinomial squares*. Each such trinomial is the square of a binomial. Thus
$$a^2 + 2ab + b = (a + b)(a + b) = (a + b)^2$$
and
$$a^2 - 2ab + b^2 = (a - b)(a - b) = (a - b)^2$$

6.10 THE QUADRATIC FUNCTION

If we replace the zero in the quadratic equation with the variable y, then we have a quadratic function with two variables, for example,
$$y = ax^2 + bx + c$$
The quadratic function consists of all ordered pairs, (x, y), that make the relation true. The graph of a quadratic function is a *parabola*, as shown in Figure 6.1, next page.

If, to each value of the variable x, we assign the number y given by
$$y = x^2 - x - 6, \text{ then}$$

Exponents, Radicals and Quadratic Equations

the resulting function is graphed like the parabola shown in Figure 6.1.

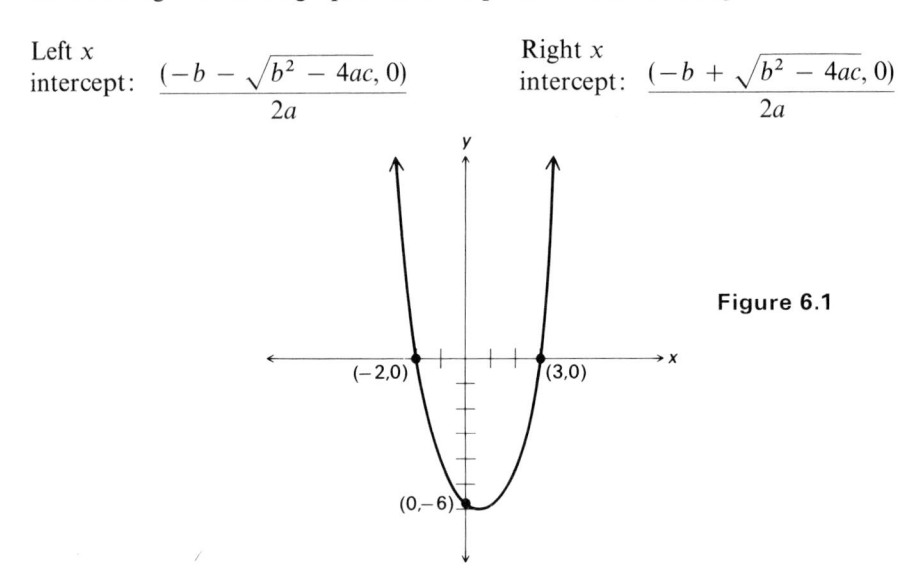

Left x intercept: $\dfrac{(-b - \sqrt{b^2 - 4ac}, 0)}{2a}$

Right x intercept: $\dfrac{(-b + \sqrt{b^2 - 4ac}, 0)}{2a}$

Figure 6.1

Since the x-axis is the line $y = 0$, by replacing y with 0 in the function and solving the resulting equation for x, we can find the points at which the line crosses the x-axis. These points are called the *x-intercepts*. The point at which the line crosses the y-axis is called the *y-intercept* and can be found by replacing x with 0 in the function and then evaluating y. The x-intercepts for the function $y = x^2 - x - 6$ are the ordered pairs $(-2, 0)$ and $(3, 0)$. The y-intercept is the ordered pair $(0, -6)$. The highest or lowest point is called the *vertex of the parabola*. The vertex is found by completing the square and determining the value for x that makes the quantity in parentheses 0.

$$y = x^2 - 2x - 8$$
$$y = x^2 - 2x + 1 - 1 - 8$$
$$y = (x - 1)^2 - 9$$

The vertex is the minimum in this parabola $(1, -9)$ and occurs when $x = 1$.

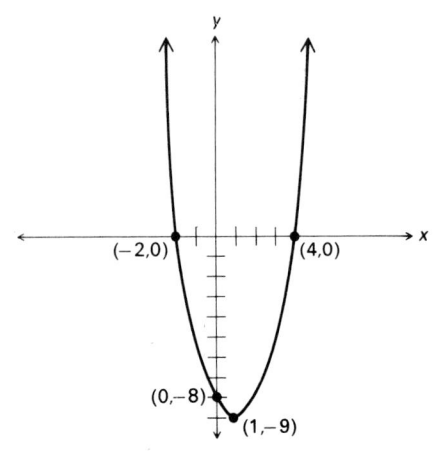

The minimum, or vertex, is at the point designated by the ordered pair $(1, -9)$.

Example 2. Find the maximum or minimum value of $y = -3x^2 - 12x + 4$

Solution. If we complete the square, we have

$$y = -3x^2 - 12x + 4$$
$$y = -3(x^2 + 4x) + 4$$
$$y = -3(x^2 + 4x + 4) + 12 + 4$$
$$y = -3(x + 2)^2 + 16$$

The vertex $(-2, 16)$ is the maximum, as shown in this diagram:

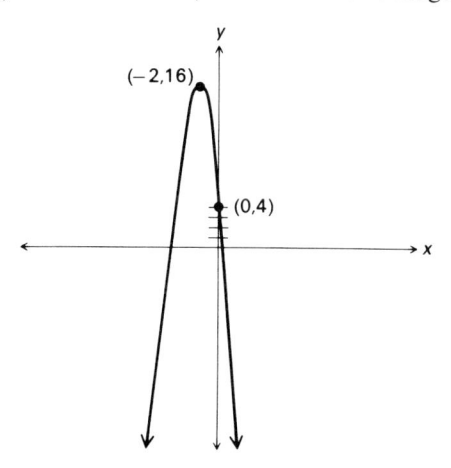

The above method is useful for solving other types of practical problems involving maximums or minimums.

The factors of a trinomial square are found by taking the square root of the first and third terms and writing these as a sum or difference squared. If all terms of the trinomial are positive, then it is a sum. If the middle term is negative, then it is a difference.

Example 1. Factor $4x^2 - 20x + 25$.

Solution. The middle term is negative. The square root of the first term is $2x$, and the square root of the third term is 5. Thus,

$$4x^2 - 20x + 25 = (2x - 5)(2x - 5) = (2x - 5)^2$$

Example 2. Factor $9x^2 + 42xy + 49y^2$.

Solution. All terms are positive. The square root of the first term is $3x$, and the square root of the third term is $7y$. Thus,

$$9x^2 + 42xy + 49y = (3x + 7y)(3x + 7y) = (3x + 7y)^2$$

Before factoring, the trinomial must be written in either descending or ascending powers of one variable. This type of factoring is called *factoring a trinomial square*.

EXERCISE 6.11

1. $x^2 + 4x^2 + 4$
2. $a^2 + 6ac + 9c^2$
3. $m^2 - 2mn + n^2$
4. $t^2 - 14t + 49$
5. $4t^2 - 4t + 1$
6. $16x^2 + 8x + 1$
7. $1 - 10a + 25a^2$
8. $12xy + 36y^2 + x^2$
9. $25a^2 - 30a - 9$
10. $25x^2 - 20x + 1$
11. $36x^2 + 60xy + 25y^2$
12. $3a^2 - 54ab + 243b^2$
13. $a^4 - 2a^2 + 1$
14. $16a^2 + 40ab + 25b^2$
15. $a^4 - 18a^2 + 81$
16. $t^2 - 4s^2t + 4s^4$
17. $t^6 - 8t^3 + 16$
18. $-8t^2 + 8t + 2t^3$
19. $144a^2 - 120ab + 25b^2$
20. $121a^2b^2c^2 - 22abc + 1$

The last type of trinomial that we shall discuss is one whose factors are *distinct*. Consider the following examples.

Example 1. Find the factors of $x^2 + 3x + 2$.

Example 2. Find the factors of $6x^2 + 7x + 2$.

For this type of trinomial, there is no set procedure for factoring. However a few clues do exist that may be helpful. For example, if we multiply the two binomials $(x + r)(x + s)$, we have the trinomial $x^2 = (r + s)s + rs$. This trinomial is similar to the trinomial $(x + 1)(x + 2) = x^2 + 3x + 2$. A comparison of the two yields:

$$(x + r)(x + s) = x^2 + (r + s)x + rs$$
$$(x + 1)(x + 2) = x + (1 + 2)x + 1 \cdot 2$$

If $r + s = 3$ and $rs = 2$, then the two trinomials would be exactly alike. Thus, to factor the trinomial $x^2 + 3x + 2$, we look for two integers, r and s, such that their sum is 3 and their product is 2; i.e., $r + s = 3$ and $rs = 2$. To factor the general expression $x^2 + bx + c$, we must find two integers, r and s, such that $r + s = b$ and $rs = c$.

Example 1. Find the factors of $x^2 + 7x + 12$.

Solution. We must find two integers such that $r + s = 7$ and $rs = 12$. The only integers that meet both requirements are 3 and 4. Thus $x^2 + 7x + 12 = (x + 3)(x + 4)$.

Example 2. Find the factors of $x^2 - 9x + 20$.

Solution. We must find two integers such that $r + s = -9$ and $rs = 20$. The integers -5 and -4 meet both requirements. Thus $x^2 - 9x + 20 = (x - 4)(x - 5)$.

Example 3. Find the factors of $x^2 + 2x - 15$.

Solution. We must find two integers such that $r + s = 2$ and $rs = -15$. The two integers that meet both requirements are 5 and -3. Thus $x^2 + 2x - 15 = (x + 5)(x - 3)$.

If the coefficient of the squared term is not 1, we must change this procedure. If we multiply the two binomials $(mx + r)(nx + s)$, we have the trinomial $mnx^2 + (ms + nr)x + rs$. This trinomial is similar to the trinomial $(2x + 1)(3x + 2) = 6x^2 + 7x + 2$. A comparison of the two yields:

$$(mx + r)(nx + s) = mnx^2 + (ms + nr)x + rs$$
$$(2x + 1)(3x + 2) = 2 \cdot 3x^2 + (2 \cdot 2 + 1 \cdot 3)x + 1 \cdot 2$$
$$= 6x^2 + 7x + 2$$

If $m = 2$, $n = 3$, $r = 1$ and $s = 2$, then the two trinomials would be exactly alike. Thus, to factor the trinomial $6x^2 + 7x + 2$, we must find integers m, n, r and s such that $mn = 6$, $rs = 2$ and $(m \cdot s + n \cdot r) - 7$. In general, to factor the trinomial

$$ax^2 + bx + c$$

we must find integers m, n, r and s that meet the requirements $m \cdot n = a$, $r \cdot s = c$ and $(m \cdot s + n \cdot r) = b$. The integers m and n will be factors of a, and r and s will be factors of c. The values selected must be such that all three requirements are met.

EXERCISE 6.12

1. $x^2 + 3x - 4$
2. $x^2 + 5x + 4$
3. $6x^2 + 5x - 6$
4. $3n^2 + 11n - 4$
5. $m^2 + 5m - 24$
6. $y^2 + 6y + 8$
7. $t^2 - 4t - 12$
8. $12t^2 + 11t - 15$
9. $a^2 - 7a - 30$
10. $15a^2 - 13a - 20$
11. $(ax)^2 - (ax) - 6$
12. $4a^2 - 9a + 2$
13. $-t^2 - 3ts + 4s^2$
14. $10t^2 + 21t + 9$
15. $5a^2 + 16a - 16$
16. $(t + n)^2 + 5(t + n) - 14$
17. $x^2y^2 - 9xy - 10$
18. $x^2y^2z^2 + 4xyz - 12$
19. $2x^2 + 11x + 12$
20. $3x^2 + 5x - 2$

6.11 THE QUADRATIC EQUATION

A polynomial equation such as

$$x^2 + 3x + 2 = 0$$

in which the variable is raised to the second power is called a *quadratic equation*.

The general form of a quadratic equation is

$$ax^2 + bx + c = 0 \quad (a \neq 0)$$

and its solution can be found by *factoring*.

If it is known that the product of the factors is zero, as in the preceding equation, then at least one of the factors is zero. That is,

If $ab = 0$, then $a = 0$ or $b = 0$

Specifically, the solution to a quadratic equation is obtained by factoring the polynomial on the left and finding the values of the variables that make each factor zero.

Example 1. Solve $x^2 + 3x = -2$.

Solution. $\quad x^2 + 3x = -2$
$\qquad x^2 + 3x + 2 = 0 \quad$ (Written in general form)
$\qquad (x + 2)(x + 1) = 0 \quad$ (Factors of the left polynomial)
$\qquad x + 2 = 0 \quad \text{or} \quad x + 1 = 0 \quad$ (Set both factors equal to zero)
$\qquad x = -2 \quad \text{or} \quad x = -1 \quad$ (Solution of the two linear equations)

Check: $\quad (-2)^2 + 3(-2) = -2 \qquad (-1)^2 + 3(-1) = -2$
$\qquad\qquad 4 + (-6) = -2 \qquad\qquad 1 + 3 = -2$
$\qquad\qquad (-2) = -2 \qquad\qquad\qquad -2 = -2$

Example 2. $6x^2 + 5x - 6 = 0$

Solution. $\quad 6x^2 + 5x - 6 = 0$
$\qquad (2x + 3)(3x - 2) = 0$
$\quad 2x + 3 = 0 \quad \text{or} \quad 3x - 2 = 0$
$\qquad 2x = -3 \quad \text{or} \quad 3x = 2$
$\qquad x = \dfrac{-3}{2} \quad \text{or} \quad x = \dfrac{2}{3}$

Check: $\quad 6\left(\dfrac{-3}{2}\right)^2 + 5\left(\dfrac{-3}{2}\right) - 6 = 0 \qquad 6\left(\dfrac{2}{3}\right)^2 + 5\left(\dfrac{2}{3}\right) - 6 = 0$

$\qquad \dfrac{27}{2} + \left(\dfrac{-15}{2}\right) + \left(\dfrac{-12}{2}\right) = 0 \qquad \dfrac{8}{3} + \dfrac{10}{3} - \dfrac{18}{3} = 0$

$\qquad\qquad\qquad 0 = 0 \qquad\qquad\qquad\qquad\qquad 0 = 0$

The ability to use quadratic equations enables us to solve many problems that would be virtually impossible to solve using regular arithmetic. These problems abound in economics, physics, engineering and other fields. Exercise care in making decisions about the quadratic solution. Those solutions that are not sensible in light of the problem must be rejected. See what can happen in these examples:

Example 3. Sue and John plan to make a patio in the back of their new home. If the patio is to cover 330 square feet and its length is 5 feet more than its width, what are its dimensions?

Solution. Let $x = $ the number of feet in width. Then $x + 5 = $ the number of feet in length, and $x(x + 5) = $ the area. Thus,
$$x(x + 5) = 310$$
$$x^2 + 5x = 310$$
$$x^2 + 5x - 310 = 0$$

$$(x - 15)(x + 22) = 0$$
$$x - 15 = 0 \quad \text{or} \quad x + 22 = 0$$
$$x = 15 \quad \text{or} \quad x = -22.$$

Check: If the area is 330 square feet and its width is 15, then its length is $15 + 7 = 22$. So, $x = -22$ must be rejected, since distance cannot be a negative number.

Example 4. A farmer sold some oranges for \$72. If he had sold 6 less boxes for the same money, he would have received \$1.00 per box more. How many boxes did he sell?

Solution. x = the number of boxes sold

$$\frac{72}{x} = \text{the price per box}$$

$$\frac{72}{x - 6} = \text{the price per box if he had sold 6 boxes less.}$$

Thus
$$\frac{72}{x} = \frac{72}{x - 6} - 1$$

which simplifies to
$$x^2 - 6x - 432 = 0.$$

Solving
$$(x - 24)(x + 18) = 0$$
$$x - 24 = 0 \quad \text{or} \quad x + 18 = 0$$
$$x = 24 \quad \text{or} \quad x = -18.$$

Check: $\dfrac{72}{24} = \dfrac{72}{24 - 6} - 1$

$$x = 3.$$

The negative root must be rejected.

EXERCISE 6.13

Solve the following equations and verify the results.

1. $t^2 - 9 = 0$
2. $s^2 + 7s + 6 = 0$
3. $y^2 - 6y + 9 = 0$
4. $y^2 + 4y + 4 = 0$
5. $4x^2 - 1 = 0$
6. $4a^2 + 4a + 1 = 0$
7. $2x^2 + 3x - 2 = 0$
8. $2x^2 - 3x = 2$
9. $72 = x^2 - x$
10. $5x = x^2 + 6$
11. $12t^2 - t - 20 = 0$
12. $6t^2 + 2t - 20 = 0$
13. $16 = x^2 - 6x$
14. $10x = 25 + x^2$
15. $6s^2 + 5s - 56 = 0$
16. $12a^2 + 25a + 12 = 0$
17. $s^2 - s - 12 = 0$
18. $a^2 - 27a + 182 = 0$

19. $6t^2 + 5t = 56$ 20. $6t^2 - 2t - 20 = 0$

21. A rectangular flowerbed is 2 feet less than three times its width and covers an area of 96 square feet. Find the dimensions.

22. When a body falls from rest from any point above the earth's surface, the distance d, which it travels in any number of seconds, t, is given by the equation

$$d = \tfrac{1}{2}gt^2$$

where g represents the velocity which the body acquires in one second. If a plane flying at an altitude of 14,400 feet drops an object, how long will it take the object to reach the ground? ($g = 32$)

23. A pebble is dropped over the railing of an overhang in a scenic park and strikes the water in a lake below in 5 seconds. How high above the lake is the overhang? (Use the formula in Problem 22.)

24. A triangular design on a new building is to cover an area of 48 feet. The base of the triangle is 4 feet less than twice its height.

25. A rancher bought a certain number of cattle for $3000. He kept 5 head for breeding stock and sold the remainder for a profit of $50.00 per head over his original investment. How many head did he buy?

26. A rectangular window is twice as high as it is wide. If 20 inches were taken from the height and 20 inches added to the width, the window would be square, containing 3600 square inches. Would this change increase or decrease the area? Justify your answer.

27. A man buys a certain number of shares of stock, paying for each share as many dollars as he buys shares. After six months, the price per share has advanced one-fifth as many dollars per share as he has shares. He sells the shares and makes a profit of $980. How many shares did he buy?

The solutions to each of the problems in the previous exercise were rational numbers. However the solutions to quadratic equations are not restricted to the set of rational numbers. The solutions may be *irrational, imaginary,* or *any complex number.*

Recall that

$$(a + b)^2 = a^2 + 2ab + b^2$$

in which each polynomial on the right is the square of a binomial. But the polynomial

$$x^2 + 6x$$

is not the square of a binomial. If we add 9, however, then it becomes

$$x^2 + 6x + 9 = (x + 3)^2$$

which is the perfect square. Adding the necessary 9 is called *completing the square.* The 9 was chosen by taking one-half of the coefficient of x and squaring it. That is,

$$\left(\frac{6}{2}\right)^2 = 9$$

Consider the following examples.

Example 1. Complete the square of $x^2 + 10x$.

Solution. One-half of the coefficient of x is 5. To complete the square, we must add 5^2. Thus we have

$$x^2 + 10x + 25$$

Example 2. Complete the square of $x^2 + 5x$.

Solution. One-half of the coefficient of x is 5/2. To complete the square we must add $(5/2)^2$. Thus we have

$$x^2 + 5x + \frac{25}{4}$$

Completing the square on the first two terms, together with the additive property of zero, enables us to factor any quadratic equation of the form

$$x^2 + bx + c = 0.$$

To solve the equation, first complete the square on $x^2 + bx$. Since a term will be added, it must also be subtracted so that the polynomial on the left is unchanged in value. The factors of the resulting polynomial can now be recognized.

Example 1. Solve $x^2 + 2x - 5 = 0$.

Solution.
$$x^2 + 2x - 5 = 0$$
$$x^2 + 2x + \left(\frac{2}{2}\right)^2 - \left(\frac{2}{2}\right)^2 - 5 = 0$$
$$(x^2 + 2x + 1) - 6 = 0$$
$$(x + 1)^2 - 6 = 0$$
$$[(x + 1) - \sqrt{6}\,][(x + 1) + \sqrt{6}\,] = 0$$
$$x + 1 - \sqrt{6} = 0 \quad \text{or} \quad x + 1 + \sqrt{6} = 0$$
$$x = -1 + \sqrt{6} \quad \text{or} \quad x = -1 - \sqrt{6}$$

Check:
$$(-1 + \sqrt{6})^2 + 2(-1 + \sqrt{6}) - 5 = 0$$
$$1 - 2\sqrt{6} + 6 - 2 + 2\sqrt{6} - 5 = 0$$
$$0 = 0$$
$$(-1 - \sqrt{6})^2 + 2(-1\sqrt{6}) - 5 = 0$$
$$1 + 2\sqrt{6} + 6 - 2 - 2\sqrt{6} - 5 = 0$$
$$5 - 5 + 2\sqrt{6} - 2\sqrt{6} = 0$$
$$0 = 0$$

When the coefficient of the squared term is some number other than 1, an additional step is necessary. Divide each term in the equation by the coefficient of the squared term. This operation reduces the coefficient of the squared term to 1 and the equation can be solved, as in the preceding example.

Example 2. Solve $3x^2 - 2x - 9 = 0$

Solution.
$$3x^2 - 2x - 9 = 0$$
$$x^2 - \frac{2}{3}x - 3 = 0$$
$$\left(x^2 - \frac{2}{3}x + \frac{1}{9}\right) - \frac{1}{9} - 3 = 0$$
$$\left(x^2 - \frac{2}{3}x + \frac{1}{9}\right) - \frac{28}{9} = 0$$
$$\left(x - \frac{1}{3}\right)^2 - \frac{28}{9} = 0$$
$$\left[x - \frac{1}{3} - \frac{\sqrt{28}}{9}\right]\left[\left(x - \frac{1}{3}\right) + \frac{\sqrt{28}}{9}\right] = 0$$
$$x - \frac{1}{3} - \frac{2\sqrt{7}}{3} = 0 \quad \text{or} \quad x - \frac{1}{3} + \frac{2\sqrt{7}}{3} = 0$$
$$x = \frac{1 + 2\sqrt{7}}{3} \quad \text{or} \quad x = \frac{1 - 2\sqrt{7}}{3}$$

Check:
$$3\left(\frac{1 + 2\sqrt{7}}{3}\right)^2 - 2\left(\frac{1 + 2\sqrt{7}}{3}\right) - 9 = 0$$
$$\frac{1 + 4\sqrt{7} + 28}{3} - \frac{2 - 4\sqrt{7}}{3} - \frac{27}{3} = 0$$
$$3\frac{1 - 2\sqrt{7}^2}{3} - 2\frac{1 - 2\sqrt{7}}{3} - 9 = 0$$
$$\frac{1 - 4\sqrt{7} + 28}{3} \frac{2 + 4\sqrt{7}}{3} - \frac{27}{3} = 0$$
$$0 = 0$$

The general quadratic equation
$$ax^2 + bx + c = 0$$
can be solved for the variable x in terms of a, b, and c by completing the square
$$ax^2 + bx + c = 0$$
$$x^2 + \frac{b}{a^x} + \left(\frac{b}{2a}\right)^2 - \left(\frac{b}{2a}\right)^2 + 6 = 0$$
$$\left(x^2 + \frac{b}{a^x} + \frac{b^2}{4a^2}\right) - \left(\frac{b^2}{4a^2} + c\right) = 0$$
$$\left(x^2 + \frac{b}{a^x} + \frac{b^2}{4a^2}\right) - \left(\frac{b^2 - 4ac}{4a^2}\right) = 0$$
$$\left(x + \frac{b}{2a}\right)^2 - \left(\sqrt{\frac{b^2 - 4ac}{4a^2}}\right)^2 = 0$$

6.11 The Quadratic Equation

$$\left[\left(x + \frac{b}{2a}\right) - \frac{\sqrt{b^2 - 4ac}}{2a}\right]\left[\left(x + \frac{b}{2a}\right) + \frac{\sqrt{b^2 - 4ac}}{2a}\right] = 0$$

$$x + \frac{b}{2a} - \frac{\sqrt{b^2 - 4ac}}{2a} = 0 \quad \text{or} \quad x = \frac{-b}{2a} + \frac{\sqrt{b^2 - 4ac}}{2a} = 0$$

$$x = \frac{-b + \sqrt{b^2 - 4ac}}{2a} \quad \text{or} \quad x = \frac{-b - \sqrt{b^2 - 4ac}}{2a}$$

The solution to the general quadratic equation is usually written as

$$x = \frac{-b \pm \sqrt{b^2 - 4ac}}{2a}$$

and is called the *quadratic formula*. To solve any quadratic equation, substitute the values for a, b, and c in the formula and evaluate.

Example. Solve $2x^2 + 4x - 1 = 0$

Solution. $a = 2$, $b = 4$, $c = -1$

$$x = \frac{-4 \pm \sqrt{4^2 - 4(2)(-1)}}{2(2)}$$

$$= \frac{-4 \pm \sqrt{16 + 8}}{4}$$

$$= \frac{-4 \pm 2\sqrt{6}}{4}$$

$$= \frac{-2 + \sqrt{6}}{2}$$

The solutions are $x = \dfrac{-2 + \sqrt{6}}{2}$ or $x = \dfrac{-2 - \sqrt{6}}{2}$

Check: $2\left(\dfrac{-2 + \sqrt{6}}{2}\right)^2 + 4\left(\dfrac{-2 + \sqrt{6}}{2}\right) - 1 = 0$

$$4 - 4\sqrt{6} + 6 - 8 + 4\sqrt{6} - 2 = 0$$

$$0 = 0$$

$$2\left(\dfrac{-2 - \sqrt{6}}{2}\right)^2 + 4\left(\dfrac{-2 - \sqrt{6}}{2}\right) - 1 = 0$$

$$4 + 4\sqrt{6} + 6 - 8 - 4\sqrt{6} - 2 = 0$$

$$0 = 0$$

EXERCISE 6.14

Use the quadratic formula and solve each equation in problems 1–20.

1. $x^2 - 4x - 3 = 0$
2. $x^2 - 8x - 8 = 0$
3. $x^2 + 5x + 5$
4. $10x^2 - 7x - 12 = 0$
5. $4x^2 + 8x = 1$
6. $9x^2 - 18x = 2$
7. $4x^2 + 4x - 5 = 0$
8. $3x^2 - 2 = 2x$
9. $2x^2 - 6x - 3 = 0$
10. $3x^2 - 8x + 2 = 0$
11. $3x^2 - 5x + 1 = 0$
12. $5x^2 + 9x + 3 = 0$
13. $4x^2 + 7x + 2 = 0$
14. $x^2 - 4x + 5 = 0$
15. $x^2 - 6x + 10 = 0$
16. $2x^2 + 10x + 13 = 0$
17. $9x^2 + 12x = -5$
18. $9x^2 + 6x + 5 = 0$
19. $2x^2 - 10x + 15 = 0$
20. $3x^2 - 5x + 3 = 0$

In the following problems, express each meaningful irrational answer to the nearest tenth, using the table of square roots in the appendix. Reject those answers that are not meaningful.

21. The length of a rectangular flowerbed is three feet less than twice its width, and the area is 54 square feet. Find the dimensions.

22. A rectangular lot, whose depth is twice its frontage, is divided by a hedge that is 20 feet from the street and parallel to it. If the rear portion of the lot contains 8400 square feet, find the dimensions of the lot.

23. Two house painters working together can paint a room in 3 hours. If it takes one painter 2.5 hours longer than the other to do the job alone, how long will it take each painter to paint a similar room?

24. A square classroom has an open space 8 feet wide across the front of the room, four feet on each of the other three sides, and the remainder is filled with chairs for 30 students. If $26\frac{2}{3}$ square feet of floor space is allowed each student, how large is the classroom?

25. A college graduate drove 270 miles to attend the homecoming game and then returned home that same night. His total driving time was 9.9 hours, and his night driving speed was 10 miles per hour slower than his day driving speed. How fast did he travel each way?

26. Two condominium apartments were sold for $720,000 each. If there were 70 apartments in all and the apartments in one building cost an average of $4000 more than in the other, find the price of each apartment.

Finding a Vertex by Completing the Square

The vertex can be found by completing the square*. For example,

$$y = x^2 - x - 6$$
$$y = x^2 - x + (\tfrac{1}{2})^2 - (\tfrac{1}{2})^2 - 6$$

---

*The vertex can also be found by evaluating the point $\left(\dfrac{-b}{2a}, \dfrac{-b^2 + 4ac}{4a}\right)$.

$$y = x^2 - x + (\tfrac{1}{4}) - \frac{25}{4}$$

$$y = (x - \tfrac{1}{2})^2 - \frac{25}{4}$$

Since $(x - 1/2)^2$ will never be negative, the least value of y will occur when $x = 1/2$. Substituting this value for x in the function and evaluating, we have

$$y = (\tfrac{1}{2})^2 - \tfrac{1}{2} - 6$$
$$= \frac{-25}{4}$$

The vertex of this is the ordered pair $\left(\tfrac{1}{2}, \dfrac{-25}{4}\right)$.

The graph of a quadratic function will open upward or downward, according to the sign before the coefficient of the squared term. If the sign is positive, the parabola will open upward, and the vertex will be the lowest point (minimum). If the sign before the squared term is negative, the parabola will open downward, and the vertex will be the highest point (maximum).

Example 1. Sketch the graph of the function $y = x^2 - 2x - 8$.

Solution. The x-intercepts are found by solving $x^2 - 2x - 8 = 0$; they are $(4, 0)$ and $(-2, 0)$. The y-intercept is found by replacing x with 0 and evaluating the function for y; it is $(0, -8)$. The vertex is found by completing the square.

Example 3. A rectangular lot is to be enclosed with 400 feet of fencing. What should the dimensions be if we want the area enclosed to be a maximum?

Solution. If the lot is rectangular and its perimeter is 400 feet, then one-half of its perimeter is 200 feet. Here we are working with area, that is, the product of the length times the width. Let

$$x = \text{the width}$$
$$200 - x = \text{the length}$$
$$y = \text{the area}$$

Then
$$y = x(200 - x)$$
$$y = -x^2 + 200x$$
$$y = -(x^2 - 200x + 10{,}000) + 10{,}000$$
$$y = -(x - 100)^2 + 10{,}000.$$

Hence y will be greatest, when $x = 100$. Since one-half of the perimeter is 200 feet and the width is 100 feet, the length must also be 100 feet. The maximum area that can be enclosed with 400 feet of fencing is a square 100 feet by 100 feet.

EXERCISE 6.15

Sketch the graph of the functions given in Problems 1–10. Label the x-intercept, y-intercept, and the vertex.

1. $y = x^2 + 2x - 3$
2. $y = -x^2 + 9$
3. $y = 2x^2 + 5x + 2$
4. $y = x^2 - 2x$

5. $y = 4x^2 + 12x + 9$
6. $y = 4x^2 - 4x - 1$
7. $y = -x^2 + 5x + 6$
8. $y = -2x^2 + 5x - 1$
9. $y = x^2 - x - 2$
10. $y = 3x^2 + 5x - 2$

11. A stone is thrown vertically from the top of a tower that is 80 feet above ground level. The height (y in feet) of the stone from the ground (at any x seconds) after it is thrown until it strikes the ground is

$$y = 80 - 64x - 16x^2$$

When does the stone reach its maximum height?

12. The cost of a ticket on an excursion boat is $6.00, if 75 or fewer people purchase tickets. For each ticket in excess of 75, the price for each person decreases by five cents. How many tickets should be sold to yield a maximum?

13. A fruit grower has 30 tons of fruit on hand ready to sell. He estimates that his present profit is $300 per ton, but if he waits he anticipates that his profit will increase $20 per ton per week. However he also knows that for each week he waits, he will lose 1 ton by spoilage. In how many weeks should he sell to realize a maximum profit?

14. A service station owner sells regular gasoline for 35 cents per gallon and averages selling 5000 gallons each week. For each 1 cent increase in price he sells 100 gallons less. How much should he charge to realize maximum income from the sale of gasoline?

15. The Transit Authority in a certain city charges a fare of 30 cents and transports an average of 10,000 passengers per day. A survey reveals that for each 5 cents increase in fare there would be 1000 less passengers. What fare should be charged for maximum income?

REVIEW EXERCISES 6.1

In Problems 1–5, evaluate each expression for the given values of the variables.

1. $2x - 3y + 4$, $x = 2, y = -1$
2. $3x - 2y + 2$, $x = -2, y = 1$
3. $x^2 - 2y^2$, $x = 1, y = -2$
4. $\dfrac{x + y^3}{z^2}$, $x = 1, y = 2, z = 3$
5. $(x + 2y)^2 - (z^2 - x)$, $x = 2, y = 3, z = -1$

Do the indicated operation and simplify.

6. $(3x^2)(2x)(4y^2)$
7. $(5x)(3xy)(2x^2y^2)$
8. $(2x^3)(3x^2y^2)(x^3y^3)$
9. $2ab(2a^2b^2)^3$
10. $(ab)^2(a^2b)(abc^3)^2$
11. $2m(m^2 + 2mn + n^2)$
12. $(2x + 1)(x - 2)$
13. $\dfrac{42x^3y^4}{6x^2y^3}$
14. $\dfrac{-64x^2y}{16x^3y^3}$
15. $\dfrac{18x^3 - 6x^2 + 12x}{6x}$
16. $\dfrac{30x^3y^2 + 45x^2y^3 + 15xy^4}{75xy^2}$

Do the indicated operation, express each as a complete quotient, and check.

17. $6x^3 + 17x^2y + 15xy^2 + 4y^3 \div 3x + 4y$
18. $3x^3 - 5x^2y + 7xy^2 - 5y^3 \div x - y$

Write each expression in its simplest form.

19. $2\sqrt{36}$ 20. $-3\sqrt{25}$
21. $\left(\dfrac{16}{25}\right)^{1/2}$ 22. $\left(\dfrac{49x^2}{64y^4}\right)^{1/2}$

Factor each polynomial. Check by multiplication.

23. $4x^2 - 9$ 24. $.25 - x^2$
25. $(x + y)^2 - 4$ 26. $4x^2 + 4x + 1$
27. $25x^2 - 30x + 9$ 28. $x^2 - 7x + 6$
29. $x^2 + 6x + 8$ 30. $2x^2 - 11x + 12$

Solve the following equations and verify the results.

31. $x^2 + 5x + 4 = 0$ 32. $9x^2 - 1 = 0$
33. $12 = x^2 - x$ 34. $6x^2 - 41x - 56 = 0$
35. $6x^2 - 20 = 2x$ 36. $x^2 + 2x - 4 = 0$
37. $x^2 + 3x - 1 = 0$ 38. $2x^2 + 2x - 3 = 0$

Sketch the graph of the functions. Label the x-intercept, y-intercept, and the vertex.

39. $y = x^2 - 4$ 40. $y = x^2 - 2x - 3$
41. What is the length and width of a rectangular flowerbed, if the area is 90 square feet and the perimeter is 46 feet?
42. The dimensions of a rectangular lawn is 20 feet by 40 feet. How wide a border must be cut all around the lawn so that three-fourths of the work of cutting the grass is completed?
43. An auditorium contains 720 seats. The number of rows is 6 less than the number of seats in each row. How many rows of seats, and how many seats are there in each row?
44. A large building is decorated with a triangular-shaped mural whose altitude is 5 feet less than the length of the base. If the mural covers 88 square feet, what are its dimensions?
45. Kathy purchased 2 square pieces of a special kind of paper for her art class. The sides of one piece of paper was 4 inches longer than the sides of the other, and the sum of the areas was 208 square inches. How large was each?

SELF QUIZ 6.1

Evaluate the expressions for the given values of the variables.

1. $3x - 4y - 7$, $x = 6, y = 3$ 2. $5x - 3y + 1$, $x = -1, y = -2$

Do the indicated operation and simplify.

3. $2x(x^2 - 3xy - 2y^2)$ 4. $\dfrac{27x^3y^4}{9x^2y^5}$

Write each expression in its simplest form.

5. $3\sqrt[3]{64}$ 6. $\dfrac{81x^4}{25y^2}$

Factor each polynomial.

7. $9x^2 - 4$ 　　　　　　　　8. $2x^2 + 3x - 2$

Solve the equations

9. $x^2 + 3x - 4 = 0$ 　　　　10. $x^2 - 2 = 0$

11. Sketch the graph of the function $y = x^2 - 1$.

Geometry 7

7.1 INTRODUCTION

The main theme in this textbook is the emphasis on the *deductive nature* of *mathematics*. When Euclid wrote his *Elements* while teaching in Alexandria, he established the model for deductive reasoning that has influenced all of modern mathematics. Today's elementary or high school pupil who studies the so-called New Math as a deductive system is following in the footsteps of Euclid's students.

The influence of Euclid's geometry on mathematics, science, and philosophy cannot be overemphasized. As originally conceived, the purpose of Euclid's text was to prepare students for the study of philosophy in the manner of Plato. In fact, Plato himself placed the following inscription over his porch, "Let no one who is unacquainted with geometry enter here." The importance of Euclid's work lies not so much in its mathematics but in the concept that a subject can be developed from a limited number of assumptions by the use of deductive reasoning. It is probably no exaggeration to say that Euclid established an ideal of logical rigor for thought.

From here we explore in a limited way the question, "What is Geometry?" The subject is so extensive that literally volumes are needed to respond to the question completely. The word geometry comes from the Greek words meaning measurement of the earth. This implies that geometry is useful as an applied subject, such as arithmetic. We will see that geometry is actually not considered an applied subject. In fact Euclid's text had not one word about the applications of his theorems to real objects.

You will recall that we have pointed out that there are many algebras. We have studied the algebra of real numbers and briefly examined the algebras of matrices and vectors. Similarly, there are also several geometries, one of which is Euclidean geometry. Each Geometry has its own set of undefined terms, defined terms, and postulates. In the modern sense, the broad areas of algebra and geometry must be viewed as fields of study rather than as mathematical systems. A single mathematical system may be studied both algebraically and geometrically. This fact is true for both the system of real numbers and the system of complex numbers. Thus it may be helpful to consider the following definitions of algebra and geometry, which were recently proposed by the American mathematician J. L. Dorsett (1928–   ).

> *Algebra:* The study of one or more operations on elements or sets of elements, each operation being characterized by postulates.
>
> *Geometry:* The study of sets characterized by postulates.

We leave these definitions for you to ponder as we progress through our discussion of geometry.

7.2 THE HISTORY OF GEOMETRY*

Geometry Prior To Euclid

There seems little doubt that man's first efforts to develop geometry were based on his need to measure physical objects. From the study of clay tablets unearthed at the sites of ancient Babylonian cities, we know that the Babylonians were able to determine the area of rectangles and some triangles, as well as the volume of several types of regular solids. They were also aware that a fixed ratio existed between the circumference of a circle and its diameter but erroneously used 3 as this ratio. $\pi = 3.1416$ approximately is what we use. The Hebrews also used this ratio (see I Kings 7:23 of the Bible). As early as 1600 B.C. the Babylonians knew the relationship among the sides of a right triangle. More than a thousand years later, a Greek philosopher and mathematician by the name of Pythagoras perfected a description of this relationship. A lasting achievement of the Babylonians is their division of the circle into 360 degrees.

There is no evidence to indicate that the geometric accomplishments of the ancient Egyptians differed significantly from the accomplishments of the Babylonians. It does seem certain that the Egyptians perfected the technique of measurement to a highly accurate process. The sides of the base of the great pyramid at Gizeh are said to be accurate to within 1 unit in 14,000 and the shape of the base is supposedly accurate to within 1 unit in 27,000.

The geometry of both the Egyptians and Babylonians is empirical in nature. Apparently they developed the subject as the need arose, based on what they could see. As might be expected, much of their geometry is incorrect. There is no record of a proved formula or an abstract concept. The ideas of proof and abstraction were to become the domain of Greek geometers.

Euclidean Geometry

The history of what we now call Euclidean geometry begins approximately three hundred years before Euclid wrote *Elements*. In a real sense, Euclid was merely the compiler and organizer of a body of knowledge to which many fellow Greeks contributed. Only a minor part of the definitions, postulates, and theorems, in *Elements* are believed to have originated with him.

---

*The geometric terms used in this section are defined in the Glossary, p. 341.

The first Greek credited with significant accomplishments in geometry is Thales (640–546 B.C.) of Miletus, a Grecian city in Asia Minor. Thales is considered the creator of the geometry of lines. The next major contributor, in chronological order, is the famed Pythagoras (circa 580–500 B.C.), who lived in a Grecian city in what we now know as southern Italy. The theorem bearing his name is his most important contribution. It states that the square on the hypotenuse of a right triangle is equal to the sum of the squares on the two legs. We illustrate the theorem in Figure 7.1.

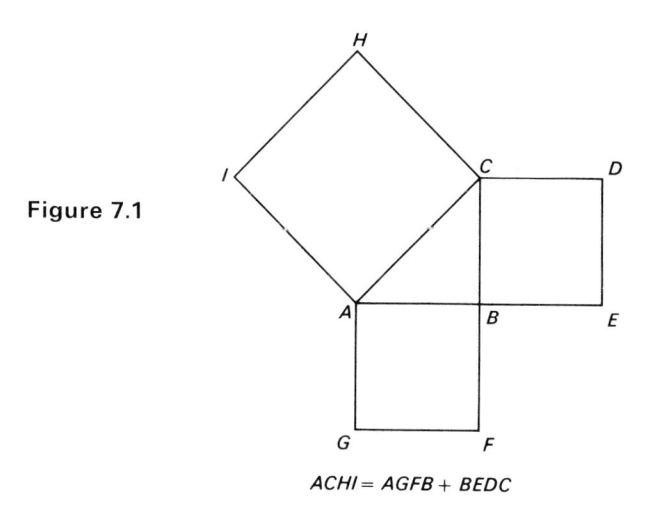

Figure 7.1

$ACHI = AGFB + BEDC$

Then Hippocrates (460–357 B.C.) (not the physician), made major contributions to describing the geometry of the circle. He is also credited with adding significantly to the logical reasoning process employed in proofs. We should also mention Plato (429–348 B.C.), for many of Euclid's definitions are said to have originated in his school. Another important contributor is Eudoxus (408–355 B.C.) of Cnidus, who contributed to the theory of proportion and to solid geometry. Aristotle (384–322 B.C.), wrote expositions on deductive logic and has become well known.

As for Euclid himself, almost nothing is known. He probably lived about 360–280 B.C. His fame rests entirely on the book *Elements*, which was completed subsequent to 300 B.C. Just how much of the book is the original work of Euclid is uncertain, but, if any, it is a very small percentage. Most of the definitions, theorems, and proofs can be traced to his Greek predecessors. Nevertheless, Euclid's fame is fully deserved. He carefully selected and listed in logical order definitions, theorems, proofs, etc., from many sources. He then showed that an entire body of knowledge can be logically deduced from a few definitions and axioms.

We list here the axioms, which he called "common notions," and postulates of Euclid's geometry. He apparently considered axioms as assumptions with general application and postulates as assumptions applying only to the subject under development.

Common Notions

1. Things which are equal to the same thing are equal to one another.
2. If equals be added to equals, the wholes are equal.
3. If equals be subtracted from equals, the remainders are equal.
4. Things which coincide with one another are equal to one another.
5. The whole is greater than the part.

Postulates

Let the following be postulated:

1. To draw a *straight line* from any *point* to any point.
2. To produce a finite straight line continuously in a straight line.
3. To describe a circle with any center and distance.
4. That all right angles are equal to one another.
5. That, if a straight line falling on two straight lines makes the interior angles on the same side less than two right angles, the two straight lines, if produced indefinitely, meet on that side on which the angles are less than two right angles.

Discussion of the Common Notions and Postulates

The common notions were considered to apply to all branches of knowledge. Today notions 1, 2, and 3 are stated as postulates of an equivalence relationship. Notion 4 appears to relate specifically to geometry and possibly should have been shown as a postulate. Notion 5 relates to our modern postulates for order.

The first three postulates tell us which geometric figures we are allowed to construct without first proving that the construction is possible. Postulate 4 appears to be present to support postulate 5. This last postulate is called the "parallel postulate." It is probably the most famous statement in the history of mathematics.

For more than two thousand years mathematicians have attempted to prove or disprove the fifth postulate. Their efforts led to a new kind of geometry, non-Euclidean geometry, which is discussed later in this section.

Euclidean geometry, in its present form is a great improvement over the original version. All modern versions limit the number of undefined terms and expand on the ten postulates and common notions. Usually the undefined terms include point, line, and plane. The postulates establish relationships between point and line, point and plane, and line and plane, with both a line and a plane being regarded as sets of points. Two mathematicians who contributed to the modernization of Euclidean geometry are the Italian Guiseppi Peano (1858–1932), and the German David Hilbert (1862–1943).

EXERCISE 7.1

1. State Euclid's common notions 1, 2, and 3 in the form of postulates for an equivalence relationship.
2. Using the theorem of Pythagoras, complete the following table of lengths of the sides of a right triangle:

Side A	Side B	Hypotenuse
a	b	—
3	4	—
9	—	15
—	20	24

3. In what way can the set of real numbers be studied geometrically?
4. In constructing the geometric figures postulated by Euclid, only a ruler and a string compass were used. These are called "Euclidean tools." Using these tools, see if you can construct the following.
   a) A triangle with all sides equal.
   b) A line that bisects a given angle.
   c) A line that bisects a given line.
5. If the diagonal of a square is 20 inches, how long is each side?
6. If the diagonal of a square is an irrational number, show that the length of the sides may be rational.
7. Prove or disprove: the diagonal of a rectangle is irrational if both of the sides are irrational.

Analytic Geometry

Some of the profound inventions of the human mind first made their appearance in relatively brief papers or books. One example is Albert Einstein's "Special Theory of Relativity," which required some 20 pages. Another is the collected works of Evarsite Galois (1811–1832), the inventor of group theory, which is about 60 pages in length. A third brief treatise of fundamental importance is René Descartes' (1596–1650) "Discours de la Méthode" written in 1637. The section of his work devoted to geometry is only 106 pages in length.

The importance of Descartes' work in geometry lies in his concept that a plane curve can be represented by an algebraic equation in two variables and that an algebraic equation in two variables can be represented by a plane curve. You will recall that we introduced the Cartesian coordinate system in Chapter 4. With this concept, we are able to study geometry from the algebraic point of view. When geometry is studied in this way, it is called *analytic geometry*.

The invention of analytic geometry added no new geometry. Analytic geometry is a method of studying geometry. It is not itself a mathematical system. There are no postulates pertaining only to analytic geometry. When geometry is studied using the Cartesian coordinate system, it is sometimes called coordinate geometry. Figures 7.2 to 7.5 show a few examples of geometric figures and the corresponding algebraic equations.

Line

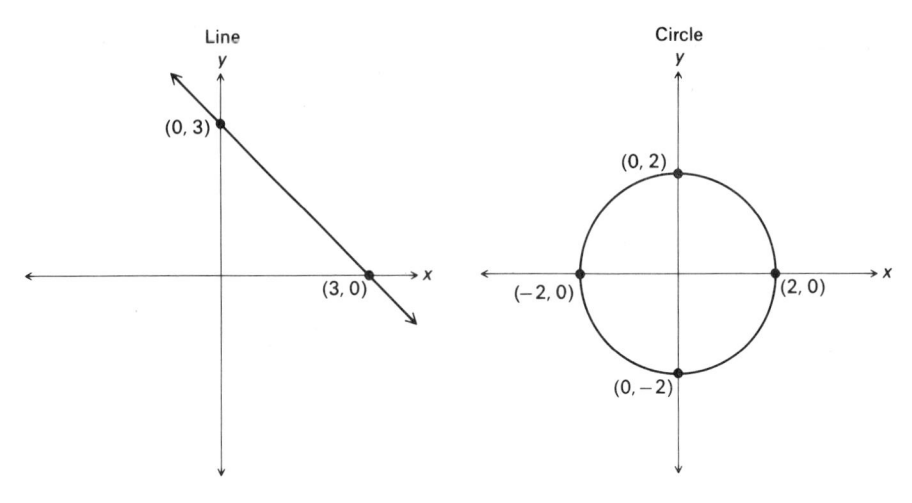

(0, 3), (3, 0)

Equation: $x + y = 3$

Figure 7.2

Circle

(0, 2), (−2, 0), (2, 0), (0, −2)

Equation: $x^2 + y^2 = 4$

Figure 7.3

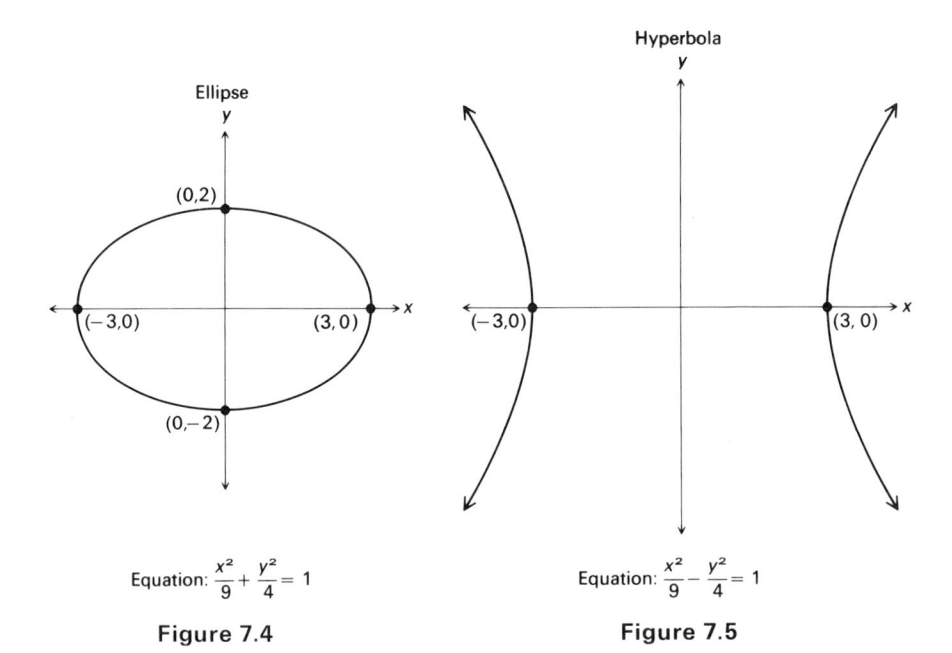

Ellipse

(0, 2), (−3, 0), (3, 0), (0, −2)

Equation: $\dfrac{x^2}{9} + \dfrac{y^2}{4} = 1$

Figure 7.4

Hyperbola

(−3, 0), (3, 0)

Equation: $\dfrac{x^2}{9} - \dfrac{y^2}{4} = 1$

Figure 7.5

Non-Euclidean Geometry

As mentioned earlier, the study of the parallel postulate of Euclid led to the invention of new kinds of geometry. About 1820 two mathematicians working independently created a new geometry by substituting another postulate for the parallel postulate. The two were the Hungarian Janos Bolyai (1802–1860) and the Russian Nicolai Lobachevsky (1793–1856). In lieu of the parallel postulate, they assumed that through a point there are at least two lines parallel to a given line. This concept of parallel lines is illustrated in Figure 7.6(a). The lines m and n through point P are both "parallel" to line l. Other lines through P, which when extended, lie entirely inside the angles formed by m and n at P, are called nonintersecting lines. Geometry based on the parallel postulate of Lobachevsky and Bolyai is called "hyperbolic geometry."

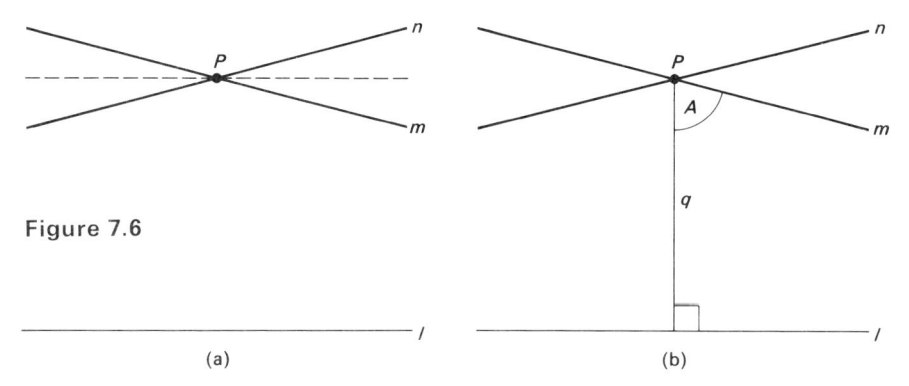

Figure 7.6

(a)   (b)

Most of the theorems in hyperbolic geometry are identical to those of Euclidean geometry. Only those theorems that depend on the parallel postulate are modified.

Let us examine a few of the consequences of the revised concept of parallel lines. Suppose that we drop a perpendicular q from P to line l as shown in Figure 7.6(b), where lines m and n are "parallel" to l. In Euclidean geometry, both the intersections of q with n and q with m would form right angles. This is not possible with the revised parallel postulate. In Euclidean geometry, these angles of intersection are right angles, no matter how far point P is from line l. In hyperbolic geometry, the angle A in Figure 7.6(b) varies as the distance of P from l varies. As P gets close to l, angle A gets close to a right angle. As P recedes, or leaves, from l, angle A gets smaller. In Euclidean geometry, the sum of the angles of a triangle is always 180°. In Hyperbolic geometry, the sum of the angles of a triangle is always less than 180°. Triangles would appear as shown in Figure 7.7.

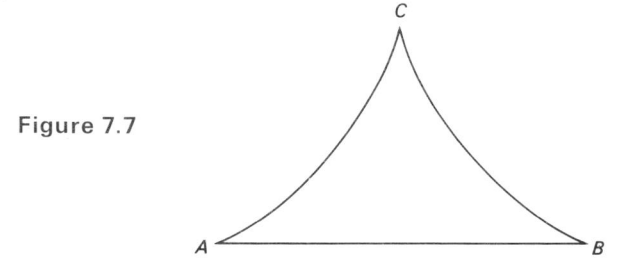

Figure 7.7

In 1854, a German mathematician, Georg Friedrich Bernhard Reimann (1826–1866), invented another non-Euclidean geometry. For the parallel postulate, he substituted the postulate that through a point in the plane there is no line parallel to a given line. Riemman also rejected Euclid's second postulate, which assumed that a straight line may be extended infinitely in both directions. For this postulate, Riemann substituted the assumption that a straight line is endless. With this assumption, a circle is a "straight line." This geometry, with two of Euclid's postulates changed, is called "elliptical geometry."

Let us examine a few of the ways in which elliptical geometry differs from hyperbolic or Euclidean geometry. In both of these geometries, only one perpendicular can be dropped from a given point to a given line. In elliptical geometry, an infinite number of perpendiculars can be dropped from a given point to a given line, as illustrated in Figure 7.8. In addition, all perpendiculars to a given line l meet in a point.

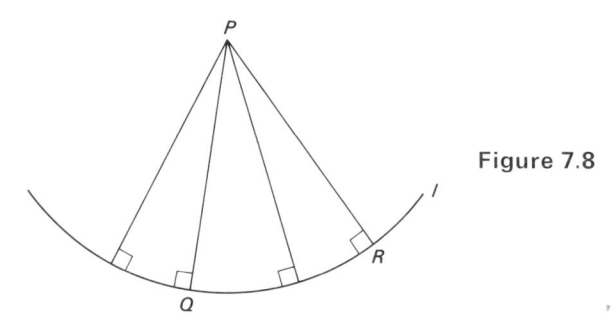

Figure 7.8

Referring to Figure 7.8, it can be seen that the angles of the triangle PQR total more than 180°. In elliptical geometry, the sum of the angles of a triangle always totals more than 180°; moreover, two lines bound an area. Three lines are required to bound an area in both Euclidean and hyperbolic geometry. Just as the plane serves as a model of Euclidean geometry, the surface of a sphere serves as a model of elliptical geometry.

The development of non-Euclidean geometry had a profound effect on the development of mathematics and science. For more than two thousand years postulates had been considered valid as "self-evident truths." The denial of some of Euclid's "self-evident truths" led to the realization that mathematics does not offer truths. Mathematicians acquired freedom to select postulates "self-evident" in the physical world or not. The stage was set for Einstein's theory of relativity and the development of abstract mathematics.

EXERCISE 7.2

1. Distinguish between analytic geometry and Euclidean geometry.
2. Can you think of any advantages that might result from studying Euclidean geometry with the methods of analytic geometry?
3. Conjecture as to whether non-Euclidean geometry might be studied with the methods of analytic geometry.
4. Illustrate by a sketch that a circle on a sphere with the diameter of the circle being equal to that of the sphere (called a "great circle") satisfies both of Riemann's revised postulates.
5. In hyperbolic geometry, a line perpendicular to two parallel lines cannot be constructed. Explain why this is true.

6. In elliptic and hyperbolic geometry, does there appear to be a relationship between the size of a triangle and the sum of the degrees in the angles of a triangle?
7. Identify the type of geometry illustrated in Figure 7.9.
8. Conjecture as to whether the Pythagorean Theorem applies in hyperbolic or elliptic geometry.
9. Would it be possible to prove that one of the three geometries—Euclidean, elliptic, or hyperbolic—is more "true" than another?
10. Does a square or parallelogram exist in hyperbolic or elliptic geometry?

7.3 SELECTED GEOMETRIC CONCEPTS

Measurement of Length

It is probable that man has measured things for almost as long as he has been able to count. Several of our present units of length originated in antiquity; e.g., foot, inch (width of a thumb), fathom (arms extended outward fingertip to fingertip), and mile (1000 paces of a Roman regiment).

Inherent in all measurement is the concept of continuity. In Chapter 3 we postulated that the real number system is complete. As we stated the postulate, we assumed a one-to-one relationship between the set of real numbers and the set of points on a line. Since the real number system is assumed to be complete, the set of points on the real number line is "complete," or, in the geometric sense, we say that the line is continuous. Completeness is an algebraic property; continuity is a geometric property.

The assumption of continuity is indispensable in measurement. We compare one continuous object of known length (a ruler, a micrometer, scale, etc.) with a continuous object of unknown length. See Figure 7.10.

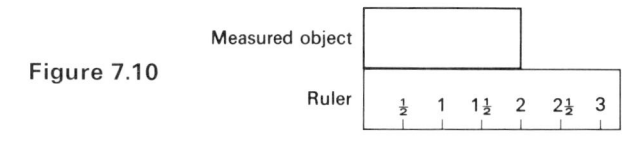

Figure 7.10

Here we are measuring an object by comparing its length with a ruler of some standard length. The assumption of continuity permits us to assume that no matter where the measured object ends, a number on the ruler corresponds to the length of the object.

Let us be more precise as to what we mean by "length." Consider the real number line with point A having coordinate a and point B having coordinate b. We define the length of the line segment between A and B, denoted by $\overline{AB}$, as follows:

Definition 7.1 If A and B are two points on a number line with coordinates a and b, where $a \leq b$, then the length of $\overline{AB} = b - a =$ length of $\overline{BA}$.

Notice that the length is always nonnegative by this definition. For instance, looking at Figure 7.11, we can see that

$$\text{Length } \overline{AB} = (-2) - (-3) = 1$$
$$\text{Length } \overline{BA} = (-2) - (-3) = 1$$
$$\text{Length } \overline{AG} = (3) - (-3) = 6$$
$$\text{Length } \overline{GA} = 3 - (-3) = |6$$

Figure 7.11

The Distance Formula

When we studied vectors, the length of vector $\langle a, b \rangle$ was defined as $\sqrt{a^2 + b^2}$. We shall now use this definition to find the distance between two points P and Q in the plane. Let the coordinate of P by (x_1, y_1) and the coordinate of Q be (x_2, y_2). See Figure 7.12.

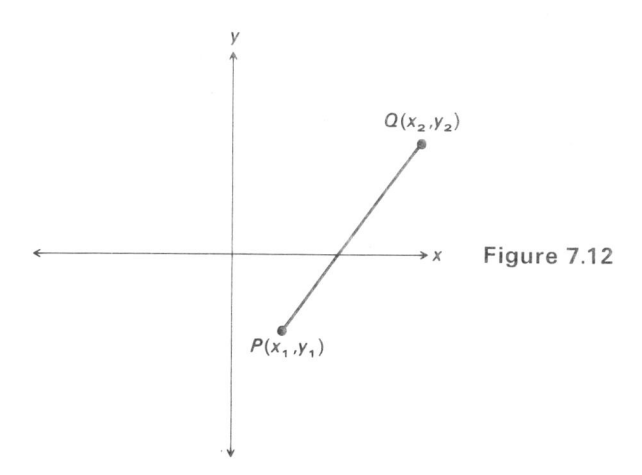

Figure 7.12

We are now able to write $\overline{PQ}$ in vector from as $\langle x_2 - x_1, y_2 - y_1 \rangle$. Applying the formula for length of a vector, we have

$$\overline{PQ} = \sqrt{(x_2 - x_1)^2 + (y_2 - y_1)^2}.$$

This is the formula for finding the distance between any two points in the Cartesian plane.

Example 1. Find the distance between the point $P(2, 3)$ and the point $Q(5, 7)$.

Solution. $\overline{PQ} = \sqrt{(5 - 2)^2 + (7 - 3)^2}$
$= \sqrt{3^3 + 4^2} = \sqrt{25} = 5.$

Example 2. Find the distance between the points $P(-2, -3)$ and $Q(7, 9)$.

Solution. $\overline{PQ} = \sqrt{[7-(-2)]^2 + [9-(-3)]^2}$
$= \sqrt{9^2 + 12^2}$
$= \sqrt{225} = 15.$

Area of a Rectangle

One of the oldest of geometric concepts is that of the area of plane figures. Many of the formulas used today were known to the Babylonians and Egyptians.

In modernized versions of Euclidean geometry, the postulate for the area of a rectangle is as follows:

> *Postulate:* The area of a rectangle is equal to the product of the length of its base and the length of its altitude. Area = base × height.

Example 1. Find the area of the following rectangle:

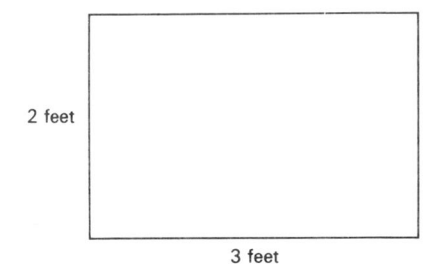

[rectangle: 2 feet by 3 feet]

Solution. Area = $3 \cdot 2 = 6$ square feet.

Example 2. Find the area of the following rectangle:

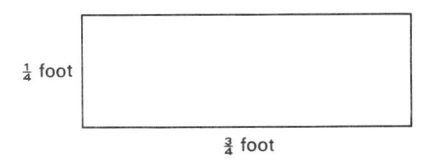

[rectangle: $\frac{1}{4}$ foot by $\frac{3}{4}$ foot]

Solution. Area = $\frac{3}{4} \cdot \frac{1}{4} = \frac{3}{16}$ square feet.

Discussion of the Concept of Area

All physical measurements, whether length, area, volume, weight, time, or whatever, are a comparison of the measured object with a standard unit. The area of the rectangle in Example 1 is 6 square feet, which means that the region enclosed by the sides is six times the size of a region enclosed by a square whose side is one foot in length. A square whose side is one unit in length is called a unit square. If the length of the sides were specified in inches, we would have compared the area of the rectangle with a "square inch." Returning to Example 1 and converting to inches,

190   Geometry   7.3

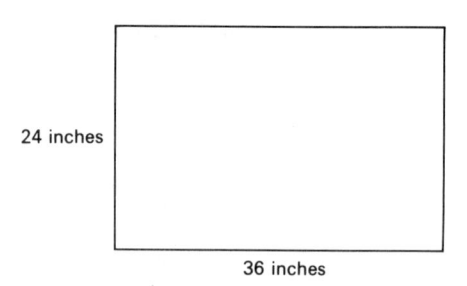

$$\text{Area} = 24 \cdot 36 = 864 \text{ square inches.}$$

We can readily visualize the comparison of a unit square with the region enclosed in any rectangular figure if the lengths of the sides are expressed in integers. In Example 2 above, the sides are not integers. Let us see how we compare this rectangle to a unit square. First we divide the unit square as shown in Figure 7.13.

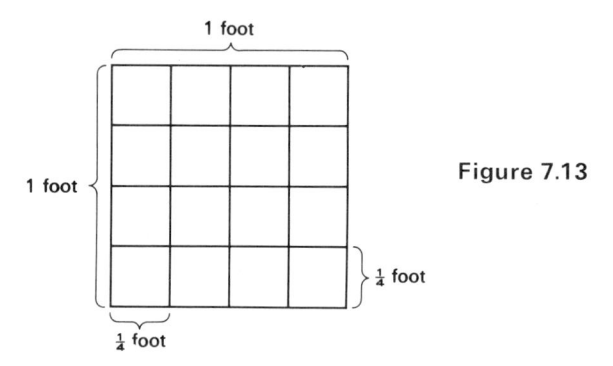

Figure 7.13

Each side of the unit square has been divided into four equal parts. It can be seen that the unit square has been divided into 16 equal regions of length $\frac{1}{4}$ foot on each side. Hence the area of a region of length $\frac{1}{4}$ foot on each side is $\frac{1}{16}$ of a square foot: $A = \frac{1}{4} \cdot \frac{1}{4} = \frac{1}{16}$. Returning now to Example 2, we divide it as shown in Figure 7.14. Each of the three regions of the rectangle is $\frac{1}{16}$ of a unit square. Hence the area $3(\frac{1}{16}) = \frac{3}{16}$ square feet.

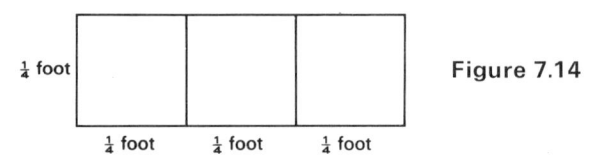

Figure 7.14

The postulated formula for the area of a rectangle applies regardless of whether the sides are rational or irrational in length.

Area of a Parallelogram

A parallelogram (see Figure 7.15) is defined to be a four-sided figure whose opposite sides lie on parallel lines. The formula for area of a parallelogram is found by transforming the parallelogram into an equivalent rectangle.

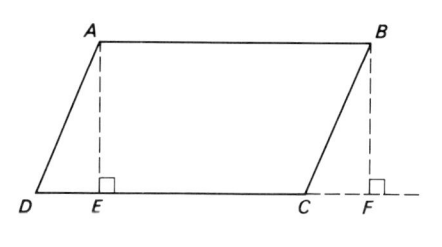

Figure 7.16

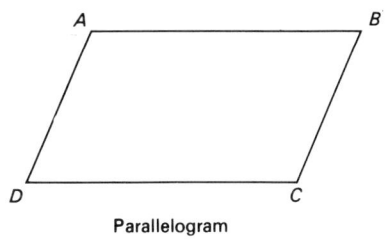

Figure 7.15 Parallelogram

This transformation is accomplished as shown in Figure 7.16. Perpendicular lines are constructed from A and B to the side DC. It can be shown that the triangle ADE is equivalent to the triangle BCF. It can also be shown that $ABFE$ is a rectangle with height of AE and base EF. Thus the area of $ABFE$ is

$$\text{Area } ABFE = \overline{EF} \cdot \overline{AE}.$$

The opposite sides of a parallelogram are equal; hence $\overline{DC} = \overline{AB} = \overline{EF}$. We are then able to state that the area of a parallelogram is equal to the base of the parallelogram times its height:

$$\text{Area } ABCD = \overline{DC} \cdot \overline{AE}.$$

Area of a Triangle

The area of a triangle can be found by using the following formula:

$$\text{Area} = \tfrac{1}{2} \text{ base} \times \text{height}.$$

The base and height are shown for two types of triangles (Figure 7.17 a and b).

Figure 7.17

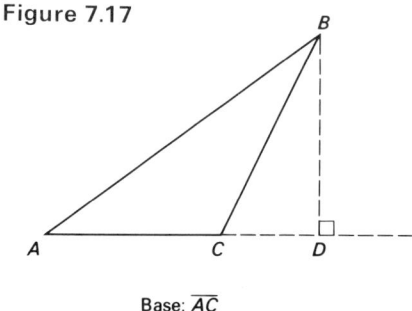

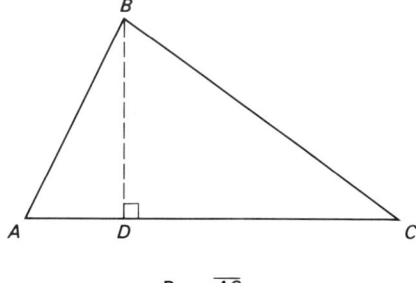

(a) Base: $\overline{AC}$ Height: $\overline{BD}$

(b) Base: $\overline{AC}$ Height: $\overline{BD}$

We shall sketch a method for deriving the area formula.

1. Any triangle may be enclosed in a rectangle. For example, triangle ABC is enclosed in rectangle $ADEC$ (Figure 7.18).

192 Geometry 7.3

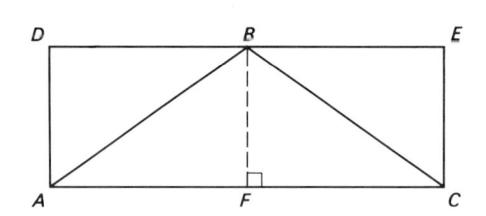

Figure 7.18

2. The rectangle $ADEC$ is separated into two regions $ADBF$ and $FBEC$ by the height BF of triangle ABC.
3. It can be shown that $\overline{AB}$ and $\overline{BC}$ divide the two regions of the rectangle into equal parts.
4. The area of $ADEC = \overline{AC} \cdot \overline{BF}$ by the postulate for area of a rectangle.
5. Hence the area of triangle ABC is

$$\text{Area} = \tfrac{1}{2} \text{ base} \times \text{height}$$

With the formulas for area of a rectangle and triangle, we can derive the formulas for area of other plane figures, such as a trapezoid, pentagon, and hexagon.

EXERCISE 7.3

1. Find the area of triangle ABC (Figure 7.19).

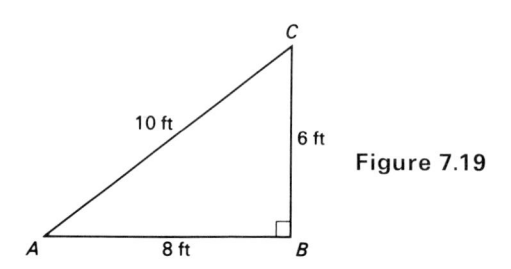

Figure 7.19

2. Find the height from B to the hypotenuse of the triangle in problem 1.
3. The hypotenuse of a right triangle is 20 and its area is 96. What is the length of the altitude of the hypotenuse? What is the length of the altitude to the longest side?
4. Find the area of the trapezoid $ABCD$ (Figure 7.20).

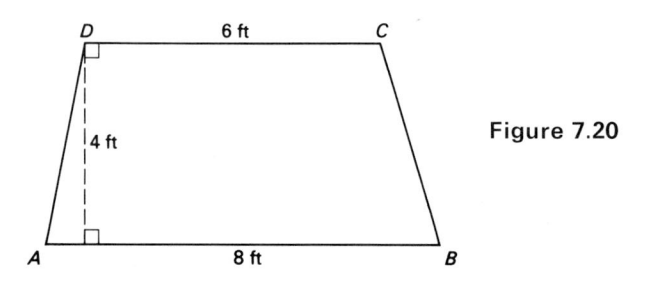

Figure 7.20

5. Two pieces of wire of equal length are bent to form a square and an equilateral triangle. Compare the relative sizes of the areas formed.
6. Illustrate a method of constructing a line of length $\sqrt{5}$.
7. When we measure objects, are fractional lengths necessary?
8. Find the area of Figure 7.21.

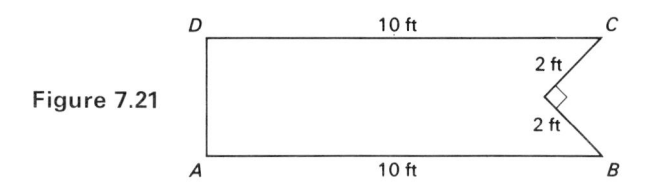

Figure 7.21

9. Find the distance between the following points.
   a) (2, 3), (5, 7)
   b) (3, 4), (−1, 0)
   c) (−2, 5), (7, 1)
   d) (−3, 6), (−1, −3)
10. Given the following points $P(2, 4)$, $Q(4, 5)$, and $R(3, 2)$, determine whether PQR is a right triangle.

Circumference and Area of a Circle

The Babylonians and Egyptians were both aware that the area of a circle depended on the ratio of the circumference of a circle to its diameter. (See Figure 7.22). However, Archimedes calculated this ratio, now designated with

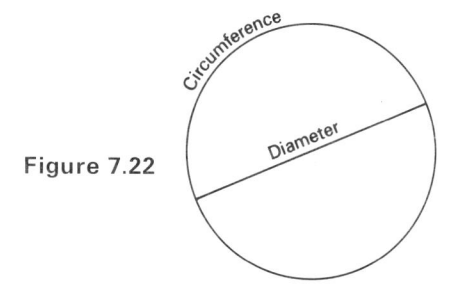

Figure 7.22

the Greek letter π (called pi), to a high degree of accuracy. This ratio is an irrational number expressible approximately as

$$\pi = 3.1416$$

$$\frac{\text{Circumference}}{\text{Diameter}} = \pi$$

or

$$\text{Circumference} = \pi \times \text{diameter}$$

Using this formula for the circumference of a circle, we shall sketch a method for showing that the area is given by the formula

$$\text{Area} = \pi \cdot (\text{radius})^2$$
$$= \pi \cdot r^2.$$

1. Cut the circle into pie-shaped pieces and place them side-by side as shown in Figure 7.23.

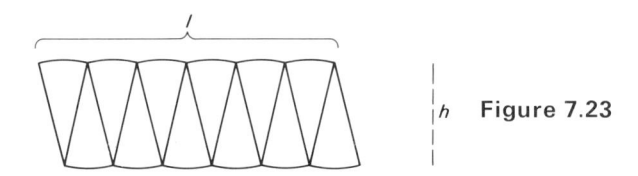

Figure 7.23

2. Since the circumference of the circle is $2\pi r$, the length of l in the figure is approximately πr. The length of h is approximately r.
3. The figure formed by placing the pieces side by side approximates a rectangle of base $\pi \cdot r$ and height r.
4. Hence the area of the circle is approximately $\pi \cdot r \cdot r = \pi r^2$
5. If we increase the number of pieces, the area of the rectangular-shaped figure approaches the area of the circle.

Formulas for Volume

We state here without discussion some of the formulas for calculating volume:

Solid	Formula
Parallelepiped (box)	$V = \text{length} \cdot \text{width} \cdot \text{height}$
Cylinder	$V = \pi r^2 \cdot h$
Cone	$V = \frac{1}{3}\pi r^2 \cdot h$
Pyramid	$V = \frac{1}{3} \text{base} \cdot \text{height}$
Sphere	$V = \frac{4}{3}\pi r^3$

EXERCISE 7.4

1. Find the area of a circle of indicated radius:
    a) 2   b) $\frac{1}{2}$ c) 5

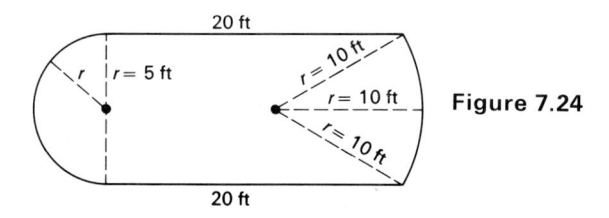

Figure 7.24

2. Find the circumference of each circle in problem 1.
3. Find the area of Figure 7.24
4. Find the perimeter of figure 7.25

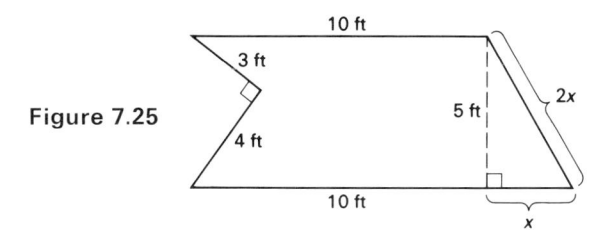

Figure 7.25

5. The formula for the surface area of a sphere is $4\pi r^2$. Consider the earth to be a sphere with a radius of 4000 miles.
   a) What is the total surface area of the earth?
   b) If the United States occupies 4 percent of the surface of the earth, what is the surface area of the United States in square miles?
6. Can the surface of the earth be accurately surveyed by using formulas based on Euclidean geometry?
7. A manufacturer makes circular tops for containers from square pieces of material. The length of the side of each square is equal to the diameter of the top and weighs 2 ounces. How many pounds of scrap are generated per week if 300,000 tops are manufactured during the week?
8. The inside and outside diameters of a spherical shell are as shown in Figure 7.26. What is the volume of the shell? If the material of which the shell is made weighs 128 pounds per cubic foot, what does the shell weigh?

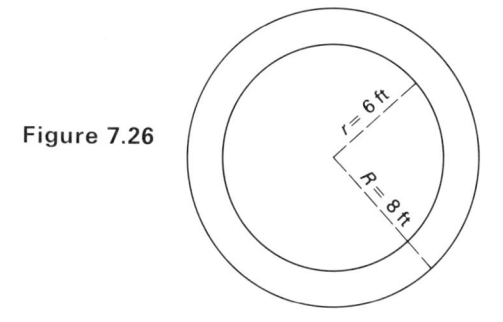

Figure 7.26

9. See if you can find a way to prove that any triangle inscribed in a circle, with the hypotenuse of the triangle being the diameter of the circle, is a right triangle.

Measurement of Angles

The oldest unit of measurement still in general use is the Babylonian unit for the measurement of angles. We call this unit a degree, written symbolically as °. One degree is one 360th part of a complete rotation. In order to define an angle mathematically, we need to know the definitions of line segment, half-line and ray. We shall consider point and line to be undefined terms. The line *l* may be represented as follows: (Figure 7.27). The arrows on l indicate that l extends indefinitely in both directions.

$\longleftarrow\!\!\!\longrightarrow\!/$ Figure 7.27

Definition 7.2 Any two distinct points on a line l determine a *line segment* of l. The segment consists of the two points and all points between them.

If two points A and B lie on l the line segment between them is denoted by the symbol $\overline{AB}$. The line l and the segment $\overline{AB}$ are illustrated in figure 7.28. the line l may be denoted by the symbol $\overline{AB}$.

Figure 7.28

Definition 7.3 Two *half-lines* are formed on l by any point P on l. (See Figure 7.29).

Figure 7.29

The point P separates the line l into three disjoint sets of points: the points to the left of P, the point P, and the points to the right of P.

Definition 7.4 A ray is the union of a half-line and the point that determines the half-line.

If Q is a point on a half-line determined by P on the line l, then the ray is denoted by $\overrightarrow{PQ}$ as illustrated in Figure 7.30.

Figure 7.30

To prepare for the definition of an angle, imagine that two distinct lines l_1 and l_2 intersect in the point P and let Q lie on l_1 and R lie on l_2 as shown in Figure 7.31.

Figure 7.31

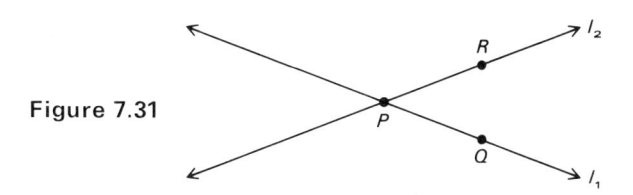

P determines two rays $\overline{PQ}$ and $\overline{PR}$. We now define an angle as follows:

> **Definition 7.5** An angle is the union of two rays with the same endpoint. The rays form the sides of the angle and the endpoint forms the vertex of the angle.

An angle is denoted by the symbol $\angle$ followed by three letters; the middle letter denotes the vertex the other letters designate points, one on each side. In Figure 7.31 we see $\angle RPQ$.

When two rays lie on the same half-line of a line l, the angle has measure $0°$, $360°$, $720°$ or any multiple of $360°$ depending on the number of times one of the rays has rotated about P. When two rays lie on both half-lines of l, the angle has measure $180°$, $540°$, etc. Angles are illustrated in Figures 7.32, 7.33 and 7.34.

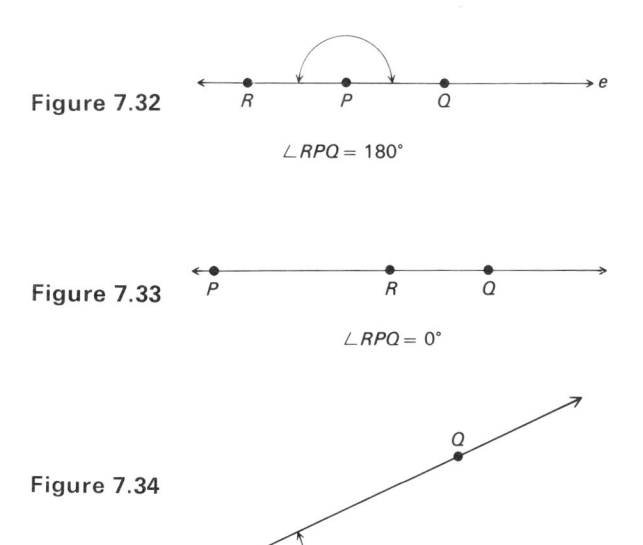

Figure 7.32

$\angle RPQ = 180°$

Figure 7.33

$\angle RPQ = 0°$

Figure 7.34

$\angle RPQ$

Similar Figures and Indirect Measurement

Geometric figures that can be made to coincide are said to be *congruent*, which is symbolized by $\cong$. Geometric figures that have the same shape are said to be *similar* and are symbolized by $\sim$. See Figures 7.35 and 7.36.

Figure 7.35
Congruent figures

△ABC ≅ △DEF

Figure 7.36
Similar figures

△ABC ~ △DEF

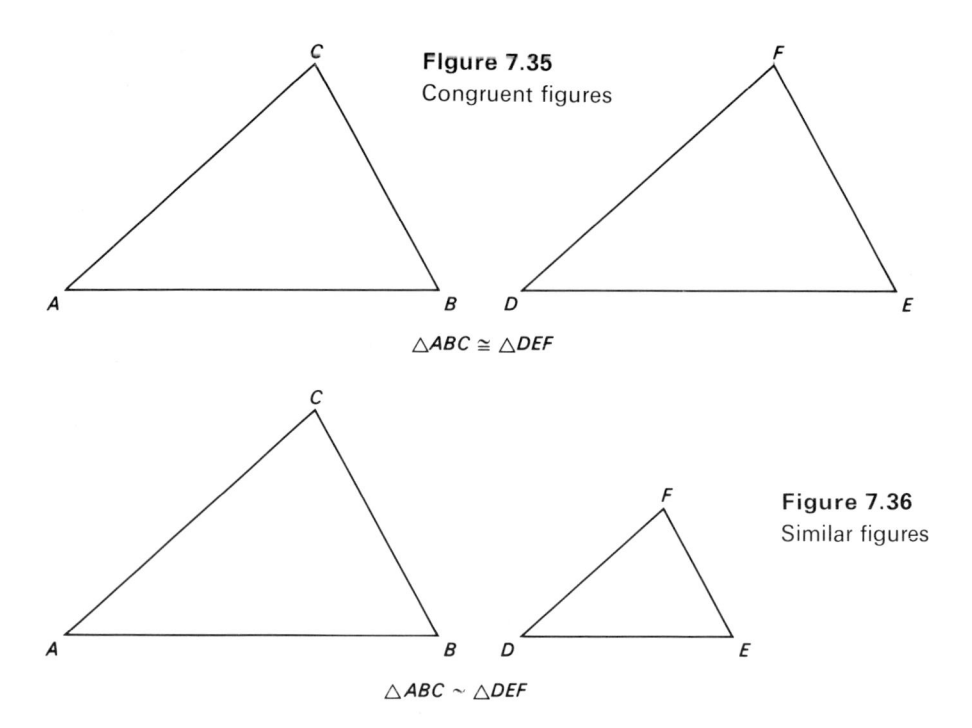

If two polygons* are similar, then their corresponding angles are repectively equal and their corresponding sides are respectively proportional. Consider the similar triangles ABC and DEF in Figure 7.36.

$$\frac{\overline{AB}}{\overline{DE}} = \frac{\overline{CB}}{\overline{FE}} = \frac{4}{6} = \frac{2}{3}.$$

The concept of proportional sides of similar figures can be used to make indirect measurements.

Example. Find the height of a building if its shadow equals 20 feet and the shadow of a 6-foot man is 2 feet. See Figure 7.37.

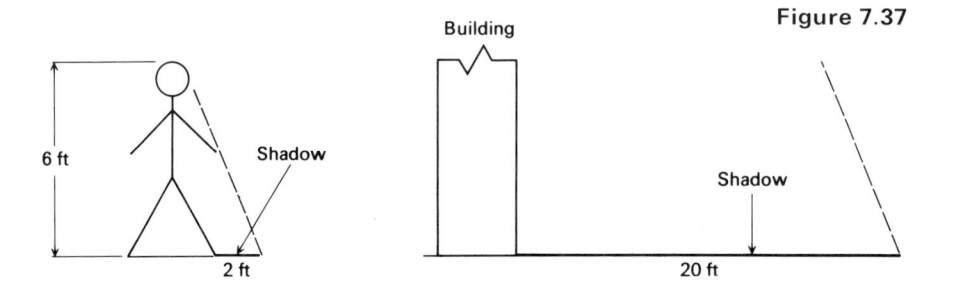

Figure 7.37

---

*See Glossary (p. 344) for definition.

Solution. $\dfrac{\text{Height of building}}{6 \text{ feet}} = \dfrac{20 \text{ feet}}{2 \text{ feet}}$

Height of building = 60 feet

7.4 OTHER GEOMETRIC CONCEPTS

Projective Geometry

If one stands in the middle of a railroad track and looks down the track, the two rails appear to meet at some point. Now, suppose a transparent material is placed between the eye and the track, and the rails are sketched on the material as they appear to the eye. The resulting sketch is called a perspective drawing. A line from the eye to any point on the rails must pass through a corresponding point on the drawing and vice versa. Any drawing constructed in this manner is a projection of the original figure and seems to be three dimensional.

The first great artist to utilize the principle of projection was the German painter Albrecht Dürer (1471–1528). Dürer believed so strongly in projective drawing that he wrote a book on the subject called *A Course in the Art of Measurement*. Intended as a text for artists, the book outlined methods for constructing perspective drawings. Dürer is considered the inventor of the theory of perspective upon which projective geometry is based. *Projective geometry* is defined as the study of properties of geometric figures that remain unchanged when the figures are projected.

Following Dürer, the French mathematician Gérard Desargues (1593–1662) made important contributions to the development of projective geometry, particularly regarding projections of the conic sections (circle, ellipse, hyperbola, parabola). Another French mathematician, Jean Victor Poncelot (1788–1867), also advanced the theory of projective geometry. Poncelot, a soldier in Napoleon's army, was captured in Russia and spent several years as a prisoner of war. While a prisoner, he studied projective geometry and wrote on the subject when he returned to France. Another French mathematician, Gaspard Monge (1746–1818), developed a branch of projective geometry—descriptive geometry—whose principles are used in modern engineering drawings.

Projective geometry has now been developed as a mathematical system with its own set of undefined terms, definitions, and postulates. It can be shown that all geometries are branches of projective geometry.

Projective geometry can be developed from the following set of postulates:

1. There exists at least one line.
2. On each line there are at least three points.
3. Not all points lie on the same line.
4. Two distinct points lie on one and only one line.
5. Two distinct lines meet in one and only one point.
6. There is a one-to-one correspondence between the real numbers and all but one point of a line.

It is interesting to note that the words "point" and "line" can be interchanged in each of the above postulates and each postulate still applies to projective geometry. When such an exchange can be made in two postulates, each is said to be the dual of the other. This principle of duality has broad application in the study of geometry.

Topology

The figures we have studied in Euclidean geometry can be moved about at will as long as they do not change their size or shape. When a Euclidean figure undergoes projection, both shape and size are subject to change but other properties remain unchanged. Even when we stretch, shrink, twist, or bend (but not tear) a geometric figure, some of its properties remain unchanged. Such properties are called topological properties. The beginning of topology as a branch of geometry can be traced to the year 1736 when the Swiss mathematician Leonhard Euler solved the famous Königsberg bridges problem.

REFERENCES

Cooley, Hollis R. and Howard E. Wahlert. *Introduction to Mathematics.* Boston: Houghton Mifflin, 1968.

Eves, Howard. *An Introduction to the History of Mathematics.* New York: Holt, Rinehart and Winston, 1961.

Eves, Howard and Carroll V. Newsom. *An Introduction to the Foundations and Fundamental Concepts of Mathematics.* New York: Holt, Rinehart and Winston, 1961.

Klein, Felix. *Elementary Mathematics from an Advanced Standpoint*, 2d ed. New York: Dover Publications, 1939.

Morrill, W. K. *Analytic Geometry*, 2d ed. Scranton, Pa.: International Textbook Co., 1965.

Probability and Statistics | 8

8.1 PROBABILITY

"Coach, what are the chances that we will win the football game this Saturday afternoon?" "Professor, what are my chances of passing this course?" "What are the odds that a team that occupied the last place in the league last season will be the winner this season?"

In each of the questions a comparison is to be made between events that have not occurred. It is impossible to make an exact comparison of events for the true answer lies in the future. We make these comparisons by expressing our answers as "very good," "a good chance," "very unlikely" or words to this effect. The basic idea of probability is the likelihood that a certain future event will occur.

The study of probability began with the first gamblers, but in the middle of the seventeenth century a systematic study of probability emerged. In 1654, the notorious gambler Chevalier De Mere proposed to Blaise Pascal the problem of how to divide the stakes in an interrupted game of dice. This intriguing problem caught the fancy of Pascal and during the next few years he exchanged letters on the solution with another mathematician, Pierre Fermat. From this correspondence the theory of probability emerged. Today the theory developed by Pascal and Fermat is used extensively by government, industry, business, science, education and many other fields of endeavor.

An understanding of how Pascal and Fermat measured the chance that a particular event would occur is illustrated by the following experiment in which a die is tossed 300 times and the result of each toss (trial) is recorded in this simple chart:

Die number	*Frequency of turning up*
1	47
2	51
3	49
4	50
5	52
6	51
Total	300

The die was tossed 300 times and, in these *trials*, the "3" turned up 49 times. Our *inductive reasoning* tells us that if the *same die* was tossed an additional 300 times for a total of 600 times the "3" would turn up a total of 98 times. We assume that the proportion of times the "3" turns up is about the same for any 300 trials. The validity of our assumption depends on having a large number of trial tosses. A small number of tosses would not be enough to validate the assumption.

The proportion of times that the "3" turned up in the above experiment is written 49/300. We call this proportion the experimental or *empirical probability* that a "3" will turn up when the die is tossed again. The empirical probabilities of each of the numbers turning up is shown here:

Die number	Frequency of turning up	Empirical probability
1	47	$\frac{47}{300}$
2	51	$\frac{51}{300}$
3	49	$\frac{49}{300}$
4	50	$\frac{50}{300}$
5	52	$\frac{52}{300}$
6	51	$\frac{51}{300}$

The empirical probability than an event will occur is equal to:

$$Pr\ (5) \quad \frac{\text{"the number of trials in which the event occurred."}}{\text{"the number of trials that are performed."}}$$

EXERCISE 8.1

In each of the problems of this exercise use the definition of empirical probability to answer the question.

1. Toss a die 25 times and find the empirical probability of:
   a) 2
   b) 1 or 5
   c) an odd number.
2. Toss three coins 10 times and find the empirical probability of getting:
   a) three heads.
   b) two heads and one tail.
   c) three heads or three tails.
3. Repeat the experiment of problem 2 except the coins are tossed 20 times.
4. On identical slips of paper write each of the numbers 1, 2, 3, 4 and put them in a box. Draw two slips of paper, record the numbers and return the papers to the box. Repeat this experiment 12 times and find the empirical probability of getting:
   a) an odd number and an even number.
   b) two even numbers.
   c) two odd numbers.
   d) two odd or two even numbers.
5. On a sheet of paper block off one inch squares and from a height of approximately two feet drop a one inch match stem and record whether or not it comes to rest across one of the lines. Repeat this experiment 25 times and find the empirical probability that it does not cross a line.

8.2 EXPECTED PROBABILITY

Each of the problems in the previous exercise asked that an experiment be conducted and the empirical probability of the occurrence of an event be determined. If another person or if several persons should carry out the same experiments it is very unlikely that the resulting probabilities would be identical but we would expect them to be approximately the same.

Often it is possible to determine without conducting an experiment the probability of an event occurring. That is, we base our deduction on experiments that have been conducted previously and on the nature of the experiment itself. To illustrate, suppose that a perfectly symmetrical die whose six faces are numbered 1, 2, 3, 4, 5, 6 is tossed. Because of the symmetry of the die each of the six sides have an equal chance of turning up. That is, the "1" has an equal chance of turning up as the "2" and so on. Since there are six numbers that can turn up and each of these is "equally likely" to turn up, *deductive reasoning* tells us that the chance that any particular number will turn up is $\frac{1}{6}$. Thus, if the die is tossed the "expected probability" of any particular number, 1 through 6, is $\frac{1}{6}$. The expected probability is usually very close to the empirical probability.

The set of all possible outcomes (results of each trial of an experiment) is called a "sample space" and is denoted by S. A sample space for the experiment of tossing the die is

$$S = \{1, 2, 3, 4, 5, 6\}$$

and each of the numbers is called a "sample point". Suppose we would like to know the expected probability of getting an odd number when the die is tossed. The sample points in the event are

$$E = \{1, 3, 5\}$$

and

$$S = \{1, 2, 3, 4, 5, 6\}$$

Since each number is equally likely to turn up, the *expected probability* is the number of sample points in E divided by the number of sample points in S. That is written

$$P_r(E) = \frac{n(E)}{n(S)} = \frac{3}{6} = \frac{1}{2}$$

where $P_r(E)$ denotes the probability of the event E and $n(E)$ and $n(S)$ denotes the number of sample points in E and S respectively.

An event is a subset of a sample space and probability is defined only for events.

Example 1. An ordinary deck of cards is shuffled and one card is withdrawn. What is the probability that it is a queen?

Solution. The experiment is "withdraw one card and record the result." The sample space of interest is:

$$S = \{\text{the 52 cards in the deck}\}.$$

The event we are interested in is

$$E = \{\text{queen of hearts, queen of diamonds,}\\ \text{queen of clubs, queen of spades}\}.$$

$$P_r(E) = \frac{n(E)}{n(S)} = \frac{4}{52} = \frac{1}{13}.$$

Example 2. Two honest coins, a nickel and a dime, are tossed. What is the probability that both are heads or both are tails?

Solution. The experiment is "toss two coins and record the result". The sample space of interest is:

$$S = \{(h, h)(h, t), (t, h), (t, t)\} \text{ where the first component is the outcome}\\ \text{of the nickel and the second is the outcome of the dime.}$$

The event we are interested in is

$$E = \{(h, h), (t, t)\}.$$

The expected probability is

$$P_r(E) = \frac{n(E)}{n(S)} = \frac{2}{4} = \frac{1}{2}.$$

Example 3. James, Tom, Sue, Mary and Joe form a club and one person is chosen president. What is the probability the person chosen is a female?

Solution. The experiment is "Choose a person and record the result". The sample space of interest is:

$$S = \{\text{James, Tom, Sue, Mary, Joe}\}.$$

The event of interest is,

$$E = \{\text{Sue, Mary}\}.$$

The expected probability is

$$P_r(E) = \frac{n(E)}{n(S)} = \frac{2}{5}.$$

A scale of probability is given in the following chart. The scale is graduated from zero to one. An event whose probability is zero is for all practical purposes an impossible event and an event whose probability is one is an event that is certain to happen.

Scale of probability

Night follows day	1
Most students pass the course	
Heads on the flip of a coin	$\frac{1}{2}$
You will make an A in this course	
You will live to be 90 years old	
You will live to be 190 years old	0

8.2 Expected Probability

A systematic approach to the solution of probability problems is given in the following steps:

1. Clearly identify the experiment to be performed.
2. Understand the event of interest.
3. Calculate the probability of the event. If the sample points in the sample space are equally likely to occur then calculate the probability by the formula

$$P_r(E) = \frac{n(E)}{n(S)}.$$

EXERCISE 8.2

1. An urn contains 5 red, 5 blue and 5 white marbles, each exactly alike except for color.
   a) If one marble is withdrawn what is the expected probability that it will be blue?
   b) The marble in part *a* is not replaced and another marble is withdrawn. What is the probability that it is white?
   c) Both marbles are replaced and another marble is withdrawn. What is the probability that it will be red or blue?

2. A die is tossed.
   a) What is the probability that the number showing is prime?
   b) What is the probability that the number showing is composite?
   c) What is the probability that the number showing is prime or composite?

3. An honest coin is flipped 5 times and lands heads up each time. What is the probability that it will land heads up on the 6th flip?

4. A number is chosen from the integers -5 to 5 inclusive.
   a) What is the probability that the number is odd?
   b) What is the probability that it is positive?
   c) What is the probability that it is 0?
   d) What is the probability that it is odd or even?

5. A pair of dice, one green and one red, is tossed.
   a) Make a sample space for this experiment by listing the possible outcomes of each die. (Hint: this sample space contains 36 sample points).
   b) What is the expected probability of each simple event? (A simple event contains one sample point).
   c) What is the sum of the probabilities of the simple events?

6. A social club conducts a raffle to raise money and sells 250 tickets. Sue Brown purchased 10 tickets. What is the probability that she will win the prize?

7. A coin is flipped and a die is tossed.
   a) Make a sample space for this experiment by listing all possible outcomes. (Hint: there will be 12 sample points).
   b) What is the probability of getting a head on the coin and a number greater than 3 on the die?
   c) What is the probability of getting a tail on the coin and a prime number on the die?

8. Two letters are chosen at random from the word *chosen*.
   a) What is the probability that the letter n is chosen?
   b) What is the probability that the letter is a vowel?
9. A card is drawn at random from an ordinary deck of 52 playing cards. What is the probability that:
   a) The card is a queen?
   b) A red card?
   c) A heart or a club?
   d) A spade and a diamond?
   e) A king or queen or ace?
10. The names of Susan, Kathy, Richard and Bill are written on slips of paper and placed in a box. Two names are to be drawn as representatives to an intra-mural contest.
    a) Make a sample space for this experiment.
    b) What is the probability that the names drawn were Susan and Bill?
    c) What is the probability that Kathy was one of the two?
    d) What is the probability that both were male?
    e) What is the probability that neither Susan nor Richard were selected?
11. In certain card games the deck is shuffled and the person who deals the cards is decided by each player drawing a card and the person drawing the highest card is the dealer. If the first person draws a 9, what is the probability that the second person who draws a card will get a higher number?
12. A football game can end in three ways; win, lose or tie. The local college team is scheduled to play two home games this season. Assume an equal chance for win, lose or tie and make a sample space for the results of the two games.
    a) What is the probability that the home team wins both games?
    b) What is the probability that both games end in a tie?
    c) What is the probability that the visiting team wins at least one game?
    d) What is the probability that the home team does not win either game?

8.3 FUNDAMENTAL PRINCIPLE OF COUNTING

Let us look more closely at problem 12 of the preceding exercise involving the outcomes of a football game. When one game is played the sample space that represents all possible results is

$$S = \{w, l, t\}$$

and contains three (3) sample points.

When two games are played, each of the three possible outcomes of the first game is paired with each of the three possible outcomes of the second game. That is shown as

$$S = \{(w, w), (w, l), (w, t) (l, w), (l, l), (l, t), (t, w) (t, l), (t, t)\}$$

and contains nine (3 · 3) sample points.

In a similar manner the sample space that represents all possible outcomes of three games can be made by pairing the nine possible outcomes of the first two games with the three possible outcomes of the third game. The sample space for the three games would contain twenty-seven $(3 \cdot 3 \cdot 3)$ sample points.

The *fundamental principle of counting* is stated as: "if one thing can be done independently in x_1 different ways, a second thing can be done independently in x_2 different ways, a third thing can be done independently in x_3 different ways and so on, then the total number of ways in which all independent things may be done is

$$x_1 \cdot x_2 \cdot x_3 \ldots$$

The following examples illustrate the fundamental principle of counting.

Example 1. In how many ways may 4 persons be seated in 4 chairs arranged in a row.

Solution. We have 4 choices for seating the first person, 3 choices for seating the second, 2 choices for seating the third and 1 choice for seating the fourth. Therefore, we have

$$4 \cdot 3 \cdot 2 \cdot 1 = 24$$

possible ways in which the four people may be seated.

Example 2. If the local college team plays 10 games (win, lose, tie), during a season how many sample points would there be in the sample space?

Solution. Since each game would be independent and each game may result in one of three ways, the number of sample points is

$$3 \cdot 3 \cdot 3 \cdot 3 \cdot 3 \cdot 3 \cdot 3 \cdot 3 \cdot 3 \cdot 3 = 3^{10} = 59{,}049$$

Example 3. How many license plates are possible if each consists of two different letters followed by four different numbers?

Solution. We have 26 choices for the first position, 25 for the second, 10 for the third, 9 for the fourth, 8 for the fifth and 7 for the sixth. Therefore, there are

$$26 \cdot 25 \cdot 10 \cdot 9 \cdot 8 \cdot 7 = 3{,}276{,}000$$

license plates possible.

Example 4. How many digit numbers (integers) can be formed from the digits 1, 2, 3, 4, 5, 6 if no digit is repeated?

Solution. $6 \cdot 5 \cdot 4 \cdot 3 \cdot 2 \cdot 1 = 720.$

It is reasonable to introduce a short-hand notation for the product of 6 and all natural numbers less than 6. The symbol is 6! (read 6 factorial). In general, *N factorial* (written N!) is the product of any natural number N and all natural numbers less than N. That is,

$$N! = n(n-1)(n-2)(n-3)\ldots(n-n+1).$$

EXERCISE 8.3

1. A student has a choice of 4 foreign languages and 5 sciences. In how many ways can he choose one of each?
2. In how many ways can two different prizes be awarded among nine contestants if both prizes:
   a) may not be given to the same person?
   b) may be given to the same person?
3. How many committees consisting of a junior, a senior and a graduate student can be chosen from 15 juniors, 17 seniors and 12 graduate students?
4. In how many ways can 5 letters be mailed if 3 mailboxes are available?
5. In how many ways can 8 books be arranged on a shelf having spaces for exactly 8 books if a particular book must be on the extreme left?
6. A baseball stadium has 4 entrances and 5 exits. In how many ways can two people enter together but leave by different exits?
7. There are 6 main roads between Sandyville and Harmony Hill, and 4 main roads between Harmony Hill and Thayer. In how many ways can a person drive from Sandyville to Thayer and return, going through Harmony Hill on both trips, without driving the same road twice?
8. How many positive even integers of three digits each can be formed from 1, 2, 3, 4, 5, 6, 7, 8 if no repetitions are allowed?
9. How many baseball teams can a coach field if there are 13 players on the squad and each player can play any position?
10. After the coach has chosen the players (problem 9) how many batting orders are possible?
11. In how many ways can a $1, a $5, a $10 and a $20 bill be distributed among 10 persons if no one gets more than one bill?

8.4 PERMUTATIONS AND COMBINATIONS

The numbers 123 and 321 consist of the same digits but they are different numbers for the digits are arranged in a different order.

Each different arrangement or ordered set of elements is called a permutation.

All examples and exercises in the preceding section involve arrangements or permutations of objects.

An expression for the total number of n elements taken r at a time ($n \geqslant r$) can be established by using the fundamental principle. The expression will be denoted by

$$P(n, r) = \frac{n!}{(n-r)!}.$$

Example 1. If 3 people enter a bus that has 9 vacant seats, in how many ways can they be seated?

Solution. Using the expression

$$P(r, r) = \frac{n!}{(n - r)!}$$

we have

$$P(9, 3) = \frac{9!}{(9 - 3)!} = \frac{9!}{6!} = \frac{9 \cdot 8 \cdot 7 \cdot 6!}{6!} = 504.$$

Example 2. In how many ways can 8 books be arranged on a shelf that has spaces for exactly 8 books?

Solution. This is problem 5 of the preceding section. If you solved this correctly, your solution was 8!. Using the formula, we have

$$P(8, 8) = \frac{8!}{(8 - 8)!} = \frac{8!}{0!} = 8! = 40,320.$$

Since the solution is 8!, we must define 0! to be 1 or the formula is not valid.

Example 3. In how many ways can a class elect a president, vice president, secretary and treasurer from a class of 80 students if no student can hold more than one office.

Solution. $P(80, 4) = \dfrac{80!}{76!} = \dfrac{80 \cdot 79 \cdot 78 \cdot 77 \cdot 76!}{76!} = 80 \cdot 79 \cdot 78 \cdot 77$

$$= 37,957,920.$$

EXERCISE 8.4

Use the formula for permutations and solve the problems.

1. Out of 9 pictures available, 3 are being hung in a row. In how many ways can this be done?
2. There are 10 buildings on a campus. In how many ways can a student visit all of them?
3. In how many ways can 6 persons be seated in 11 vacant chairs that are arranged in a row?
4. Find the number of permutations of the seven letters in the word "algebra". (Be careful—two letters are the same).
5. How many different ways can the manager of a 9-man baseball team arrange his batting order if he has 15 members on the squad?
6. A baseball manager has his best hitter batting fourth and the pitcher last. How many batting orders are possible under these conditions?
7. How many numbers can be formed by using four digits from the digits 1, 2, 3, 4, 5, 6, if
    a) the digits may not be repeated in any number?
    b) the digits may be repeated.
    c) the digits may not be repeated and the number formed must be even.
8. How many signals can be made with four different flags by raising them any number at a time?

210   Probability and Statistics   8.4

9. How many four-digit numbers greater than 2000 can be formed from the digits 1, 2, 3, 4, 5 if repetitions
   a) are not allowed?
   b) are allowed?
10. A family of 6 children including a set of triplets and a set of twins have 12 aunts and uncles. In how many ways can the children visit their aunts and uncles if all members of a multiple birth must go to the same relative and no relative can take more than one child unless it is of multiple birth?
11. A woman buys 4 sweaters, 5 blouses and 6 skirts. How many "outfits" that includes one of each can she wear assuming any garment can be worn with any other?
12. In how many ways can 6 women and 4 men be seated in a row if the men are seated together and the women seated together?

Combinations

A particular set of elements selected without regard to the order in which they are arranged is called a "combination". Consider the following coins: a nickel, dime, quarter and half-dollar. How many different sums of money could be formed from these coins if exactly two coins are selected? We list the sums as follows: 15¢, 30¢, 55¢, 60¢, and 75¢. Instead of counting in this manner which would not be convenient in many problems, we use this formula:

$$C(n, r) = \frac{n!}{(n-r)!r!}.$$

Since we are selecting 2 coins from the set of coins, we have

$$C(4, 2) = \frac{4}{(4-2)!2!} = \frac{4!}{2!2!} = \frac{4 \cdot 3 \cdot 2!}{2!2!} = 2 \cdot 3 = 6$$

different sums of money.

The distinction between a permutation and a combination is a very important one. If arrangement or order of elements is important, we are dealing with a *permutation*. If order of the elements is not important, then we are dealing with a *combination*. The six permutations "abc," "acb," "bac," "bca," "cab," and "cbc" are only one combination since the same elements are used in each.

Permutations are *ordered* arrangements and combinations are *unordered* arrangements.

Example 1. How many committees of 3 persons can be selected from a group of 9?

Solution. The order in which the committee members appear is not important so we are dealing with a combination and we may write it this way:

$$C(9, 3) = \frac{9!}{(9-3)!3!} = \frac{9!}{6!3!} = \frac{9 \cdot 8 \cdot 7 \cdot 6!}{3!6!} = \frac{9 \cdot 8 \cdot 7}{3 \cdot 2 \cdot 1} = 84$$

Example 2. In how many ways can a committee of 6 seniors and 4 juniors be selected from 10 seniors and 8 juniors?

$$\text{Solution.} \quad C(10, 6) \cdot C(8, 4) = \frac{10!}{4!6!} \cdot \frac{8!}{4!4!} = 14,700$$

Example 3. How many different sums of money could be formed from a penny, nickel, dime, quarter, and half-dollar if at least one coin is selected?

Solution. $C(5, 1) + C(5, 2) + C(5, 3) + C(5, 4) + C(5, 5) =$
$$5 + 10 + 10 + 5 + 1 = 31.$$

EXERCISE 8.5

1. In how many ways can a group of 12 ladies be divided into groups of 4 to play bridge?
2. At a certain trial 9 of 12 jurors voted for acquittal and 3 for conviction. In how many ways might this have occurred?
3. a) In problem 2 did you compute $C(12, 3)$ or $C(12, 9)$?
   b) Does it make a difference? Explain.
4. Is a so-called "combination lock" correctly named by our standards? Explain.
5. How many non-empty subsets can be formed from the set $\{a, b, c, d, e\}$?
6. How many different "hands" of 13 cards each can be dealt from a deck of 52 cards?
7. In how many ways can a committee of 4 Democrats and 3 Republicans be selected from a group of 20 Democrats and 14 Republicans?
8. A family of 7 persons plan to take a trip and take two cars. If 4 people can ride in one car and 3 in the other, in how many ways can they be seated?
9. In how many ways can 15 persons be seated at 3 tables if one table can seat 6 people, another 5, and another 4? Assume the order of seating at a table is not important.
10. In how many ways can a group of 10 students be divided into 3 sub-groups of 5, 3 and 2?

8.5 PROBABILITY INVOLVING ARRANGEMENTS

Permutations and combinations provide us with a method for determining the number of sample points in a sample space or event without the laborious task of listing all of the arrangements. We are now ready to solve problems in probability when there is a large number of ways that an event can occur or fail to occur.

Example 1. Two cards are drawn from an ordinary deck of fifty-two cards. What is the probability that both are hearts?

Solution. The experiment is "draw 2 cards". The event is "both cards are hearts." The sample space consists of all combinations of two cards and is $C(52, 2)$. The event consists of all those sample points in which both cards are hearts and is $C(13, 2)$. Using the definition of probability, we have

$$P_r(E) = \frac{n(E)}{n(S)} = \frac{C(13, 2)}{C(52, 2)} = \frac{\frac{12 \cdot 12 \cdot 11!}{2!11!}}{\frac{52 \cdot 51 \cdot 50!}{2!50!}} = \frac{13 \cdot 12}{52 \cdot 51} = \frac{1}{17}$$

There is one chance in 17 that both cards will be hearts.

Example 2. A hat contains 14 poker chips of which 7 are red and 7 are black. If 5 chips are drawn at random what is the probability that 3 chips are red and 2 are black?

Solution. The experiment is "draw 5 chips." The event is "3 chips are red and 2 are black." The sample space consists of all combinations of 5 chips and is $C(13, 5)$. The event consists of all combinations of 3 red and 2 black chips and is $C(7, 3) \cdot C(7, 2)$.

$$P_r(E) = \frac{C(7, 3) \cdot C(7, 2)}{C(13, 5)} = \frac{\frac{7!}{3!4!} \cdot \frac{7!}{2!5!}}{\frac{13!}{5!8!}} = \frac{245}{429}$$

EXERCISE 8.6

1. What is the probability of drawing 3 spades from an ordinary deck of 52 playing cards?
2. What is the probability of selecting a man from a group of 10 men and 15 women?
3. Five persons are to be selected for a committee out of a group of 20 men and 10 women.
   a) What is the probability that 3 men and 2 women will be selected?
   b) What is the probability that 1 man and 4 women will be selected?
4. Corky drew 2 tickets from a hat that contained 10 tickets numbered 1 to 10.
   a) What is the probability that the numbers on both tickets were odd?
   b) What is the probability that the sum of the numbers on the tickets drawn was odd?
   c) What is the probability that the sum of the tickets drawn was less than 6?
5. Four cards are drawn from an ordinary deck of 52 cards. What is the probability that:
   a) all will be hearts?
   b) all will be kings?
   c) all will be red?
6. Two bills are drawn simultaneously from a hat that contains ten $1 bills, six $5 bills and four $10 bills. What is the probability that the sum is
   a) $2?
   b) $15?
7. If 3 bills are drawn from the hat in problem 6 what is the probability that the sum of the two bills will be:
   a) $3?
   b) $25?
8. Two men and three women take seats at random in five vacant chairs arranged in a row. What is the probability that the men and women are sitting alternately in the seating arrangement?
9. If 3 cards are withdrawn from an ordinary deck of 52 cards, what is the probability that all 3 cards are from the same suit?

10. A bridge club is made up of 4 married couples. The men draw numbers from 1 to 4 and so do the wives. The man and woman with equal numbers are partners. What is the probability that each man has his wife as a partner?

8.6 PROBABILITY OF COMPOUND EVENTS

The probability of most compound events can be determined from the probability of the simpler parts that make up the event. To illustrate, suppose that a die is tossed twice and we are interested in the event that a 2 will turn up both times. There are six possible outcomes on the first toss, one of which is 2. Thus, the probability of a 2 is $\frac{1}{6}$. The second toss of the die is independent of the first toss and the probability of 2 on the second toss is $\frac{1}{6}$. The event requires that a 2 turn up on both tosses and by the fundamental principle we calculate the probability of a 2 on the first toss *and* a 2 on the second toss to be

$$\tfrac{1}{6} \cdot \tfrac{1}{6} = \tfrac{1}{36}.$$

This probability may be verified by making a sample space for the experiment and using

$$P_r(E) = \frac{n(E)}{n(S)}.$$

There is one sample point (2, 2) in the event and 36 sample points in the sample space. Thus

$$P_r(E) = \tfrac{1}{36}.$$

This type of compound probability, the probability that two events will both happen, is the product of their separate probabilities.

Example 1. A coin is flipped and a die is tossed, what is the probability that a head and a 3 turn up?

Solution. Experiment: "flip a coin and toss a die."
Event: "a head and a 3 will turn up."

$$P_r(E) = P_r(\text{head on coin})\, P_r(3 \text{ on die}) = \tfrac{1}{2} \cdot \tfrac{1}{6} = \tfrac{1}{12}.$$

Example 2. In a round-robin tournament each of the six teams invited has an equal chance of winning any one game and each team must play 3 games. What is the probability that a particular team will win all 3 games?

Solution. Experiment: "play 3 games."
Event: "a particular team will win all 3 games it plays."

$$P_r(E) = \tfrac{1}{2} \cdot \tfrac{1}{2} \cdot \tfrac{1}{2} = \tfrac{1}{8}.$$

Example 3. A box of chocolates contains 50 pieces of candy that are exactly alike except 30 pieces have nougat centers and 20 have nut centers. If 2 pieces are selected at random what is the probability that the first has a nut center and the second a nougat center?

Solution. Experiment: "select 2 pieces of candy at random."
Event: "the first has a nut center and the second a nougat center."
The probability that the first has a nut center is $\frac{20}{50}$ and the probability that the second has a nougat center is $\frac{30}{49}$. Thus $P_r(E) = \frac{20}{50} \cdot \frac{30}{49} = \frac{12}{49}$.

Another type of compound probability involves the probability that one or both of two events will occur. To illustrate, suppose that one die is tossed and we want to find the probability that the number that turns up is odd. This event will occur if a 1, 3, or 5 turns up. The probability of a 1 is $\frac{1}{6}$, the probability of a 3 is $\frac{1}{6}$ and the probability of a 5 is $\frac{1}{6}$. The probability of an odd number turning up on any one throw is $\frac{1}{6} + \frac{1}{6} + \frac{1}{6} = \frac{1}{2}$. This probability can be verified by making a sample space and using the formula

$$P_r(E) = \frac{n(E)}{n(S)}.$$

This type of compound probability, that one or both of two events will happen, is the sum of the two separate probabilities minus the probability that both will happen.

Example 4. What is the probability of getting at least one head when a coin is flipped twice?

Solution. Experiment: "flip a coin two times."
Event: "at least one head will turn up."

The probability that a head will turn up on the first flip is $\frac{1}{2}$ and also $\frac{1}{2}$ on the second flip. However the correct answer is not $\frac{1}{2} + \frac{1}{2} = 1$ for if a sample space is made only 3 of the 4 sample points will contain at least 1 head. Thus, the probability is the sum of the separate events minus the probability of a head on both coins and

$$P_r(E) = \tfrac{1}{2} + \tfrac{1}{2} - \tfrac{1}{4} = \tfrac{3}{4}.$$

Example 5. One card is drawn from an ordinary deck of 52 cards. What is the probability that it is a queen or heart.

Solution. Experiment. "draw one card from a deck of 52 cards."
Event: "the card is a queen or a heart."
The probability that it is a queen is $\frac{1}{4}$ and the probability that it is a heart is $\frac{1}{13}$. Thus,

$$P_r(E) = \tfrac{1}{4} + \tfrac{1}{13} - (\tfrac{1}{4} \cdot \tfrac{1}{13}) = \tfrac{16}{52} = \tfrac{4}{13}.$$

Example 6. A class in art has 21 students, 11 of whom are sophomores and 10 are freshmen. Two students are selected at random, one at a time. What is the probability that a sophomore and a freshman are selected?

Solution. Experiment: "two students are selected, one at a time."
Event: "a sophomore and a freshman are selected."
The event will occur if a sophomore is selected first with probability of $\frac{11}{21}$, and a freshman is selected second with probability of $\frac{10}{20}$. The event will also occur if the first selected is a freshman and the second a sophomore. Thus

$$P_r(E) = \frac{11}{21} \cdot \frac{10}{20} + \frac{10}{21} \cdot \frac{11}{20} = \frac{11}{21}.$$

EXERCISE 8.7

1. Three coins are tossed. What is the probability that,
   a) all three fall heads up?
   b) exactly 2 fall heads up?

2. A die is tossed. What is the probability that an odd number or a prime number turns up?

3. The probability that it will rain in Memphis on the fourth of July is $\frac{1}{10}$ and the probability that it will rain on Christmas day is $\frac{3}{10}$. What is the probability that it will rain
   a) on both days?
   b) on at least one of the days?

4. What is the probability of throwing a number less than 3 with a die if we have 2 tries?

5. A drawer contains six black and four white socks that are unattached. If two socks are drawn, one at a time, what is the probability that
   a) one will be black and the other white?
   b) both socks will be white?
   c) the socks match?

6. Kathy and Joe are a newly wed couple and plan to have three children. What is the probability that
   a) all three will be boys?
   b) that the first child will be a boy, the second a girl and the third a boy?
   c) there will be two girls and a boy?
   d) all three children will be of the same sex?

7. A local soft drink distributor sponsors both a boys' softball team and a girls' softball team. A game for each team is scheduled for a Saturday afternoon. The probability that the boys' team will win is $\frac{2}{3}$ and the probability of the girls' team winning is $\frac{3}{5}$. What is the probability that
   a) both teams win?
   b) neither team wins?
   c) at least one team will win?

8. Joe Sample is enrolled at a community college and has three classes, English, Mathematics and Chemistry that meet on Fridays. On a particular Friday, the probability that Joe will have a test on English is $\frac{1}{3}$, a test on Mathematics $\frac{1}{2}$ and a test on Chemistry $\frac{2}{5}$. What is the probability that on that particular Friday that Joe will have
   a) a test on all three subjects?
   b) a test on English and Mathematics but not on Chemistry?
   c) no tests at all?

9. A group consists of 7 juniors, 4 of whom are boys, and 9 seniors, of whom 4 are boys. A president is to be selected by lot. What is the probability that the person chosen is
   a) a senior girl?
   b) a junior or a boy?
   c) a senior boy or a junior girl?

10. Mr. and Mrs. Jones live on a farm and, except for an elderly couple across the road, their nearest neighbor lives ten miles away. Mr. and Mrs. Jones have one child, a seven year old boy named Sammy, who is lonesome and longs for a boy about his own age as a playmate. The elderly couple tells Mr. Jones that they have sold their home to a family about whom they know nothing except they have ten children all under twelve years of age and that they plan to move in the next day. Mr. Jones says to his son, "Sammy, beginning tomorrow you will have a boy to play with." Could Mr. Jones be wrong? If so, calculate the probability?

8.7 MATHEMATICAL EXPECTATION

One application of the use of probability is in finding the mathematical value of expectation. If a wager is made that a certain event will occur, the mathematical value of expectation or simply *mathematical expectation*, denoted by $E(A)$, is "the product of the amount to be won and the probability that the event will occur."

Any time a person pays more to take part in a game of chance or invests more in a business endeavor than is the value of his expectation he is bound to lose in the long run.

Example 1. A toaster that retails for $20 is to be raffled off at a school bazaar. If 250 tickets at 25 cents each are sold and Mr. Jones buys 10 tickets, what is the value of his expectation? Is he paying too much?

Solution. The probability that Mr. Jones will win the toaster is $\frac{10}{250}$ or $\frac{1}{25}$. His expectation is

$$E(A) = \$20(\tfrac{1}{25}) = .80.$$

Mr. Jones is paying too much for he has paid $2.50 to play the game. If Mr. Jones plays this game a larger number of times, he will lose. His net gain per game is $17.50 and he stands to lose $2.50. Thus, on the average, loss per game is

$$\$17.50(\tfrac{1}{25}) + (-\$.250)(\tfrac{26}{25}) = -\$1.70.$$

Example 2. Suppose that a person pays $0.75 to play a game in which two coins are tossed. The person tossing the coins is to receive $0.50 for each head that turns up. What is the expected value in this game?

Solution. The probability of obtaining two heads is $\frac{1}{8}$, the probability of one head is $\frac{1}{2}$ and the probability of no heads is $\frac{1}{4}$. Therefore,

$$\begin{aligned} E(A) &= \$1.00(\tfrac{1}{4}) + \$0.50(\tfrac{1}{2}) + \$0.00(\tfrac{1}{4}) \\ &= \$0.25 + \$0.25 + 0 \\ &= \$0.50. \end{aligned}$$

If the person continues to play the game he can expect to lose approximately $0.25 per game. A fair price to pay would be $0.50.

EXERCISE 8.8

1. A person is to receive $10 if he tosses two coins and both coins turn up heads. What is his mathematical expectation?

2. A women's club sold 1000 lottery tickets at $1.00 each. The prize to be won is worth $600.00. Are the tickets fairly priced? If your answer is no, what would be a fair price?

3. A hat contains ten counterfeit $10.00 bills and fifteen $10.00 bills that are authentic. Kathy agrees to pay $0.50 for the privilege of drawing one bill from the hat. Did Kathy pay too much?

4. A player in a dice game throws two dice and is paid $10.00 if the number that turns up is 8 or more. What should he expect to pay to play?

5. An honest coin is tossed 25 times. What is the expected number of heads that will turn up?

6. A man has $10,000 to invest in stocks. His agent tells him that the probability the stock will double in value is $\frac{2}{5}$. On this basis what is his mathematical expectation at the end of one year?

7. A man pays $1.00 and draws 2 cards from an ordinary deck of cards. He will receive $3.00 if either is a heart. Is this a good bet?

8. Tom and Sam are playing a game that consists of tossing 3 coins. Tom makes Sam the following bet. "I will pay you $3.00 every time you throw 3 heads or 3 tails and you will pay me $1.00 if you don't." Is this a fair game for Sam?

9. An objective test consists of ten questions that are to be answered true or false. If the question is answered correctly the student is credited with 10 points, however, if the question is answered incorrectly then the student is penalized 10 points. What should a student expect to score if he is completely unprepared?

10. Two bills are drawn from a purse that contains five $10.00 bills and seven $20.00 bills. What is the mathematical expectation?

11. The face cards are taken from a deck of cards shuffled and two cards are dealt face down. The dealer says he will bet even money that one of the cards is a queen. Is this a good bet?

SELF QUIZ 8.1

1. What is the expected probability of drawing a face card by selecting a card at random?

2. An experiment consists of testing light bulbs. If a bulb is good "g" is recorded and "b" if the bulb is not good. Make a sample space showing all possible outcomes when:
    a) one bulb is tested.
    b) two bulbs are tested.
    c) three bulbs are tested.

3. A large sofa has a seating capacity for four people. There are six people in the room. How many seating arrangements are possible for sitting on the sofa?

4. A five digit number is to be made from the digits 1, 2, ..., 9. In how many ways can this be done?

5. In how many ways can three door prizes be given to a group of four people if:

a) no person can receive more than one prize.

b) there is no restriction on the number of prizes a person may win.

6. An instructor gives a review sheet containing fifty questions and tells the class that five of the questions will be selected at random and used as a test.

   a) How many sets of five questions are possible?

   b) What is the probability that the five questions selected will be questions 10, 20, 30, 40, 50?

7. In the baseball world series between the winner of the National and American leagues, the winner of four of the seven games becomes World Champion.

   a) In how many ways can either team become World Champion?

   b) What is the probability that the National team will become champion after playing four games?

   c) If the National league team wins the first game, what is the probability that the American league team will win the next four games?

8. If a person is dealt five cards from an ordinary deck of cards

   a) How many different hands are possible?

   b) What is the probability all five cards are red?

9. A man pays two dollars and tosses a die. If the die turns up a 3 or 5 he wins five dollars. Is this a good bet?

8.8 INTRODUCTION TO STATISTICS

We shall begin our introduction to statistics with a quote attributed to Disraeli, "There are three kinds of lies: lies, damned lies and statistics." Such a statement might lead you to believe that statistics has no place in a mathematics course and we would tend to agree if the statement was altogether true. Also, it has often been said that anything can be proved using statistics. This statement like the first is not altogether true. When statistics are used to support an argument that is not valid, it is not a use but rather a *mis-use of statistics*.

Evidence of the use of statistics is found in the earliest recorded history of mankind. Today, the use of statistics is almost limitless and, as we move forward, it will become more important that a study of the elementary concepts be included in the curriculum.

In the study of statistics, as in the study of probability, we are concerned with a set of elements, usually a large set, and a subset of that larger set. In statistical language the large set is called a *population* and the subset is called a *sample* of that population. If we are concerned with a study of the student body of City Community College then the population is the entire student body at that college and the freshmen class would be a sample.

Whether the data, a set of measurements or observations, is collected first-hand or received complete, the statistician's job is to (a) summarize, analyze and interpret this data and (b) to draw conclusions about the population from which the data was obtained.

The data may include the whole population but usually it is only a sample, a small fraction of the population. In either case, it is important that the data be accurate. In a sample, the observations must be as nearly as possible representative of the entire population. To get a representative sample, we make a subset of measurements selected at random from the population. When each measurement in the population has an equal chance of being selected as a member of the sample. Such a subset is called a *random sample*.

The part of statistics that deals with summarizing, analyzing and interpreting the data is called *descriptive statistics*. The part that deals with making inferences about the population on the basis of information contained in a random sample is called *statistical inference*.

8.9 NUMERICAL DESCRIPTION OF DATA

After the data has been collected and organized the next step is usually to give a numerical description of that data. These measures are called *measures of central tendency* and *measures of variation*.

The Measures of Central Tendency

> The most important measure of central tendency is the arithmetic mean. The *arithmetic mean*, commonly called the *mean* and denoted by $\bar{x}$, is the arithmetic average of the measurements.

Example 1. Find the mean of the sample of observations

$$8, 10, 12, 15, 22.$$

Solution.

$$\bar{x} = \frac{8 + 10 + 12 + 15 + 30}{5}$$

$$= \frac{75}{5} = 15$$

Example 2. The ages of a sample six children to the nearest year are 6, 8, 8, 7, 6, 4. Find the mean age of the group.

Solution.

$$\bar{x} = \frac{6 + 8 + 8 + 7 + 6 + 4}{6} - \frac{39}{6} = 6.5 \text{ years}.$$

The mean is the most commonly used measure of central tendency; in most sets of data it is the number around which most of the other measurements are clustered. If there are a few extreme values, very small or very large in the data, then the mean may not be of much help in describing the data accurately.

Example 3. Tommy went fishing and caught fish whose weights were $\frac{1}{2}, \frac{3}{4}, 1, 1$ and 12 lbs. What is the mean weight of the catch?

Solution. $\bar{x} = \dfrac{\frac{1}{4} + \frac{3}{4} + 1 + 1 + 12}{5} = \frac{15}{5} = 3$ lbs.

The mean weight, 3 pounds, is larger than any fish caught except the one whose weight was 12 pounds. In such cases, the mean does not give a good description of the sample. For the mean to be useful it should be somewhere around the middle of the sample.

For those samples where the mean is not very helpful as a measure of central tendency, another number called the *median* may be used. To find the *median*, arrange the observations in order from the smallest to the largest; the number such that one-half of the observations are below it and one-half are above, is the median. With an odd number of observations in the array, the *middle value* is the median. When there is an even number of observations, find the mean of the *two middle values* and that becomes the median.

Example 4. Find the median of the sample composed of the observations 6, 8, 9, 12, 15.

Solution. The observations are arranged from the smallest to the largest and since there is an odd number, one-half the observations fall below and one-half fall above the middle value. The median is the observation "9".

Example 5. Find the median of the sample composed of the observation 25, 15, 20, 23, 22, 10.

Solution. The observations in order of smallest to largest are 10, 15, 20, 22, 23 25. Since there is an even number of observations, the mean of the observations "20" and "22", the two middle values, is figured. The median is

$$\frac{20 + 22}{2} = 21.$$

Sometimes a third measure of central tendency called the *mode*, the observation that appears most frequently, is useful. The mode is easily determined by counting. It is useful when considering a large number of observations. For example, a supermarket manager would find the mode useful in making out the work schedule for his employees. He should assign more employees during the hours with the most customers.

EXERCISE 8.9

1. Find the measures of central tendency of the sample made up of these observations:
    a) 3, 2, 5, 4, 7, 3
    b) 6, 11, 5, 8, 5
    c) 2, 2^2, 2^3, 2^4
2. A random sample of seven families living in Calhoun City had annual yearly incomes of $50,000, $3,000, $2,500, $8,000, $6,500, $7,000, $7,140.

a) What is the mean yearly income?

b) What is the median yearly income?

c) Which of the measures, mean or median, better describes the sample?

3. On a sheet of paper list the last names of ten of your friends. Count the number of letters in each name. Find the mean, median and mode for your data. Which measure best describes the data?

4. A small manufacturing company's annual report gives the average weekly wage of all employees to be $120.00. Sam Jones works in the shipping department as a clerk and is the highest paid employee in his department. Yet his weekly earning is $90.00. Can you explain statistically how this is possible if the company's report is true?

5. Over the past five years the amount of rainfall recorded each year for the month of August by the weather bureau at Tampa was 19.2 inches, 20.5 inches, 18.6 inches, 16.4 inches and 22.3 inches.

a) What is the mean fainfall?

b) What is the median rainfall?

6. If a sample is composed of numbers that are not the same, why must the mean be smaller than the largest number? Can the median be the largest number?

7. The heights of a random sampling of nine four year old fir tree seedlings yielded measurement to the nearest one-tenth foot of:

4.2, 6.5, 4.6, 5.4, 4.8, 5.6, 5.2, 5.8, 5.3.

a) What is the mean height?

b) What is the median height?

8. Esther received grades of 88, 92, 93 and 85 on the first four tests during a semester in a mathematics class. What must she make on the fifth test if she is to have an average of 90?

9. The contributions of five members of the mathematics department of a community college to the United Fund were $5, $25, $30, $5, $100.

a) What was the mean contribution?

b) What was the median contribution?

10. The times recorded for five athletes in the 100 yard dash were 9.2, 9.3, 9.2, 9.4 and 10.6 seconds respectively.

a) What is the mean time?

b) What is the median time?

c) Which measure best describes the data?

Measures of Variation

The mean, median and mode represent central tendency, where the data is clustered at some *central number*. However, we often want a description of the scatter or spread, of the data. The measures that show how the data are *scattered* about some central number are called *measures of variation*.

The *range* is a measure of variation but has very limited use. It is easy to calculate because it is the difference between the largest and smallest measurements in the set. For example if we have the set of data {2, 5, 9, 12} the range is 12 − 2 = 10.

Although the most used measure of variation is the *standard deviation,* we need the variance to calculate the standard deviation.

> The *variance* of a set of data is the average of the sum of the squares of the difference between each measurement and the mean. The *standard deviation* is the square root of the variance.

Example 1. Find the variance and standard deviation of the set of data $\{5, 8, 10, 12, 15\}$.

Solution. We first find the mean,

$$\bar{x} = \frac{5 + 8 + 10 + 12 + 15}{5} = \frac{50}{5} = 10$$

The variance denoted by s^2 is

$$s^2 = \frac{(5 - 10)^2 + (8 - 10)^2 + (10 - 10)^2 + (12 - 10)^2 + (15 - 10)^2}{5}$$

$$s^2 = \frac{(-5)^2 + (-2)^2 + 0^2 + (2)^2 + (5)^2}{5}$$

$$s^2 = \tfrac{58}{5} = 11.6$$

The standard deviation denoted by s is

$$s = \sqrt{11.6} \cong 3.4$$

Example 2. The weekly earnings of each of five brothers were $100, $120, $125, $150, $110. Find the variance and standard deviation in their weekly earnings.

Solution. $\bar{x} = \$121$

$$s^2 = \frac{(100 - 121)^2 + (120 - 121)^2 + (125 - 121)^2 + (150 - 121)^2 + (110 - 121)^2}{5}$$

$$= \tfrac{1420}{5}$$

$$= 284$$

$$s = \sqrt{284}$$

$$\cong \$16.90$$

One great advantage of the standard deviation over the variance is that the standard deviation is always in the same units of measure as the original observations. This usually makes it more meaningful than the variance as a description measure.

EXERCISE 8.10

1. Find the variance and standard deviation of the samples whose observations and measurements are
   a) 8, 10, 12, 16, 19: when $\bar{x} = 13$.
   b) 22, 24, 35, 26, 30, 25: when $\bar{x} = 29$.
   c) 61, 73, 68, 58, 60, 63, 65: when $\bar{x} = 64$.
   d) 500, 550, 450, 525, 475: when $\bar{x} = 500$.

2. Find the variance and standard deviation of the samples whose measurements are
   a) 5, 7, 3, 4, 5, 6.
   b) 17, 15, 12, 20.
   c) 2, 4, 7, 6, 5, 6.

3. A random sample of twelve students at City College had grade point averages of 3.2, 4.0, 3.8, 1.2, 2.5, 2.4, 1.8, 3.0, 2.4, 2.5, 2.2, 1.0. Find the mean, variance and standard deviation.

4. The Game and Fish Commission tagged one-thousand bass fingerlings and stocked them in the Tallahatchie River. Five years later, the Commission returned and collected a sample of eight bass wearing the identifying tags. The individual weights to the nearest tenth of a pound were 4.5, 6.1, 5.3, 5.2, 5.4, 4.9, 5.0, 5.2. Find the standard deviation in weight.

5. During the summer Olympic games at Munich the times for the eight contestants recorded in seconds were 10.84, 10.82, 10.88, 10.90, 10.89, 10.91, 10.86, 10.85. What is the mean time and the standard deviation?

6. Over the past five years the amount of rainfall each year for the month of August recorded by the weather bureau at Tampa was 19.2 in., 20.5 in., 18.6 in., 16.4 in. and 22.3 in. What is the variance and standard deviation in rainfall? (This is problem 5 of Ex. 8.9).

7. The weights to the nearest tenth of a pound of each of a random sample of ten toy fox terrier dogs were 6.5, 4.2, 4.6, 5.4, 5.6, 5.6, 4.8, 5.8, 5.2, 5.3. Find the mean weight and standard deviation.

8. During a recent golf tournament, the top five contestants shot scores on the first round of 66, 64, 65, 68, 72. What was the mean score and the standard deviation?

9. On a spelling test of ten commonly used words the number of words spelled incorrectly by a random sample of thirty tenth grade students were 1, 2, 1, 0, 3, 4, 1, 0, 0, 1, 1, 1, 2, 2, 3, 4, 4, 3, 2, 1, 0, 0, 1, 2, 1, 2, 1, 0, 1, 1. Find the mean number of words spelled incorrectly and the standard deviation.

10. On an arithmetic test of twenty elementary problems the number of problems missed by each of the same thirty students in problem 9 were 2, 0, 6, 8, 1, 3, 2, 4, 3, 5, 1, 2, 0, 1, 2, 1, 2, 0, 1, 0, 2, 1, 2, 5, 0, 1, 1, 2, 0, 2.
    a) Find the mean number of problems solved incorrectly and the standard deviation.
    b) If Johnny was one of those thirty students and he misspelled 2 words and solved 4 problems incorrectly, in which test did he do best in comparison with the other students? On what do you base your answer?

8.10 THE NORMAL CURVE

The data in a sample or population are often presented in the form of a graph. The purpose of the graph is to give a visual picture of the distribution of measurements. The graph, the measures of central tendency, and variation give a complete description of the data.

If a sample has a large number of measurements we expect to find a majority of them near the mean. As we move away from the mean, below or above, we expect the number of measurements to become fewer and fewer. The following data on pine tree seedlings will demonstrate how a normal curve can give a visual picture of the distribution of measurements. A random sample of one-hundred, four year old pine tree seedlings were measured and the heights in feet were recorded and separated into classes. Since seedling height was measured to the nearest foot, each tree fits one of the classes. Seedling height data is set up in a chart:

Height classes	Number	Percent
1.5–2.5 ft	2	$\frac{2}{100} = 2\%$
2.5–3.5 ft	8	$\frac{8}{100} = 8\%$
3.5–4.5 ft	20	$\frac{20}{100} = 20\%$
4.5–5.5 ft	40	$\frac{40}{100} = 40\%$
5.5–6.5 ft	15	$\frac{15}{100} = 15\%$
6.5–7.5 ft	10	$\frac{10}{100} = 10\%$
7.5–8.5 ft	5	$\frac{5}{100} = 5\%$
	100	100%

In Figure 8.1, a bar graph, using this seedling height data, shows the distribution of measurements.

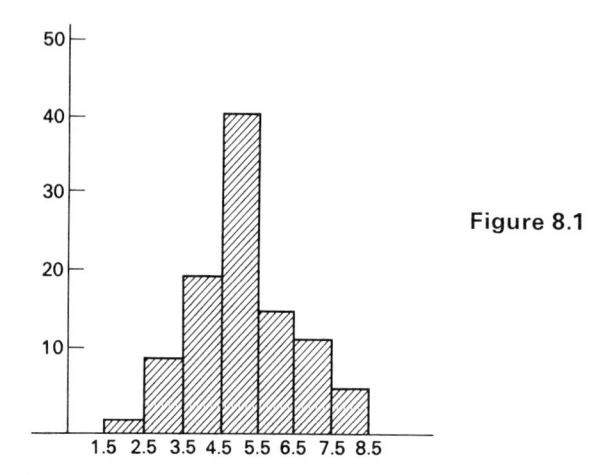

Figure 8.1

This type of bar graph is called a *histogram*. The width of each bar represents a seedling height class. The height of each bar corresponds to the number of seedlings in that class. Each bar shows us that class's percentage of the total. Since all the classes are represented, the total area of the bars (the total shaded area) must be 100 percent. Thus, we visualize by using a histogram, that the sum of class percentages is 100 percent. We may wonder if this relationship of percentages holds true on samples over 100.

If the number of trees in the sample were increased to one-thousand, then we could assume, on the basis of empirical probability, that the number of measurements in each class would be distributed like this:

Height classes	Number	Percent
1.5–2.5 ft	20	$\frac{20}{1000} = 2\%$
2.5–3.5 ft	80	$\frac{80}{1000} = 8\%$
3.5–4.5 ft	200	$\frac{200}{1000} = 20\%$
4.5–5.5 ft	400	$\frac{400}{1000} = 40\%$
5.5–6.5 ft	150	$\frac{150}{1000} = 15\%$
6.5–7.5 ft	100	$\frac{100}{1000} = 10\%$
7.5–8.5 ft	50	$\frac{50}{1000} = 5\%$

Even though the number of measurements may change, the percentage of trees in each class would remain the same. In a sample the total percentage of all classes will still be 100 percent. Now we will apply what we've learned from the seedling sample to other data.

If we have a large sample of measurements and arrange them in many small classes, the bar bases in the histogram will be small. The many small bars will rise in many small steps, so that the histogram appears to *fit* underneath a smooth curve.

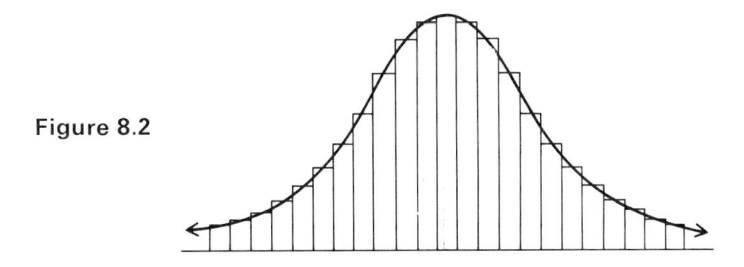

Figure 8.2

One of the most used curves in statistics resembles a bell and is called a *normal curve*.

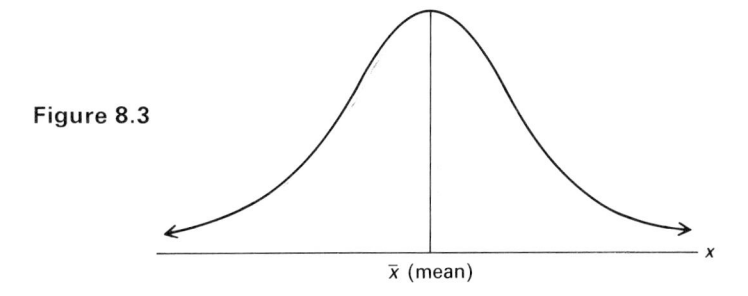

Figure 8.3

$\bar{x}$ (mean)

A set of data that graphically conforms to a normal curve is said to be *normally distributed*. A normal curve is symmetrical about a line drawn perpendicular to and intersecting the horizontal axis at the mean. If a population is normally distributed then a random sample taken from this population is assumed to be normally distributed.

If a set of population or sample data is normally distributed, we can attach significance to the mean and standard deviation in determining percentage. The percentage of distribution that lies between the mean and one or more standard deviations on each side is shown in Figure 8.4.

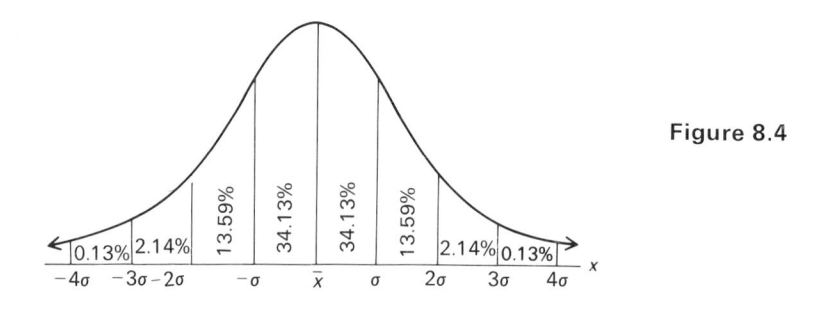

Figure 8.4

From the statistical information in a random sample, we make assumptions and predictions about the population which the sample represents. Studies in science, business, economics, nature, government, and other fields are based on normally distributed data. Thus, the information contained in a random sample is often the only source of information upon which we base our predictions.

Example 1. The mean score on a standardized IQ test is 100 and the standard deviation is 15.

   a) Represent this distribution with a normal curve.
   b) What percent of the people have an IQ greater than 130?
   c) What percent have an IQ greater than 70?
   d) What percent have an IQ between 85 and 115?

Solution.

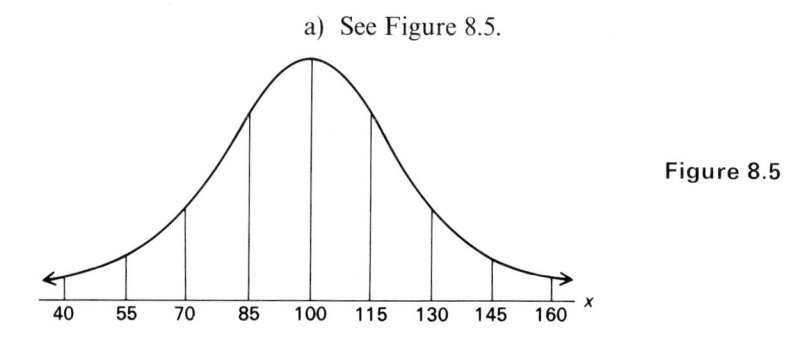

a) See Figure 8.5.

Figure 8.5

b) Using the percentages contained in Figure 8.4 we find that 130 on Figure 8.5 is 2 standard deviation to the right of the mean. Thus we have 2.14% + .13% = 2.27 with IQ above 130. (shaded area Figure 8.6).

Figure 8.6

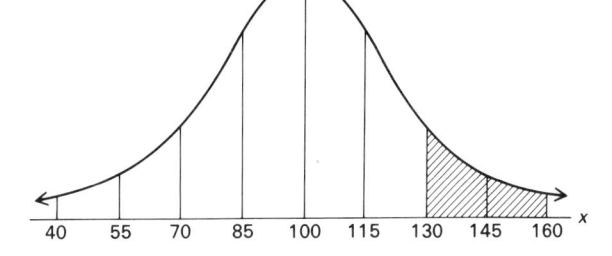

c) An IQ of 70 is 2 standard deviations to the left of the mean. The percentage of IQ greater than 70 is 13.59% + 34.13% + 34.13% + 13.59% + 2.14% + .13% = 97.73%. (shaded area Figure 8.7)

Figure 8.7

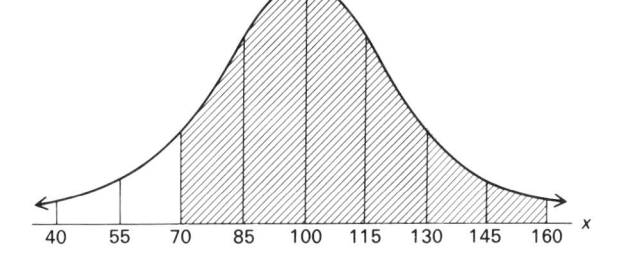

d) An IQ of 85 is one standard deviation to the left of the mean, while an IQ of 115 is one standard deviation to the right. The percentage of IQ's between 85 and 115 is 34.14% + 34.13% = 68.26%. (shaded area Figure 8.8).

Figure 8.8

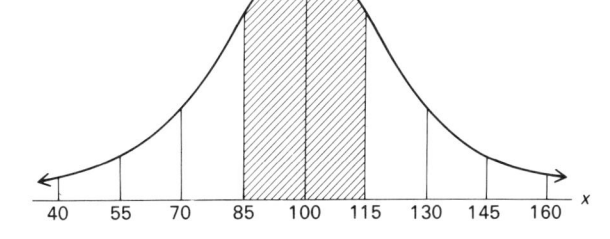

In a histogram we note that the percentage of each class is equal to the number of measurements in that class divided by the number of measurements in the sample. That is:

$$\frac{\text{number of measurements in the class}}{\text{number of measurements in the sample}} = \text{the percentage of any class}$$

Consider this definition the same as our definition of probability when the sample points are equally likely to occur. The probability that any measurement chosen at random from a normal population will be in a particular class is the same as the percentage of that particular class area. In the previous example, if we ask "what is the probability of the event a person chosen at random has an IQ between 100 and 115", the solution is the same as the percentage of area in the "rectangle" (bar of the histogram) between $\bar{x}$ and s. In Figure 8.9 the bar of the histogram has become a "rectangle" in normal curve terminology.

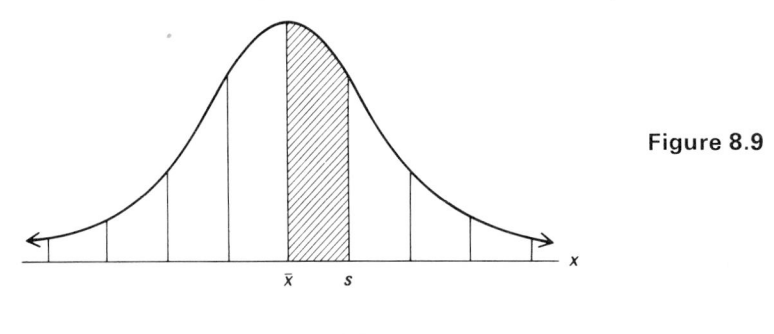

Figure 8.9

$P_r(E) = 34.13\% = .3413$

EXERCISE 8.11

1. A sample of data has a mean of 25 and a standard deviation of 5. Assume the distribution is normal.
    a) What percent of the distribution has measurements between 15 and 25?
    b) What percent of the distribution has measurements less than 30?
    c) What percent of the distribution has measurements less than 20 or greater than 30?
    d) If a measurement is chosen at random, what is the probability that the measurement is between 30 and 35?

2. The average wage per hour in a small manufacturing company is $3.00 per hour with a standard deviation of $0.60. If the wages follow a normal distribution, what percent of the workers make:
    a) less than $2.40?
    b) more than $4.20?
    c) between $2.40 and $4.20?

3. In a poll a random sample of 50 people were asked how many hours per week they spent watching TV. The average time spent per person was 10 hours with a standard deviation of 1.5 hours. On the basis of this poll, how many people spent more than 13 hours watching TV per week? (Population 200,000,000). What is the probability that a person chosen at random spent less than 8.5 hours per week in watching TV?

4. A random sample of students at City College had a mean grade point average of 2.5 and a standard deviation of .3. Assume a normal distribution.
    a) What percent of the students had a grade point average between 2.2 and 3.1?
    b) What is the probability that a student chosen at random will have a grade point average greater than 3.4?

8.10 The Normal Curve 229

5. The random sample of fish caught by the Game and Fish Commission (problem 4, ex. 8.10) had a mean weight of 5.2 pounds and a standard deviation of .43 pounds. What is the probability that one of the tagged fish caught at random weighs between 4.77 and 5.63 pounds? Assume normal distribution.

6. The mean weight of a random sample of toy fox terrier dogs (problem 7, ex. 8.10) was calculated to be 5.3 pounds and a standard deviation of 1.93 pounds. What is the probability that a toy fox terrier chosen at random weighs between 3.37 and 7.23 pounds? Assume normal distribution.

7. The blood pressure of seven adults was 105, 115, 130, 144, 136, 140, 154. If the distribution is normal, what is the probability that an adult picked at random will have a blood pressure between 116.04 and 147.96?

8. The mean high temperature in Jackson for the month of September is 84° with a standard deviation of 3°. What is the probability that on a particular day in September that the temperature will be above 90°?

9. The mean number of words spelled incorrectly by a random sample of students (problem 9, ex. 8.10) was 1.5 with a standard deviation of .38. If a student is picked at random what is the probability that the student will miss more than 1.12 words?

10. On the arithmetic problems (problem 10, ex. 8.10) the mean number of problems worked incorrectly was 2.9 and the standard deviation 1.93. What is the probability that a student chosen at random will miss more than 4.83 problems?

9 Introduction to Computers

9.1 HISTORICAL DEVELOPMENT OF COMPUTATIONAL DEVICES

People did not invent the first computing device. Nature provided us with a ten digit computer that is still in general use and requires no electric power, maintenance or special training for the operator. It seems paradoxical that the Latin word for finger is now used to describe the incredibly fast modern device —the digital computer.

The origins of the first human-designed computation device, the abacus, are buried in antiquity. The abacus is known to have been in use in Europe and China more than 2000 years ago. It is still in use in the Orient. The beads of a modern abacus were apparently pebbles in ancient times. The Latin word for pebble, calculus, is still prominent in mathematics. The abacus was used in Europe until the present-day base ten numeral system replaced Roman numerals in business usage about 400 years ago. Pencil and paper (originally slate and crayon) computations with base ten numerals are easily performed but such computations are not feasible with Roman numerals. Try multiplying MDCCCCLXXII by MDCCCCLXXI without converting to base ten.

The beginnings of modern computations devices go back to the 17th Century. The French mathematician Blaise Pascal invented a mechanical calculator in 1642. Pascal employed a series of wheels each with ten teeth to represent the digits. The principal contribution that Pascal made was the design of a "carry" mechanism. The difficulty of carrying quantities mechanically still exists for the designers of modern computers. Pascal's invention was followed in 1672 by the "Reckoning Machine" of Gottfried Wilhelm Liebnitz, the German mathematician and philosopher. Despite these developments it was not until 1885 that William Burroughs produced a salable adding machine. Desk calculators that could perform multiplication did not appear until World War I.

Modern computers differ markedly from desk calculators and adding machines. The words "automatic" and "high speed" explain the essential differences in performance. A computer is automatic in that no operator is required from after the data input until the "answer" is given. The speed of a computer is limited only by the speed of transmission of electric impulses.

An automatic digital computer was conceived in 1833 by Charles Babbage, a professor of mathematics at Cambridge University. The Babbage computer was to consist of a memory or "store", an arithmetic unit or mill and a control unit. Punched cards, already in use in textile mills, were to be used to furnish instructions and data to the computer. Babbage worked on his machine until his death in 1871. Thousands of parts were required for the Babbage computer and a complete machine was never constructed. The work of Babbage was unknown to 20th Century developers of the computer.

The computer has undergone continuous development since 1937 when Howard Aiken of Harvard University began work on an electromechanical computer. This machine was completed in 1944. The first electronic computer was completed in 1946 by a group from the University of Pennsylvania. This computer contained 19,000 vacuum tubes and weighed 30 tons.

In 1945 John von Neumann, a Princeton University mathematician, suggested that the binary number system (base two) be used in building computers. He also suggested that machine instructions as well as data be stored internally. The suggestions of von Neumann have since been followed by virtually all manufacturers of computers. The desirability of the binary number system in computer design will be discussed later in this chapter. The first commercial computer utilizing the von Neumann concepts became available in 1951. Since that time, the development of computers has been so rapid that we speak of generations of computers. Four generations, characterized as follows, are recognized.

First generation: 1945–1957—Vacuum tubes, calculations in milliseconds. (10^{-3}).
Example: IBM 650

Second generation: 1957–1965—Transistors, calculations in nucroseconds. (10^{-6}).
Example: IBM 1401

Third generation: 1965–1972—Solid state and integrated circuits, calculations in nanoseconds. (10^{-9}).
Example: IBM 360

Fourth generation: 1972– Monolithic chip circuitry, calculations in nanoseconds.

9.2 TYPES OF COMPUTERS

In this textbook we shall limit ourselves to the study of digital computers. These computers perform their operations by adding binary digits. The majority of all computers are of this type.

There is another type of computer which performs its operations based on the concept of measurement. Some type of measurement is made and the result is converted to an analogous number. Computers which operate in this manner are called "analog computers". The analogy most often employed relates to changes in voltage and quantities to be measured. An analog computer is best suited for solving problems which require calculus and other higher mathematics.

9.3 COMPUTER COMPONENTS

The components of a computer must be organized to perform five functions as illustrated in Figure 9.1.

Figure 9.1

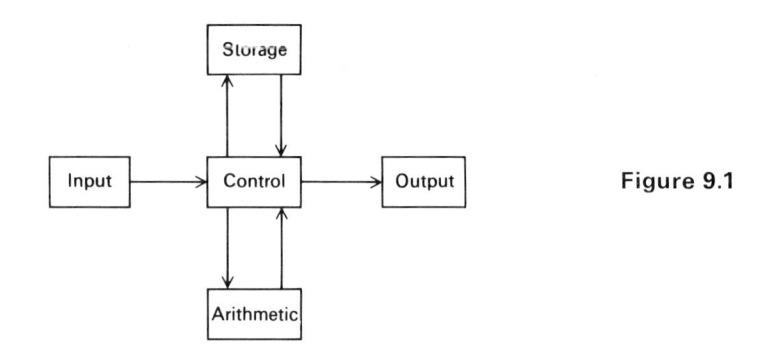

Input

Words and numbers must be translated into machine language before computation can proceed. This translation process begins with the input components of the computer. Input devices can "read" and translate punched cards, punched tape, magnetic tape, magnetic characters and even ordinary printed characters.

Instructions and data may be input directly (online) from operator to computer by means of a typewriter. Visual input is also possible. Limited voice communication input has been accomplished.

Storage

Two kinds of information must be stored in the memory of a computer, the instructions to follow and the data to be handled. Computer storage may be provided internally only or both internally and externally. If part of the memory is external, it may be "online" or "offline." A computer memory is made up of a large number of small units called "locations" or "addresses". A permanent address code is assigned to each unit in the memory. Data and instructions stored at the address are completely independent of the code used for the address. Devices used for computer storage or memory, include:

Device	*Description*
1. Magnetic core	May be internal or external online. Consists of many very small rings which can be magnetized in both directions.
2. Magnetic drum	About 1 foot in diameter. Data and instructions are stored by magnetizing parts of the drum, now used primarily for external storage.
3. Thin fim devices	Made of a very thin fim of alloys of nickel and iron. Tiny rectangular storage locations are used. Used for internal storage.
4. Punched cards or tape	Used for external offline storage.
5. Magnetic tape	Used for external offline storage.
6. Magnetic disk	Used for external on and offline storage.

Control

The control unit of a computer selects, interprets and executes the program instructions in the proper sequence.

Arithmetic

The arithmetic-logic unit does the processing of the program.

Output The primary output device is a high speed printer. If the information is stored for later use it may be output on cards or tape.

9.4 COMPUTER ARITHMETIC

It is possible to become relatively skilled in solving algebraic equations without understanding algebraic theory. It is merely necessary to follow a step-by-step process developed by a person who understands algebraic theory. The step-by-step procedure employed in solving a type of problem is called an algorithm.*

A computer program is based on an algorithm. One can become relatively skilled in writing computer programs without understanding the theory on which an algorithm for a program is based. Similarly, one can program a computer without any knowledge of the type of arithmetic in which the computer performs it operations. However, an understanding of computer arithmetic should remove some of the mystery that surrounds a computer for most of us, whether we are future programmers or passive recipients of the advantages and disadvantages of the computer age. The achievement of this understanding is our purpose here.

The Hindu-Arabic Numeration System

The Hindu-Arabic numeration system is the familiar system of writing symbols for numbers. An important feature of this system is the concept of place value. Each of the digits 0, 1, 2, . . . , 9 has value, depending on the place the digit occupies in the numeral.* Another feature of our numeration system is the use of the number 10 as the basis for assigning value to each digit in a numeral. Let us review the meaning of the symbol 2351:

$$2351 = \text{two thousand} + \text{three hundred} + \text{fifty} + \text{one}$$
$$2351 = 2000 + 300 + 50 + 1$$
$$2351 = 2 \times 10^3 + 3 \times 10^2 + 5 \times 10^1 + 1 \times 10^0$$

As illustrated, we are able to write any Hindu-Arabic numeral in four ways: (1) the usual symbolic way, (2) in English words, (3) in expanded numeral notation, and (4) in exponential notation. We shall find that the exponential

---

*The word algorithm is derived from the work of al-Khowarizmi, as is the word algebra.

*Numeral is defined as a symbol for a number. Several numerals often represent the same number, that is 1 and *I*.

form of notation is most helpful in understanding the binary numeration system of the computer.

The Binary Numeration System

We are aware that ten digits are required in base 10. In any base, the number of "digits" (single symbols) needed is always the same number as the base. In base 2, two symbols—0 and 1—are needed. To see what number the numeral 101 in base 2 symbolizes we write the numeral in exponential notation:

$$101 \text{ (base 2)} = 1 \times 2^2 + 0 \times 2^1 + 1 \times 2^0$$
$$= 4 + 0 + 1$$
$$= 5.$$

Following the same pattern, we are able to determine the number represented by any numeral in base 2. Table 9.1 lists the base 2 numerals for the numbers 1 through 20.

Table 9.1

Base 2	Conversion	Base 10
1	none	1
10	$1 \times 2^1 + 0 \times 2^0$	2
11	$1 \times 2^1 + 1 \times 2^0$	3
100	$1 \times 2^2 + 0 \times 2^1 + 0 \times 2^0$	4
101	$1 \times 2^2 + 0 \times 2^1 + 1 \times 2^0$	5
110	$1 \times 2^2 + 1 \times 2^1 + 0 \times 2^0$	6
111	$1 \times 2^2 + 1 \times 2^1 + 1 \times 2^0$	7
1000	$1 \times 2^3 + 0 \times 2^2 + 0 \times 2^1 + 0 \times 2^0$	8
1001	$1 \times 2^3 + 0 \times 2^2 + 0 \times 2^1 + 1 \times 2^0$	9
1010	$1 \times 2^3 + 0 \times 2^2 + 1 \times 2^1 + 0 \times 2^0$	10
1011	$1 \times 2^3 + 0 \times 2^2 + 1 \times 2^1 + 1 \times 2^0$	11
1100	$1 \times 2^3 + 1 \times 2^2 + 0 \times 2^1 + 0 \times 2^0$	12
1101	$1 \times 2^3 + 1 \times 2^2 + 0 \times 2^1 + 1 \times 2^0$	13
1110	$1 \times 2^3 + 1 \times 2^2 + 1 \times 2^1 + 0 \times 2^0$	14
1111	$1 \times 2^3 + 1 \times 2^2 + 1 \times 2^1 + 1 \times 2^0$	15
10000	$1 \times 2^4 + 0 \times 2^3 + 0 \times 2^2 + 0 \times 2^1 + 0 \times 2^0$	16
10001	$1 \times 2^4 + 0 \times 2^3 + 0 \times 2^2 + 0 \times 2^1 + 1 \times 2^0$	17
10010	$1 \times 2^4 + 0 \times 2^3 + 0 \times 2^2 + 1 \times 2^1 + 0 \times 2^0$	18
10011	$1 \times 2^4 + 0 \times 2^3 + 0 \times 2^2 + 1 \times 2^1 + 1 \times 2^0$	19
10100	$1 \times 2^4 + 0 \times 2^3 + 1 \times 2^2 + 0 \times 2^1 + 0 \times 2^0$	20

The familiar addition and multiplication tables of base 10 are greatly simplified for base 2.

Addition—Base 2

+	0	1
0	0	1
1	1	10

Multiplication—Base 2

×	0	1
0	0	0
1	0	1

Using these tables, we are able to perform addition and multiplication for base 2 with the same algorithms as for base 10. Addition Examples, Base 2

Exxmple 1. $\quad\;\;1$
$\qquad\quad\;\;\underline{+1}$
$\qquad\quad\;\;10$

Example 2. $\quad\;\;10$
$\qquad\quad\;\;\underline{+10}$
$\qquad\quad\;\;100$

Example 3. $\quad\;\;11$
$\qquad\quad\;\;\underline{+1}$
$\qquad\quad\;\;100$

Example 4. $\quad\;\;101$
$\qquad\quad\;\;\underline{+1101}$
$\qquad\quad\;\;10010$

Multiplication Examples, Base 2

Example 1. $\quad\;\;1$
$\qquad\quad\;\;\underline{\times 1}$
$\qquad\quad\;\;1$

Example 2. $\quad\;\;10$
$\qquad\quad\;\;\underline{\times 10}$
$\qquad\quad\;\;100$

Example 3. $\quad\;\;11$
$\qquad\quad\;\;\underline{\times 1}$
$\qquad\quad\;\;11$

Example 4. $\quad\;\;101$
$\qquad\quad\;\;\underline{\times 111}$
$\qquad\quad\;\;101$
$\qquad\quad\;\;101$
$\qquad\quad\;\;\underline{101}$
$\qquad\quad\;\;100011$

Notice in Table 9.1 that the base (in this case 2) does not appear in the base 2 column. When the base is reached, the symbol is 10, just as in base 10. We should not verbalize the symbol for the base with the word "ten" except in base 10. In other bases, the symbol 10 should be read "one zero." It should also be noted that, once the base is reached, the usual verbalization of the numeral is incorrect. For example, 1000 in base 2 is read as "one zero zero zero," not "one thousand."

In base 2, the symbols 0 and 1 are called *binary digits*. This phrase is contracted to *bit* in computer applications. The symbol 1011 in base 2 consists of four bits.

Let us now extend the binary system to provide numerals for decimal fractions. We first review a decimal fraction written in exponential form:

$$.756 = 7 \times 10^{-1} + 5 \times 10^{-2} + 6 \times 10^{-3}$$
$$= 7 \times \tfrac{1}{10} + 5 \times \tfrac{1}{100} + 6 \times \tfrac{1}{1000}.$$

Now examine the following, written in base 2:

$$.101 = 1 \times 2^{-1} + 0 \times 2^{-2} + 1 \times 2^{-3}$$
$$= 1 \times \frac{1}{2} + 0 \times \frac{1}{2^2} + 1 \times \frac{1}{2^3}$$
$$= \tfrac{1}{2} + 0 + \tfrac{1}{8}$$
$$= \tfrac{5}{8} = .625 \text{ in base } 10.$$

The following example illustrate the conversion of base 2 numerals to decimal form.

Base 2 to Base 10 Conversion

Example 1. Convert 101.11 to decimal form.

Solution. We write 101.11 in exponential form:

$$101.11 = \underline{1} \times 2^2 + \underline{0} \times 2^1 + \underline{1} \times 2^0 + \underline{1} \times 2^{-1} + \underline{1} \times 2^{-2}$$
$$= (1 \times 4) + (0 + 1) + (1 \times \tfrac{1}{2}) + (1 \times \tfrac{1}{4})$$
$$= 5.75.$$

Example 2. Convert .00011 to decimal form:

Solution. $.00011 = \underline{0} \times 2^{-1} + \underline{0} \times 2^{-2} + \underline{0} \times 2^{-3}$
$$+ \underline{1} \times 2^{-4} + \underline{1} \times 2^{-5}$$
$$= 0 + 0 + 0 + \tfrac{1}{16} + \tfrac{1}{32}$$
$$= \tfrac{3}{32} = .09375.$$

Conversions from Base 10 to Base 2

We have seen that it is a simple matter to convert a numeral from base 2 to base 10. The technique of converting from base 10 to base 2 is not quite so straightforward. Let us begin by converting 16 in base 10 to base 2. We see in Table 9.1 that 16 in the base 10 column is equal to 10000 in base 2. We reproduce the conversion column for 16 from Table 9.1.

$$1 \times 2^4 + 0 \times 2^3 + 0 \times 2^2 + 0 \times 2^1 + 0 \times 2^0.$$

If a conversion table is not available, we must determine the highest power of base 2 that equals or is less than the base 10 number. In this case the highest power is 2^4, which exactly equals 16. 2^4 always occupies the fifth position in a base 2 numeral, 2^3 the fourth position, etc. Hence we could write

$$\underline{} \times 2^4 + \underline{} \times 2^3 \underline{} \times 2^2 + \underline{} \times 2^1 \underline{} \times 2^0$$

and fill in the blank places with 10000, for we require only 1×2^4 and none of the other powers of 2.

Let us try another conversion of base 10 to base 2.

Example. Convert 71 in base 10 to base 2.

Solution.
1. Determine the highest power of base 2 that is equal to or is less than 71; this is $2^6 = 64$. Hence we need $1 \times 2^6 = 64$.
2. If next we use 1×2^5, this would give a total of 96. Hence we need $0 \times 2^5 = 0$.
3. If next we use 1×2^4, this would give a total of $1 \times 2^6 + 0 \times 2^5 + 1 \times 2^4 = 80$, which is too much. Hence we need $0 \times 2^4 = 0$.
4. If next we use 1×2^3, this would give a total of $1 \times 2^6 + 0 \times 2^5 + 0 \times 2^4 + 1 \times 2^3 = 72$, which is also too much. Hence we need $0 \times 2^3 = 0$.

5. If next we use 1×2^2, this gives us a total of $1 \times 2^6 + 0 \times 2^5 + 0 \times 2^4 + 0 \times 2^3 + 1 \times 2^2 = 68$, which is less than 71. Hence we need 1×2^2.
6. A total of 3 is still required; it is provided by 2^1 and 2^0. If we use 1×2^1 and 1×2^0, we would have $1 \times 2^6 + 0 \times 2^5 + 0 \times 2^4 + 0 \times 2^3 + 1 \times 2^2 + 1 \times 2^1 + 1 \times 2^0 = 64 + 0 + 0 + 0 + 4 + 2 + 1 = 72$.
7. 71 in base 10 = 1000111 in base 2.

We now state an algorithm for converting from base 10 to any other base b.

1. Prepare a list of powers of b until the base 10 symbol is reached or exceeded.
2. Beginning with the first power, say n, below the base 10 symbol write the powers of b in conversion form as follows:

$$\underline{\quad} \times b^n + \ldots + \underline{\quad} \times b^2 + \underline{\quad} \times b^1 + \underline{\quad} \times b^0.$$

3. Determine the number of times b^n is required, say c times.
4. Subtract $c \times b^n$ from the base 10 numeral.
5. Determine the number of times b^{n-1} is required, say d times. Subtract $d \times b^{n-1}$ from the result of step (4).
6. Continue until the base 10 symbol has been entirely converted to the new base.

EXERCISE 9.1

1. Write the following decimal numerals in expanded exponential form.
    a) 675
    b) 2300.0001

2. Convert the following numerals in base 2 to base 10.
    a) 101
    b) 10101
    c) 11.11
    d) .000101

3. Convert the following base 10 numerals to base 2.
    a) 72
    b) 601
    c) 659
    d) 1111

4. Add in base 2.
    a) 111
       +11

    b) 111
         11
       +1011

    c) 10101
       +11111

    d)   101
         101
        1011
       +10111

5. Check your answers in problem 4 by converting to base 10.

6. Add in base 2.

   a)   1.11
        +.01

   b)   1.01
        101.1
       +11.11

   c)   .0011
       +1.01

   d) 100.001
          1.1
        +1.01

7. Multiply in base 2.

   a)   11
       ×11

   b) 101
       ×11

   c) 1011
       ×111

   d) 1111
       ×111

8. Refer to parts (c) and (d) of problem 2. Should the symbol "." be called a decimal point?

9. Prepare an algorithm for converting the following base 10 numerals to base 2.
   a) Base 10 numeral .52
   b) Base 10 numeral $\frac{1}{10}$

10. State any advantages that you think might result if a base higher than 2 could be used directly for computer computations.

Other Numeration Systems Used by Computers

The binary system is ideal for the internal operations of a computer, for its digits 0 and 1 can be represented by electrical impulses, lack of electrical impulses, or direction of flow of an impulse. As we have seen, however, even small base 10 numerals become cumbersome in base 2. Consequently, many computers, while performing operations in base 2, are designed to accept and put out numerals in other bases. In particular, bases 8 and 16 are used for this purpose. We shall discuss each of these systems briefly.

The base 8 or octal numeration system has as its digits the symbols 0, 1, 2, ..., 7. The base 8 numeral 242 written in exponential form is as follows:

$$242 \text{ base } 8 = 2 \times 8^2 + 4 \times 8^1 + 2 \times 8^0$$
$$= 128 + 32 + 2$$
$$= 162 \text{ base } 10.$$

If we wished to convert 162 in base 10 to base 8, we proceed as follows:

1. Find the highest power of 8 that is less than or equal to the base 10 symbol. In this case it is $8^2 = 64$.

2. Determine the number of times 8^2 divides 162. It is 2; hence we need $\underline{2} \times 8^2 = 128$.

3. Determine the number of times 8^1 divides the remainder of 34. It is 4; hence we need $\underline{2} \times 8^2 + \underline{4} \times 8^1 = 160$.

4. Determine the number of times 8^0 is required. It is 2; hence the base 8 symbol for 162, base 10, is $\underline{2} \times 8^2 + \underline{4} \times 8^1 + \underline{2} \times 8^0$.

An octal number in a computer is "coded" in binary digits. The following examples illustrate the process.

Example 1. Write 735 base 8 in binary code.

Solution. Each digit 735 is written in a 3 bit code:

$$7 = 111$$
$$3 = 011$$
$$5 = 101$$

Hence 735 base 8 = 111, 011, 101 base 2.

Example 2. Write 2672 base 8 in binary code.

Solution.

$$2 = 010$$
$$6 = 110$$
$$7 = 111$$
$$2 = 010$$

Hence 2672 base 8 = 010, 110, 111, 010 base 2.

Example 3. Convert 111, 111, 011, 000 base 2 to base 8.

Solution.

$$111 = 7$$
$$111 = 7$$
$$011 = 3$$
$$000 = 0$$

Hence 111, 111, 011, 000 base 2 = 7730 base 8.

When a base that is a power of two is used in a computer, the bits are grouped according to the base. If base 8 is used, the bits are grouped in units of 3. Each unit (or usually a multiple thereof) is called a byte. For example, computers using base 8 may symbolize a letter with a byte of six bits. However, digits would still be symbolized with three bits. See Table 9.2.

Table 9.2 Binary Code for Base 8

Letter or Digit	Binary Code
1	001
2	010
3	011
4	100
5	101
6	110
7	111
A	010,001
B	101,010
C	010,011
D	010,100
E	010,101
F	010,110

Some large modern computers use binary-coded bytes for base 16. This means that four bits must represent each "digit." A new requirement arises when we use a base larger than 10. We require new "digits." Any single symbol may be used for a new digit. We shall use six letters of the alphabet. A partial base 16 table is shown in Table 9.3.

Table 9.3 Binary Code for Base 16

Base 16	Binary Code	Base 10
1	0001	1
2	0010	2
3	0011	3
4	0100	4
5	0101	5
6	0110	6
7	0111	7
8	1000	8
9	1001	9
A	1010	10
B	1011	11
C	1100	12
D	1101	13
E	1110	14
F	1111	15
10	10000	16

Base 16 binary-coded symbols are readily converted to base 2 by use of this table.

Base 16	Base 2	Base 10
AA	1010, 1010	170
89F	1000, 1001, 1111	2207

EXERCISE 9.2

1. Write the following base 8 symbols in exponential form.
    a) 717   b) 603
    c) 521   d) 603.05
2. Convert the following base 8 symbols to base 10
    a) 72   b) 635
    c) .05   d) 603.05
3. Convert the following base 10 symbols to base 8.
    a) 565   b) 230
    c) 5631
4. Convert the following base 8 symbols to binary code.
    a) 5   b) 201
    c) 2.004   d) 301.1

5. Convert the following binary code symbols to base 8.
   a) 101   b) 1101
   c) 11.11   d) .001
6. Convert the following base 16 symbols to binary code.
   a) AAA   b) 8FA
   c) 9AB   d) F00F
7. Is a new algorithm needed for converting .007 base 16 to base 10?
8. Which is larger?
   a) .001 base 2 or .005 base 10   b) .9 base 16 or .111 base 2
   c) .808 base 10 or .AA base 16

REFERENCES

Anderson, Decima M. *Computer Programming Fortran IV.* New York: Appleton-Century-Crofts, 1966.

Dorn, William S. and Herbert J. Greenberg. *Mathematics and Computing with Fortran Programming.* New York: Wiley, 1967.

McCammon, Mary. *Understanding Fortran.* New York: Crowell, 1968.

Pennington, Ralph H. *Introductory Computer Methods and Numerical Analysis.* New York: Macmillan, 1965.

Appendix A
Computer Programming in BASIC

A.1 INTRODUCTION

The purpose of any computer language is to enable "communication" between human and computer. We communicate with the computer by means of a series of statements written in a language that the computer is able to "understand." The series of statements designed to instruct the computer to perform a specific task is known as a "program." Modern digital computers are usually designed to receive programs in several languages. Therefore it is often not necessary to learn a new language each time a different computer is used. In this course we shall study a language called "BASIC." This is one of the easiest languages to learn and it is acceptable to many computers. In this chapter words in BASIC are capitalized.

A.2 ARITHMETIC STATEMENTS

The BASIC word that informs the computer that an arithmetic operation is to be performed is LET. Consider the following computer instruction.

```
LET X = A + 1
```

This statement tells the computer to add two numbers A and 1, where A has a numerical value. The addition symbol in this statement has the same meaning as an addition symbol in ordinary arithmetic. However, the symbol for equality has a new meaning. This symbol instructs the computer to replace any current value of X which may be in the computer "memory" with the value of X found by adding two numbers. The last value calculated for X erases the previous value and places the last value in the computor memory location called "X".

Arithmetic operations in a LET statement are symbolized as follows:

- $+$ addition
- $-$ subtraction
- $*$ multiplication
- $/$ division
- $\uparrow$ exponentiation

X and A in the statement LET $X = A + 1$ designate variable quantities and are called "variables." Variables may be represented with a single letter or with a single letter followed by a single digit 0 thru 9. For example, $X1$ and $A1$ could be used in place of X and A. Ordinary numerals such as "1" in the above statement are constants.

The rules for evaluating the LET statement are almost the same as those for regular arithmetic. Quantities in parenthesis are evaluated first, followed by exponentiation, multiplication and division and finally by addition and subtraction. Consider the LET statement given below:

$$\text{LET } A = P * (1 + R) \uparrow N$$

The computer calculates A in the following order:

1. Adds $1 + R$
2. Raises the sum of 1 and R to the Nth power.
3. Finds the product of P and $(1 + R)$ raised to the Nth power.

Additional examples of LET statements follow.

Basic Statement	Algebraic Statement
1. LET P = A/T * 100	$P = \frac{A}{T} 100$
2. LET Y = .5 * (X + Z/X)	$y = .5 \left(x + \frac{z}{x} \right)$
3. LET U = V + P * A	$U = v + pa$
4. LET D = A1 * B2 - B1 * A2	$D = a_1 b_2 - b_1 a_2$
5. LET Y = X ↑ 2 + 3 * X + 4	$y = x^2 + 3x + 4$

A.3 READ AND DATA STATEMENTS

In order for the computer to perform the operations specified in a LET statement, variables to the right of the equal sign must be given numerical values before the evaluation. This is called "defining" the variable. The symbols used to denote the variables which must be given numerical values can be supplied to the computer in a READ statement. The numerical values of the variables may be furnished in a DATA statement. It is not important whether the DATA statements procedes or follows the READ statement.

When the computer encounters a READ statement, memory cells in the computer are earmarked for each variable. Multiple variables in the READ statement are separated by commas. Numerical values to be placed in the memory cells are obtained from the DATA statements. Numbers in the DATA statement must be written in decimal form (common fractions are not allowed). If a decimal point is not included the computer assumes the number is an integer. Numbers may be positive or negative and may contain as many as nine digits. Commas may *not* be used in numerals. If there are three variables in the READ statement, a minimum of three constants must be given in the DATA statement. The first constant is placed by the computer in the cell labeled for the first variable in the READ statement, the second constant is placed in the cell labeled for the second variable and the third constant in the cell for the third variable. If additional constants appear in the DATA statement, they are placed in the variable memory cells in sequence as listed in the READ statement. If all constants in the DATA statement are used, the number of such constants must be integral multiple of the number of variables. For three variables, there may be 3 constants, 6 constants, 9 constants and so forth. As we shall soon see, the computer may be instructed to seek automatically the constants in the DATA statement to use in the LET statement until all entries in the DATA statement have been used.

A.4 PRINT STATEMENT

Each of the BASIC language statements discussed thus far either supplies information to the computer or informs the computer of the arithmetic operations to be performed. The primary purpose of the PRINT statement is to obtain the results of the arithmetic operations. The computer is instructed to PRINT whatever variables have been computed. For the statement LET $A = P*(1 + R)\uparrow N$, the PRINT instruction to obtain the numerical value of A may be as follows:

```
PRINT A
```

When sufficient instructions have been given to the computer so that the desired calculations can be made, the computer is informed by the BASIC statement:

```
END
```

A.5 THE COMPUTER PROGRAM

With the five BASIC words, READ, DATA, LET, PRINT and END, we are ready to write a simple program for a computer. Each statement in the program is given a line number to inform the computer of the order in which instructions are to be compiled. Let us instruct the computer to compute how much $1,000 is worth if invested at 8% interest compounded annually for 10 years. If a principal P is invested at the rate of interest R for N investment periods, the worth A of the investment at the end of the N periods is given by the formula $A = PX(1 + R)^N$.

Program 1
```
10  READ P, R, N
20  DATA 1000, .08, 10
30  LET A = P * (1 + R) ↑ N
40  PRINT A
50  END
```

When instructed to do so, the computer will run this program and print the result,

```
2158.92
```

If we wish to instruct the computer to find another value of A we must furnish another set of DATA and instruct the computer to again run the program. This may be accomplished with a GO TO statement.

A.6 LOOPING

GO TO ＿＿＿. This instruction tells the computer to transfer to a specified line in the program. The computer then performs its operations in sequence as before. Let us return to the program to compute A. In addition to the computation already indicated, we wish to know how much $5,000 is worth when invested at 5.5% compounded annually for 20 years. The program to accomplish this is shown in Program 2.

Program 2

```
10  READ P, R, N
20  DATA 1000, .08, 10, 5000, .055, 20
30  LET A = P * (1 + R) ↑ N
40  PRINT A
50  GO TO 10
60  END
```

The computer performs the first calculation, prints the result, returns to line 10, finds the new data, computes and prints the new value of A. This process will continue as long as unused DATA remains in the program. The program may contain as many DATA lines as required. The procedure resulting from the GO TO statement is known as "looping."

A.7 ADDITIONAL PRINTING INSTRUCTIONS

Sometimes it is desirable to PRINT more than the numerical values found by the computer. For Program 2, let us assume that we wish to print the variables P, R and N as well as the computed values of A. The computer can be instructed to do this by modifying line 40 in Program 2 as follows.

```
40  PRINT P, R, N, A
```

The following would be printed on two lines, one line for each set of variables.

```
1000        .08         10          2158.92
5000        .055        20          14588.8
```

The commas in the PRINT statement determine the spacing between the entries in the printed line. Each comma reserves a "print zone" which consists of 15 columns. With this spacing a maximum of 5 variables and/or constants may be printed on each line which contains 75 columns. If more than 5 variables and constants are to be printed, the sixth, etc., would be printed on a new line. As we shall see later in the chapter more than 5 print zones can be established by modifying the instructions to the computer.

If only variables and constants could be printed, sometimes it would be difficult to interpret the printout, particularly for a long program with several printouts. This difficulty may be remedied by instructing the computer to print column headings or "labels." Again referring to Program 2, it would be helpful for the printed columns to be labeled as follows.

```
PRINCIPAL   INTEREST    YEARS       AMOUNT
1000        .08         10          2158.92
5000        .055        20          14588.8
```

The computer may be instructed to print the column headings or "labels" by placing a PRINT statement in the program as shown in line 5, Program 3.

Program 3

```
 5  PRINT "PRINCIPAL", "INTEREST", "YEARS", "AMOUNT"
10  READ P, R, N
20  DATA 1000, .08, 10, 5000, .055, 20
30  LET A = P * (1 + R) ↑ N
40  PRINT P, R, N, A
50  GO TO 10
60  END
```

The computer will now print the following

PRINCIPAL	INTEREST	YEARS	AMOUNT
1000	.08	10	2158.92
5000	.055	20	14588.8

Notice that the labels in line 5, Program 3, are enclosed in quotation marks. A minimum of 15 columns is reserved for each label as is the case for variables and constants. If a label requires more than 15 but 30 or less columns, a total of 30 columns is reserved, etc.

The positioning of the PRINT statement for the labels is significant. For example, if the labels are to be printed on only one line for Program 3, the instructions in line 5 must not be included in the "loop"; otherwise, the labels would be printed for each computation of A. It is a good idea to place label printing instructions at the beginning of the program when labels are to be printed only one time.

The PRINT statement has some other important properties. If the word PRINT alone is shown on a line in the program the computer skips a line in the printout. If two successive lines are to be skipped the instruction PRINT would appear on two successive lines in the program. Let us rewrite Program 3 to make our printout easier to read. The revision is shown in Program 4.

Program 4

```
 5  PRINT "PRINCIPAL", "INTEREST", "YEARS", "AMOUNT"
 6  PRINT
 7  PRINT
10  READ P, R, N
20  DATA 1000, .08, 10, 5000, .055, 20
30  LET A = P * (1 + R) ↑ N
40  PRINT P, R, N, A
50  GO TO 10
60  END
```

The printout now appears as follows.

PRINCIPAL	INTEREST	YEARS	AMOUNT
1000	.08	10	2158.92
5000	.055	20	14,588.8

Exercise A.1

1. Which of the following programs are correct? If a program is not correct, revise it so that it will run.

    a) 1 READ A, B
        2 DATA 3, 5, 7, 9, 11, 13
        3 LET X = A + B
        4 PRINT X, "IS THE SUM OF", A, AND, B
        5 GO TO 1
        6 END
    b) 10 DATA X,Y
        20 READ 2, 4, 6,.8
        30 LET Z = X2 + Y2
        40 PRINT
        50 END
    c) 5 DATA 1, 2, 3, 4, 5, 6, 7, 8, 9, 10
        6 READ X
        7 LET X = X ↑ 3
        8 PRINT "THE CUBE", OF X, "IS", Y
        9 GO TO 5
        10 END

2. What is the printout for 1a) as written or as you corrected it? For 1b) and 1c)?

3. Find the error in the following LET statements.

    a) LET A = B(C + D)
    b) LET B2 = X1 + X2 + X3
    c) LET X + Y = 2 * Z - Y
    d) LET 5Z - 2 * (5 + .03 * X)
    e) LET W7 = X2 * 7X

4. Which of the following constants are permitted in a BASIC program?

    a) 22.925   d) -3027.5   g) $\sqrt{15}$
    b) 7,421   e) 0.02   h) 164324683222
    c) 007   f) 5/7

5. Write a BASIC program to compute and print how much each person owes based on the following tabulation.

PURCHASER	UNITS PURCHASED	UNIT COST	OWED
John	3,000	.035	
Mary	5,150	.022	
Jim	10,310	.018	

A.8 SPACING THE PRINTOUT

Sometimes column labels are not needed for all columns. The computer can be instructed to skip column labels in the following manner:

                    PRINT "   "

For each pair of quotation marks, the computer omits a label for 15 spaces. Consider the following instruction:

```
PRINT "        ", "RATE", "        ", "AMOUNT"
```

In this instance, the computer omits a label for the first print zone (15 spaces), prints RATE in the second zone of 15 spaces, omits a label in the next 15 spaces, and prints the label AMOUNT in the fourth print zone.

After a PRINT statement has been executed, the next PRINT statement spaces to a new line if the program instructions are in the form already specified. However, it is possible to use one line for several PRINT statements until all print zones are used. The computer can be so instructed by the use of commas at the ends of the PRINT statements. For example,

```
PRINT P,
PRINT R,N,
PRINT A
```

The printout would now appear on one line, unless more than 5 print zones (75 spaces) were needed. In that case printing would continue on the next line after using up the 75 spaces.

Exercise A.2

1. What is the printout for the following program?

```
10  PRINT "QUANTITY", "UNIT COST", "TOTAL COST"
20  READ Q, U
30  DATA 10000, .01, 12000, .012, 16000, .025
40  LET C1 = Q * U
50  PRINT Q, U, C1
60  GO TO 20
70  END
```

2. What is the printout of the following program?

```
10  READ Q1, U1, Q2, U2, Q3, U3
20  DATA 10000, .01, 12000, .012, 16000, .025
30  LET C1 = Q1 * U1
40  LET C2 = Q2 * U2
50  LET C3 = Q3 * U3
60  PRINT "THE COST OF C1 IS", C1
70  PRINT "THE COST OF C2 IS", C2
80  PRINT "THE COST OF C3 IS", C3
90  PRINT "THE TOTAL IS", C1+C2+C3
```

3. A company employs five people. The owner decides to perform his payroll calculations by computer. Assume a tax deduction rate of 10% and a Social Security deduction of 5%. Write the program (net salary = gross salary − deductions) and show the complete printout in the following format:

Emp	Gross	Tax	SS	NET
1	500			
2	1000			
3	700			
4	900			
5	400			

Appendix A Computer Programming in BASIC   249

4. Write the program and show the printout for finding the value of $Y = X^2 + 2X^{\frac{1}{2}} + 3$ when X has the following values; 4, 9, 16, 25, 36.
5. You work for the SIPJAC Supermarket; the manager instructs you to work up a model computer program for finding the present value of the store stock. He suggests the following format.

```
ITEM   QUANTITY   UNIT COST   TOTAL COST
A
B
 .
 .
 .
```

Write a program to produce the desired format.

A.9 COMPUTER DECISIONS BY COMPARING NUMBERS

We have seen that useful programs are possible utilizing only 6 types of BASIC statement.

```
DATA
READ
LET
GO TO
PRINT
END
```

By adding two types of statements the usefulness of the computer can be greatly increased. The first that we shall discuss is called an IF ... THEN statement. IF _ _ _ THEN _____. The basic purpose of this statement is to instruct the computer to proceed to a specified line in the program IF certain conditions are met. Consider the statement

```
IF X = 6 THEN 10
```

If the computed value of X is equal to 6 then the computer switches to line 10. If $X \neq 6$, then the computer proceeds to the next line in sequence. In addition to equality, the computer is able to make 5 other comparisons.

COMPARISON	SYMBOL in BASIC
1. Not equal to	< >
2. greater than	>
3. greater than or equal to	> =
4. less than	<
5. less than or equal to	< =

Illustrations of the first three follow.

```
IF X < > 2 * Y THEN 20
```

If the variable X is not equal to $2Y$ then the computer transfers to line 20. Otherwise, the next line is executed.

```
IF A 2 > 2 ↑ X THEN 80
```

If the variable $A2$ is greater than 2^x, then the computer goes to line 80; otherwise, to the next line.

```
IF X ↑ 2 + 3 * X + 2 > = 0 THEN 60
```

If $X^2 + 3X + 2 \geqslant 0$ then the computer switches to line 60; otherwise, the next line is executed.

The two expressions that are to be compared can be simple as illustrated above, or complicated as in the following example.

```
IF (X > 2) / (X | 2 + 1) > 1/2 * (X + 2) / (X + 5) THEN 180
```

No matter how complicated the compared expressions may be, the computer calculates each expression and compares the two numbers.

Program 5 illustrates the use of an IF ... THEN statement.

Program 5

```
10  LET N = 0
20  READ A
30  DATA 9, 7, 5, 1, 6, 11, 12, 24, 3, 2
40  LET N = N + 1
50  PRINT A
60  IF N < 10 THEN 20
70  END
```

Program 5 instructs the computer to PRINT the numbers 9, 7, 5, etc., in one column. The IF ... THEN statement causes the computer to "loop" until $N = 10$. Program 5 illustrates another use of a LET statement. In line 10 we assign an initial value to N, a process called "initializing the variable." The number "0" is stored in the memory cell reserved for "N" until another value of N is computed in step 40. The new N then replaces the value "0."

A.10 ANOTHER METHOD OF LOOPING

The eighth BASIC statement that we shall consider is known as a FOR ... NEXT statement. The use of this instruction leads to a "loop" as do the IF ... THEN and GO TO statement.

FOR ... NEXT. This statement is best explained by examining first the BASIC word FOR. Consider the statement.

```
20  FOR N = 1 to 50
```

Line 20 instructs the computer to assign an initial value of 1 to the variable N for the first computation. In subsequent computations N will be assigned each integer from 2 thru 50. Consider Program 6 in which line 20 above appears.

Program 6

```
10  PRINT "N", "N SQUARE"
20  FOR N = 1 TO 50
30  LET X = N ↑ 2
40  PRINT
50  PRINT N, X
60  NEXT N
70  END
```

The output of this program is as follows.

```
         N              N SQUARE
         1              1
         2              4
         3              9
         .
         .
         .
        50              2500
```

Line 60 in Program 6 accomplishes the loop in this program. The first computation is made for $N = 1$, the number 1 is printed under the label "N" and the number 1^2 is printed under the label "N SQUARED." Line 60 then instructs the computer to return to line 20 for the NEXT value of N which, of course, is 2. Steps 30, 40 and 50 are then performed for $N = 2$. This procedure is repeated through $N = 5$.

In Program 6, N was increased by 1 in each step. This change in the variable in a FOR statement is called the "increment." The increment of 1 in program 6 can be changed by modifying the FOR statement in the following manner.

```
20 FOR N = 1 to 50 STEP .5
```

1 now changes by .5 in each step. The first N would be 1, the second 1.5, etc. Consider another example for a FOR statement with an increment other than 1.

```
FOR I = 0 TO 1 STEP .001
```

The first I is 0, the second .001, the third .002, etc.

Another procedure known as "nesting" can be accomplished with the FOR and NEXT statements. Nesting is the process of placing one loop inside another loop. Consider the following nest.

```
FOR I = 1 TO 10
FOR J = 1 TO 5
    .
    .
    .
NEXT J
NEXT I
```

For $I = 1$, the inside or J loop repeats 5 times; for $I = 2$, the inside loop repeats 5 times. In other words, the J loop is performed a total of 50 times. This procedure is illustrated in Program 7.

Program 7

```
10   FOR I = 1 TO 5
20   FOR J = 1 - 3
30   IF I = J THEN 60
40   PRINT "0"
50   GO TO 70
60   PRINT "1"
70   NEXT J
80   PRINT
90   NEXT I
100  END
```

The printout is as follows:

```
    1       0       0
    0       1       0
    0       0       1
    0       0       0
    0       0       0
```

A.11 SUBSCRIPTED VARIABLES

From our discussion of variables, you recall that $A0$, $A1$, $A2$, $A3$, and up to $A9$ are permissible variables. There is another method of defining a variable which removes the restriction that a specific letter can be used for only ten variables. This method is called "subscripting." If we wish to use A for more than 10 variables, say 50, we may denote the first variable by $A(1)$—note the parenthesis about 1—and continue to $A(60)$. If more than 10 subscripts are to be used on the variable A the computer must be informed of the number of times A will be subscripted by a dimension statement written as "DIM" in the BASIC language.

DIM. This statement is normally placed in the program preceding the variable, or variables, to which it applies. Usually it is the beginning statement in the program. One DIM statement may be used to specify the dimensions of several variables. For example

```
10   DIM A (50), B (50), C (50)
```

This statement tells the computer to reserve 50 storage locations for A, 50 for B, and 50 for C. When a DIM statement is not used, 10 storage locations are automatically reserved for each of the subscripted variables. Consider Program 8 which includes a DIM statement.

Program 8

```
10   DIM A (20)
20   LET S = 0
30   FOR I = 1 TO 20
40   READ A (I)
50   LET S = S + A(I)
60   NEXT I
70   PRINT "SUM=", S
80   DATA 5, 10, 15, 20, 25, 30, 35
90   DATA 40, 45, 50, 55, 60, 65, 70, 75
100  DATA 80, 85, 90, 95, 100
110  END
```

Program 8 will cause the twenty numbers in DATA to be added with the sum shown in the following printout.

```
                SUM = 1050
```

Variables may also be defined with two subscripts. The general form is $A(I, J)$ where I and J are nonnegative integers. In this case a DIM statement with the dimension of both *I* and *J* must be included in the program if either *I* or *J* is ever larger than 10.

A.12 ADDITIONAL BASIC WORDS

Three additional BASIC statements can often be used to advantage. They are the INPUT, STOP and REMARK statements.

    INPUT. This statement can be used instead of READ and DATA statements. Program 9 could replace Program 1.

Program 9

```
10  INPUT P, R, N
20  LET A = P * (1 + R) ↑ N
30  PRINT A
40  END
```

When the computer is instructed to run this program, a question mark will be printed. The programmer then furnishes the data:

1000, .08, 10

When *A* is printed, the computer again prints a question mark, and additional data may be supplied. If there is no more data to be supplied, the programmer can inform the computer by the statement STOP.

    STOP. This statement can be used at any point in the program. Execution of the program ceases when the computer encounters this statement.

The BASIC language word REM is an abbreviation of "remark." A REM statement can be inserted at any point in a program before the END statement. The REM statement is never executed, but is used for program documentation. Programmers can use this statement to explain steps in the program. Several examples of REM statements follow.

```
10  REM PROGRAM FOR FINDING COMPOUND INTEREST
50  REM BE SURE TO PUT INTEREST IN DECIMAL FORM
15  REM IS THE FIRST OF FIVE PRACTICE PROGRAMS
```

Exercise A.3

1. What is the printout for the following program?

```
 5  INPUT X
10  PRINT "TABLE OR POWERS OF", X
15  PRINT
16  PRINT "EXPONENT", "2 ↑ E"
20  FOR E = 0 TO 10
25  LET A = X ↑ E
30  PRINT E, A
35  NEXT E
40  END
RUN
```

2. What is the printout for the following program?

```
 5  PRINT "AMOUNT", "PERCENTAGE"
10  DIM A(10)
12  LET T = 0
15  FOR I = 1 TO 10
20  READ A(1)
25  DATA 6, 8, 10, 12, 14, 16, 18, 20, 22, 24
30  LET T = T + A(1)
40  NEXT I
45  FOR I = 1 TO 10
50  LET P = A(1)/T * 100
55  PRINT A(1), P
60  NEXT I
60  END
```

3. Write a program to find a print sum of the first 100 integers.
4. Write a program to compute the squares of the integers from 1 through 100, printing each integer and its square.
5. Write a program to compute the square roots of the integers from 1 through 10, printing each integer and its square root.
6. Write a program to compute the square roots of numbers between 2 and 3 in intervals of .01, printing each number and its square root.

A.13 CORRECTING PROGRAM ERRORS

Computer programs often contain errors. The process of correcting errors in a program is known as *editing* or *debugging*. Program errors are of three types: typing errors, BASIC language (including punctuation) errors, and logical errors.

Typing errors and language errors are detected by the computer when it is instructed to RUN a program. The computer prints a brief description of each error and gives the line number in which the error appears. For instance, a line in a program might be

$$10 \text{ LAT} = A + B$$

This is not a BASIC language statement. The computer will so inform the programmer by printing

$$\text{ILLEGAL INSTRUCTION IN 10.}$$

The programmer may then correct line 10 by rewriting the entire line, again using 10 for the line number. The computer always uses the last statement when a line number is repeated. For the illegal line 10 the program should probably be:

$$10 \text{ LET } X = A + B$$

A partial listing of BASIC error messages is given in Table A.1.

Table A.1

1. ILLEGAL FORMULA IN _____   Missing ( ), illegal operation or illegal variable

2. ILLEGAL INSTRUCTION IN _____   Misspelled words, or words not in BASIC
3. NO DATA   The programmer forgot to include a DATA following a READ statement
4. ILLEGAL VARIABLE IN _____   Form of the variable is wrong.
5. NEXT WITHOUT FOR or FOR WITHOUT NEXT   A FOR or NEXT statement is missing
6. INCORRECT FORMAT IN _____   Incorrect punctuation or spelling
7. NO END INSTRUCTION   Program has no END statement

After studying the error messages and making corrections in the indicated lines, the computer is again instructed to RUN the program.

The computer is able to find only the errors in typing or language—not logic. If the programmer has instructed the computer to "multiply" when he meant to "divide," no error message will be received. The program may RUN giving an incorrect answer. It is always desirable to check a program with data which will yield a known answer. It is possible to write additional steps into a program to enable the programmer to find errors in logic. A discussion of such procedures is left for a more sophisticated treatment.

A.14 PROGRAM INPUT TO THE COMPUTER

A completed program may be given to the computer in several ways depending upon the computer facilities available. A teletypewriter resembling an ordinary typewriter may be used. When this type of input devise is available the program may be fed directly to the computer as it is typed. Programs are often input to the computer by the familiar punched card. The cards may be punched by hand with a key punch machine or machine punches from cards marked with an electrographic pencil. In lieu of punched cards punched tapes may be used. Other methods for entering the program include magnetic tape, printed magnetic characters (such as those on a bank check), magnetic discs and visual display consoles. Because of the great computational speed of most computers, researchers are continually seeking faster methods of furnishing programs to computers.

Appendix B
Student Research Topics

The topics listed here have been found suitable for student research projects. These projects may take the form of oral or written reports. The authors have employed both types of reports in teaching the material covered in this text.

APPLICATIONS OF MATHEMATICS

1. Mathematics in Art
2. Mathematics of Chance
3. Mathematics of the Calendar
4. Mathematics in Finance
5. Mathematics in Business
6. Mathematics in Navigation
7. Mathematics in Stock Brokerage
8. Mathematics in Medicine
9. Mathematics in Music
10. Mathematical Proportions
11. Mathematics in Electricity
12. Mathematics in Physics
13. Mathematics in (students' choice)

HISTORY OF MATHEMATICS

14. Babylonian Mathematics
15. Egyptian Mathematics
16. Mayan Mathematics
17. René Descartes and Analytic Geometry
18. The Geometry of Bolyai and Lobachevsky
19. Lewis Carroll and Mathematical Logic
20. Simon Stevin and the Invention of Decimals
21. J. Willard Gibbs and the Invention of Vectors
22. Sir Isaac Newton
23. Gottfried Leibnitz and His Computer
24. Evariste Galois and the Theory of Groups
25. Charles Babbage and the Computer
26. Arthur Cayley, James Joseph Sylvester and Matrices
27. G. F. B. Riemann and His Elliptical Geometry
28. The Newton–Leibnitz Dispute

29. History of Mathematical Symbols
30. Three Famous Math Problems of Antiquity
31. History of π

JUST FOR FUN

32. Magic Squares
33. Prove $2 = 4$
34. Misuse of Logic in Advertising
35. Numerology
36. Achilles and the Tortoise (Zeno's Paradoxes)

TEACHING MATHEMATICS

37. Mathematics of the Elementary School
38. Mathematics of the Secondary School

MISCELLANEOUS

39. Abacus: Operation and/or History
40. Mathematics in Nature
41. Mathematics for Citizenship
42. Map Coloring
43. Networks and the Traveling Salesman
44. The Bridges of Königsberg
45. Topology
46. Numeration Systems

Appendix C
Selected Answers

EXERCISE 1.1

1. a) simple proposition.
   c) not a simple proposition.
   e) not a simple proposition.
   g) simple proposition.
   i) not a simple proposition.
   k) not a simple proposition.
3. a) Four can be expressed as two times two or four can be expressed as four times one.
   c) Football players are sweet and colds are sweet.
   e) Geometry is the science of earth measurement and geometry is abstract.

EXERCISE 1.2

1. It is not raining.
3. John is not happy or John is not well fed.
5. Some Irishmen do not wear green ties or some Irishmen do not live in Ireland.
7. Some heavenly bodies are not planets and some heavenly bodies are not stars that shed no light.
9. Some men are not cowards and some men are not heroes.

EXERCISE 1.3

1. a) Hypothesis: You are a minor.
      Conclusion: You will not be admitted.
      If you are a minor then you will not be admitted.
   c) Hypothesis: It rains.
      Conclusion: It is always cloudy.
      If it rains then it is always cloudy.
   e) Hypothesis: I did not have to work.
      Conclusion: I could relax and enjoy playing golf.
      If I did not have to work then I could relax and enjoy playing golf.
   g) Hypothesis: If a thing goes up.
      Conclusion: A thing must come down.
      If a thing goes up then it must come down.

i) Hypothesis: Wishes were horses.
   Conclusion: Beggars would ride.
   If wishes were horses then beggars would ride.
2. a) Eight and four are twelve and four and eight are not twelve.
   c) It is an axiom and it is not assumed.
   e) $a(b + c) = d$ and $(b + c)a \neq d$.

EXERCISE 1.4

I. 1. John Brown lives in Texas.
   3. Horses can fly.
II. 1. Jack is not a politician.
   3. You do not watch TV seven hours a day.
III. 1. All rectangles are trapezoids.
   3. If it rains I will be sick.
IV. 1. $p \to q$
   3. $p \lor q$
   5. $p \to q$

EXERCISE 1.5

I. 1.

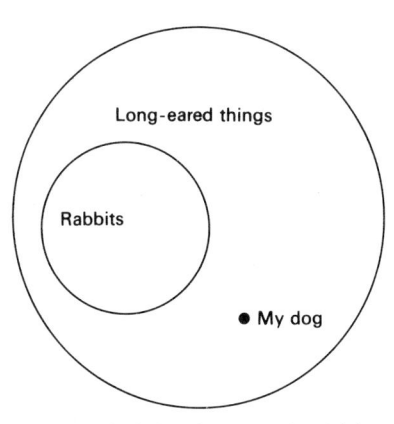

It is not necessary that "my dog" be included in the set of rabbits. The conclusion does not follow from the given statements.

3.

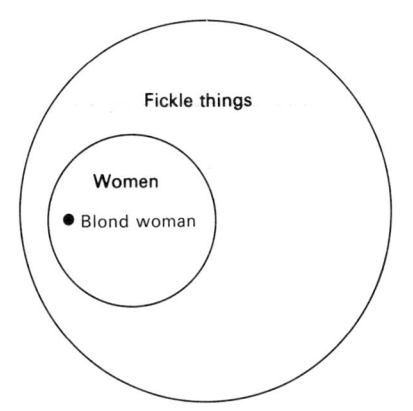

The conclusion is correct.

5.

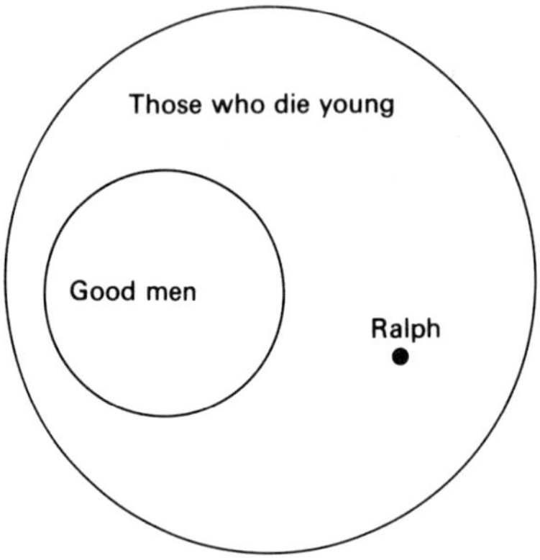
Those who die young
Good men
Ralph

The conclusion is not correct.

7.

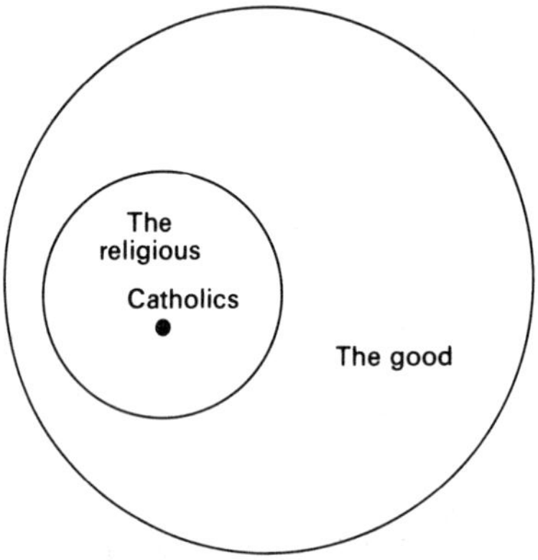
The religious
Catholics
The good

The conclusion is uncorrect. It should read "Therefore, all Catholics are good."

9.

The evil
Evil person not from Europe
Not evil
a German

The conclusion is not correct.

II. 11. Jack Blue is not a college student.
13. This is not a rose.
15. No conclusion.
17. All x's are w's.
    Some z is w.
19. Mathematics is the true.

EXERCISE 1.6

I. a) Converse: If a man is good he is honest.
      Inverse: If a man is not honest then he is not good.
      Contrapositive: If a man is not good then he is not honest.
   c) Converse: If it rains I will cut the grass.
      Inverse: I will not cut the grass if it does not rain.
      Contrapositive: If it does not rain then I will not cut the grass.
   e) Converse: If a student does not study then the course is too difficult or the instructor does not give exams.
      Inverse: If the course is not too difficult and the teacher gives exams then a student will study.
      Contrapositive: If a student studies then the course is not too difficult and the instructor gives exams.

II. a) If it is a rose then it is a flower.
       Converse: If it is a flower it is a rose.
       Inverse: If it is not a rose then it is not a flower.
       Contrapositive: If it is not a flower then it is not a rose.
    c) If it is a game of sport then it has a large following.
       Converse: If it has a large following then it is a game of sport.
       Inverse: If it is not a game of sport then it does not have a large following.
       Contrapositive: If it does not have a large following then it is not a game of sport.
    e) If it is a Blue Grass cigarette then it is more flavorful.
       Converse: If it is more flavorful then it is a Blue Grass cigarette.
       Inverse: If it is not a Blue Grass cigarette then it is not more flavorful.
       Contrapositive: If it is not more flavorful then it is not a Blue Grass cigarette.

EXERCISE 1.7

1. a) Converse: If hares are hairy then fish are fishy.
      It is possible that the given implication be true when p is F and q is true; hence, we cannot conclude that the converse is true.
      Inverse: If fish are not fishy then hares are not hairy.
      Since we cannot determine the truth value of the converse, we cannot determine the truth value of the inverse.
   c) Converse: If it is wet then it is wet. Both the inverse and converse are true.

EXERCISE 1.8

1. a)
p	q	$\sim q$	$p \wedge \sim q$
T	T	F	F
T	F	T	T
F	T	F	F
F	F	T	F

b) Continuing the table of 1a.

$p \vee (p \wedge \sim q)$	$p \vee (p \wedge \sim q) \Rightarrow q$
T	T
T	F
F	T
F	T

c) Continuing the tables of 1a and 1b,

$\sim p$	$p \wedge \sim p$	$q \vee \sim q$	$(p \wedge \sim p) \to (q \vee \sim q)$
F	F	T	T
F	F	T	T
T	F	T	T
T	F	T	T

d) Continuing the tables of 1a, 1b, 1c,

$p \wedge q$	$\sim p \vee q$	$(p \wedge q) \vee (\sim p \vee q)$
T	T	T
F	F	T
F	T	T
F	T	T

e) Continuing the tables of 1a, 1b, 1c, 1d,

$p \to q$	$q \Rightarrow p$	$(p \to q) \vee (q \to p)$	$(p \to q) \vee (q \to p) \to (p \to q)$
T	T	T	T
F	T	T	F
T	F	T	T
T	T	T	T

3. p: it purrs
   q: it is a cat

p	q	a) $p \Rightarrow q$	b) $p \wedge \sim q$
T	T	T	F
T	F	F	T
F	T	T	F
F	F	T	F

5. a) Mary does not go to college or Sue does not work in an office.
   b) Squirrels are furry and squirrels are not hairy.
   c) Jane is not a senior and John is not a junior.
   d) You study and think and a problem does not become a mountain and it does not become a molehill.

7. Propositions 6e is the negation of the given proposition. Propositions f and b are opposites.

EXERCISE 2.2

1. a) {1, 2, 3, ..., 10, 12, 14} b) {1, 2, 3, ..., 10, 12, 14}
   c) {1, 2, 3, ..., 10} d) {1, 2, 3, ..., 10, 12, 14}
   e) {1, 2, 3, ..., 10, 12, 14} f) {1, 2, 3, ..., 10}
   g) {11, 12, 13, 14} h) {1, 3, 5, 7, 9, 11, 13}
   i) {2, 4, 6, 8, 10, 11, 12, 13, 14} j) {13}
3. a) 10 b) 5
5. a) {(s, s), (s, f), (f, f)} b) {(s, f)}
   c) {(f, s), (f, f)} d) {(s, s), (f, s)}
7. a) Caucasian humans 21 years of age or older.
   b) All Caucasians and all human beings 21 years of age or older.
   c) All Caucasians and all Negroes.
   d) All Negroes and all human beings 21 years of age or older.
   e) All Negroes and all Caucasians.

EXERCISE 2.3

1. a) {(1, x), (1, y), (1, z), (2, x), (2, y), (2, z), (3, x), (3, y), (3, z)}
   b) {(x, 1), (x, 2), (x, 3), (y, 1), (y, 2), (y, 3), (z, 1), (z, 2), (z, 3)}
   c) {(1, 1), (1, 2), (1, 3), (2, 1), (2, 2), (2, 3), (3, 1), (3, 2), (3, 3)}
   d) {(x, x), (x, y), (x, z), (y, x), (y, y), (y, z), (z, x), (z, y), (z, z)}
3. a) {(a, 1), (a, 5), (a, 7), (a, 9), (b, 1), (b, 5), (b, 7), (b, 9), (c, 1), (c, 5), (c, 7), (c, 9), (d, 1), (d, 5), (d, 7), (d, 9)}
   b) {(a, a), (a, 2), (a, b), (a, 3), (b, a), (b, 2), (b, b), (b, 3), (c, a), (c, 2), (c, b), (c, 3), (d, a), (d, 2), (d, b), (d, 3)}
   c) {(1, a), (1, 2), (1, b), (1, 3), (5, a), (5, 2), (5, b), (5, 3), (7, a), (7, 2), (7, b), (7, 3), (9, a), (9, 2), (9, b), (9, 3)}
   d) {a, 1, a), (a, 1, 2), (a, 1, b), (a, 1, 3) ...}
5. The Cartesian product is not commutative; however, the number of elements in $A \times B \times C$ is unchanged by commuting.

EXERCISE 3.1

1. a) Commutative b) Associative
   c) Commutative d) Commutative
   e) Commutative

3. $\left.\begin{array}{c}2\\3\end{array}\right\}$ 5 Associative $\left.\begin{array}{c}4\\3\end{array}\right\}$ 7 Associative $\left.\begin{array}{c}\\ \\ \\ \end{array}\right\}$ Commutative

   $\dfrac{4\ \ 4}{9}$ $\dfrac{2\ \ 2}{9}$

5. a) Yes   b) Yes   c) No

7. Cardinal—the number of elements in a set.
   Ordinal—a number indicating the ordering of a set of elements—first, etc.
9. a) False—zero is not a counting number.
   b) False.
   c) The system includes postulates, theorems—the set consists of elements only—False.
   d) False—two operations are required.

EXERCISE 3.2

1. A mathematic proof is deductive based on the laws of logic. It may be direct using the Fundamental Rule, chain rule etc. or indirect using the contrapositive. Each proposition must be related to the hypothesis or the contrapositive of the conclusion by using axioms, definitions or previously proved propositions.
3. Commutative
   Commutative
   Transitive
5. Disprove by counter example. Let $a = 1, b = 3, c = 4$

$$2 + (3 + 4) \stackrel{?}{=} (2 + 3) + (2 + 4)$$
$$9 \stackrel{?}{=} 5 + 6$$
$$9 \neq 11$$

EXERCISE 3.3

1. a) Rewrite as $(-5) + (-8) = -(5 + 8) = -13$
      Def 3.4, Def 3.5, addition table.
   b) Rewrite as $(-9) + (+9) = 0$ identity.
   c) Rewrite as $((-2) + (+1)) + 3 = -1 + 3 = 2$
      Association, Def 3.6, addition, Def 3.3
   d) Rewrite as $((-4) + 1) + 3 = -3 + 3 = 0$
      Identity, association, Def 3.6, addition table, Def 3.3
   e) Rewrite as $((+10) + 2) + (-5) + (-3) =$
      $(12 + (-5)) + (-3) =$
      $7 + (-3) = 4$
      Association, Def 3.6, Def 3.3, addition table.
   f) Rewrite as: $((-a) + (-6a)) + ((-5b) - (-b)) =$
      $-7a + ((-5b) + b) = -7a - 4b$
      Def 3.4, association, Def 3.3
   g) Rewrite $(2x + (-3x)) + (4y + (-2y))$
      $-x + 2y$
      Same as f.
3. a) Binary   b) not binary
   c) Binary   d) Binary

5. a) 2   b) $-a$
   c) $-6x$ d) $-(2 + x)$
   e) $-(-3 - 2) = 5$ f) $2 - 2y$
7. a) $(-a)(b + (-b)) = 0$
   $-ab + (-a)(-b) = 0$
   The inverse of $-ab$ is ab
   $\therefore -ab + ab = 0 = -ab + (-a)(-b)$
   $\therefore ab = (-a)(-b)$
   b) $a(b + (-b)) = 0$
   $ab + a(-b) = 0$
   The inverse of $ab = -ab$
   $ab + -ab = ab + a(-b)$
   $\therefore -ab = a(-b)$
   c) $b > a \rightarrow b - a = c$ and $-(b - a) = -c$
   $a - b = -c$
   $\therefore a - b = -(b - a)$
   If $a < b = a - b = -(b - a)$.

EXERCISE 3.4

1. a) $3 \cdot 5 \cdot 5$ b) $5 \cdot 5$
   c) $3 \cdot 5 \cdot 7$ d) $3 \cdot 3 \cdot 13$
   e) $13 \cdot 17$ f) $3 \cdot 13 \cdot 31$
   g) $2^6 \cdot 3^3$ i) $3^3 \cdot 2^2 \cdot 7^4$
3. a) $6 = 2 \cdot 3$ b) $12 = 3 \cdot 2^2$
   $15 = 3 \cdot 5$ L.C.M. $= 2 \cdot 3^2 \cdot 5$ $33 = 3 \cdot 11$ L.C.M. $= 2^2 \cdot 3 \cdot 11$
   c) $28 = 2 \cdot 2 \cdot 7$ d) $14 = 2 \cdot 7$
   $56 = 2 \cdot 2 \cdot 2 \cdot 7$ L.C.M. $= 2^3 \cdot 7$ $21 = 3 \cdot 7$
   e) $38 = 2 \cdot 19$ $35 = 5 \cdot 7$
   $57 = 3 \cdot 19$ L.C.M. $= 2 \cdot 3 \cdot 5 \cdot 7$
   $95 = 5 \cdot 19$ L.C.M. $= 2 \cdot 3 \cdot 5 \cdot 19$
   f) $16 = 2^{4\prime}$
   $32 = 2^5$
   $96 = 3 \cdot 2^5$
   $128 = 2^7$ L.C.M. $= 2^7 \cdot 3$

EXERCISE 3.5

1. a) $\dfrac{2}{-5} + \dfrac{-2}{-3} = \dfrac{(-3)2 + (-2)(-5)}{(-5)(-3)} = \dfrac{-6 + 10}{15} = \dfrac{4}{15}$

   b) $\dfrac{1}{3} + \dfrac{-3}{1} = \dfrac{1 + (-3)(3)}{3 \cdot 1} = \dfrac{-8}{3}$

   c) $\dfrac{6}{7} + \dfrac{-1}{1} = \dfrac{6 - 7}{7 \cdot 1} = \dfrac{-1}{3}$

   d) $\dfrac{2a}{3} + \dfrac{3b}{2} = \dfrac{2 \cdot 2a + 3b \cdot 3}{3 \cdot 2}$

3. a) $\dfrac{63}{84} = \dfrac{9 \cdot 7}{4 \cdot 21} = \dfrac{3 \cdot 3 \cdot 7}{2 \cdot 2 \cdot 3 \cdot 7} = \dfrac{3}{4}$
   b) 4
   c) 15
   d) $\dfrac{.1}{7} = \dfrac{1}{70}$
   e) 5

5. a) $\dfrac{-10}{21}$ b. -1
   c) $\dfrac{1}{2}$ d) 2
   e) $8\dfrac{5}{21}$

7. a) $\dfrac{7}{3}$ b) $\dfrac{5}{2}$
   c) $\dfrac{3}{2}$ d) $\dfrac{-7}{8}$
   e) $-\dfrac{7}{15}$

9. a) 0   b) Indeterminate
   c) Undefined   d) 1
   e) Undefined

11. a) $.5 = \dfrac{1}{2}$ b) $1 = \dfrac{1}{1}$
    c) $\dfrac{31}{100}$ d) $\dfrac{1040}{1000}$
    e) $\dfrac{14303}{1000}$

13. Yes
15. No largest or smallest

EXERCISE 3.6

3.

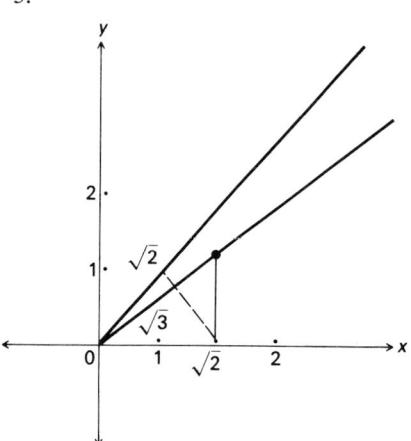

5. Conjecture
$S = n^2 + n$
$1 + 1 = 2$ verified for $n = 1$
$2 + 4 + 6 + 8 \ldots 2k = k^2 + k$
$2 + 4 + 6 \ldots 2k + 2(k + 1) = K^2 + k + 2(k + 1)$
$= k^2 + 3k + 2$
$= (k + 1)^2 + k + 1$
∴ the formula is true for the *n*th natural no.

7. a) $8 + 5\sqrt{2}$
b) $\dfrac{4.1414}{5} = .8283$
c) $1 - 5 + \sqrt{2} = -4 + \sqrt{2}$
d) $\frac{19}{12}$
e) $\frac{1}{48} = .208 \ldots$

EXERCISE 4.1

1.

+	1	2	3	4	5
1	2	3	4	5	1
2	3	4	5	1	2
3	4	5	1	2	3
4	5	1	2	3	4
5	1	2	3	4	5

3. a)

□	a	b	c
a	a	a	c
b	b	b	c
c	c	c	c

b) No. There is not a unique identity element.

5.

0	1	2	3	4	5	6	7
1	2	3	4	5	6	7	1
2	3	4	5	6	7	1	2
3	4	5	6	7	1	2	3
4	5	6	7	1	2	3	4
5	6	7	1	2	3	4	5
6	7	1	2	3	4	5	6
7	1	2	3	4	5	6	7

This operation satisfies the requirements for a group. It is commutative.

7. None

EXERCISE 4.2

1.

⊕	0	1	2	3	4	5	6
0	0	1	2	3	4	5	6
1	1	2	3	4	5	6	0
2	2	3	4	5	6	0	1
3	3	4	5	6	0	1	2
4	4	5	6	0	1	2	3
5	5	6	0	1	2	3	4
6	6	0	1	2	3	4	5

⊗	0	1	2	3	4	5	6
0	0	0	0	0	0	0	0
1	0	1	2	3	4	5	6
2	0	2	4	6	1	3	5
3	0	3	6	2	5	1	4
4	0	4	1	5	2	6	3
5	0	5	3	1	6	4	2
6	0	6	5	4	3	2	1

3.
Element	Inverse ⊕	Element	Inverse ⊗
0	0	0	None
1	6	1	1
2	5	2	4
3	4	3	5
4	3	4	2
5	2	5	3
6	1	6	6

5. a) 11 b) 5
   c) 10 d) 1, 4, 7 or 10
   e) 11

7. Thursday. Christmas is the 359th day.
   $\frac{185}{7} = 26$ rem 3 (Friday)
   $\frac{359}{7} = 51$ rem 2 (Thursday)

EXERCISE 4.3

1. a) $x = 5$ b) $x = \frac{1}{2}$
   c) $x = -2$ d) $x = .4$
3. a) $x = 1, y = -2$ b) $x = 2, y = -6$
   c) $x = 0, y = \frac{1}{2}, z = 1, 2 = 0$ $x = -4, 2 = -5$

5. $\begin{matrix} 1 & 2 & 1 \\ 2 & 0 & 2 \\ 0 & 3 & 4 \end{matrix}$

EXERCISE 4.4

1. a) $AB = \begin{pmatrix} 7 & 13 \\ 15 & 23 \end{pmatrix}$ $BA = \begin{pmatrix} 28 & 13 \\ 15 & 7 \end{pmatrix}$

   b) $AB = \begin{pmatrix} 2x + y & 6x + 5y \\ 2z + 2 & 6z + 5w \end{pmatrix}$ $BA = \begin{pmatrix} 2x + 6z & 2y + 6w \\ x + 5z & y + 5w \end{pmatrix}$

   c) $AB = BA = \begin{pmatrix} 5 & 6 \\ 1 & 2 \end{pmatrix}$

d) $AB = \begin{pmatrix} 13 & 13 \\ 8 & 8 \end{pmatrix}$ $BA = \begin{pmatrix} 11 & 10 \\ 11 & 10 \end{pmatrix}$

3. a) $\begin{matrix} -\frac{1}{5} & \frac{2}{5} \\ \frac{3}{10} & -\frac{1}{10} \end{matrix}$ b) $\begin{matrix} -2 & 1 \\ \frac{5}{3} & -\frac{2}{3} \end{matrix}$

   c) $\begin{matrix} -1 & -2 \\ -2 & -3 \end{matrix}$ d) $\begin{matrix} -\frac{1}{9} & \frac{1}{3} \\ \frac{2}{9} & -\frac{1}{6} \end{matrix}$

5. a) Yes b) Yes

EXERCISE 4.5

1. a) (5, 4) b) $5 + 4i$
   c) (0, −2) d) (8, 5)
   e) (9, 12)

3. $i = \sqrt{-1}$
   $i^2 = -1$
   $i^3 = -\sqrt{-1} = -i$
   $i^4 = 1$
   $i^5 = i$
   $i^6 = -1$
   $i^7 = -i$
   $i^8 = 1$
   $i^9 = i$
   $i^{10} = -1$
   $i^{11} = -i$
   $i^{12} = 1$

5. Yes. The rational numbers.
7. $-i$
9. (a, b, c). Yes. The system is called Quarternious developed by the English mathematician Hamilton in the 19th Century.

EXERCISE 4.6

1. a) (5, 12)....b) (1, 0)   c) (−4, 10)   d) (1, 0)

3.

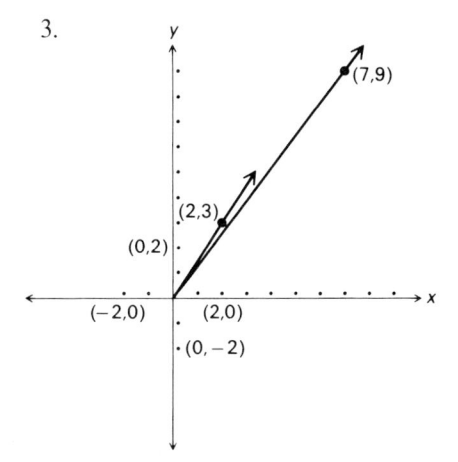

5. a) $\langle 6, 8 \rangle$ b) $\langle ac, ad \rangle$
   c) $\langle 12, 15 \rangle + \langle 9, 6 \rangle = \langle 21, 21 \rangle$ d) $(12 \langle 5, 6 \rangle) = \langle 60, 72 \rangle$
   e) $(3 \times 4) \langle 5, 6 \rangle = \langle 60, 72 \rangle$
7. a) No. The product is a scalar.   b) No. Not defined.
   c) Yes
9. a) $\langle -7, 9 \rangle$ b) $(-7, 9)$

EXERCISE 4.7

1. Speed is a scalar. Velocity is a vector. When the velocity vector is of the form $\langle a, 0 \rangle$ or $\langle 0, a \rangle$, speed $= \sqrt{a^2} = a$.
3. The resultant force vector is $\langle 3000, -400 \rangle$

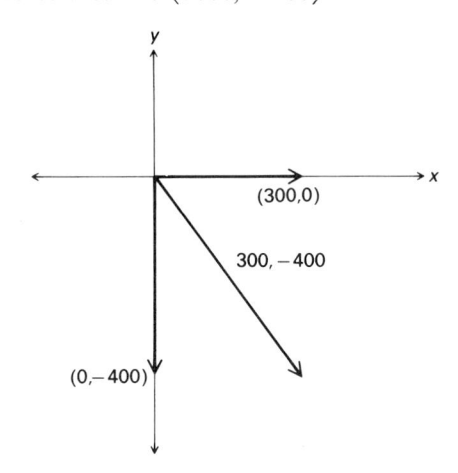

5. $400 = \sqrt{a^2 + a^2}$
   $400 = \sqrt{2}\, a$
   $a = \frac{400}{\sqrt{2}} = 200\sqrt{2}$ m.p.h. both east and north

EXERCISE 5.1

1. 5   3. $4\frac{2}{3}$
5. $-\frac{4}{45}$ 7. 160
9. 2.727   11. 78
13. 55; 300

EXERCISE 5.2

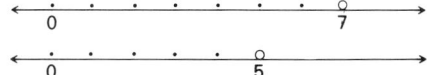

1. $\{7\}$
3. $\{5\}$
5. $\{7\}$ 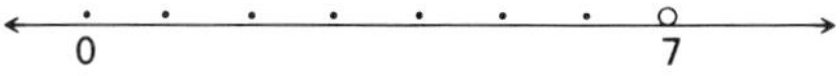
7. $\{1, 3\}$

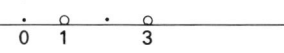

9. $\{2, 4, 6\}$
11. $\emptyset$
13. $\{3, 4, 5, 6\}$
15. $\{-3, -2, 3\}$
17. $(0, 0)F, (0, 2)F, (1, 0)F, (0, 2)F$
19. $(2)F, (1)T$
21. $(2, 2)$ undefined, $(2, 4)T, (4, 2)T,$ $(4, 4)$ undefined.
23. $(a)T, (b)T$
25. $(a)T, (b)T$

EXERCISE 5.3

1. 5
3. 2
5. 15
7. 4
9. 6
11. 1.5
13. 12
15. 2
17. -6
19. 2.5
21. 2
23. 1
25. $h = \dfrac{2A}{b}$
27. $\pi = \dfrac{C}{2r}$
29. Mary 7, John 14
31. 9, 12, 15
33. 72′ by 90′
35. 9
37. Stocks $4000; bonds $1000
39. 24, 30, 48

EXERCISE 5.4

1. $3x > 3y$
3. $x - 5 \leqslant y - 5$
5. $x > z - 2$
7. $2x = y$
9. F, let $x = -7$ and $y = 2$
11. T
13. $x > -2$
15. $x > 5$
17. $x < -6$
19. $x \leqslant 10$
21. $x \geqslant 3$ or $x \leqslant -2$
23. 93
25. 55 minutes
27. $10.00
29. 6 roses
31. 3 ozs.

EXERCISE 5.5

1. $|x| + 2$
3. -12
5. 4
7. -5

9. $6x$

11. $\{5, -5\}$

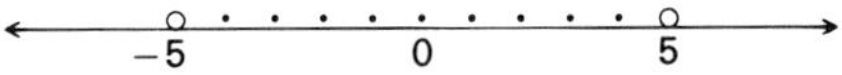

13. $\{3, -3\}$

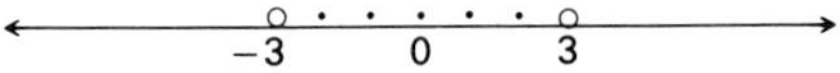

15. $x < 4 \cap x > -4$

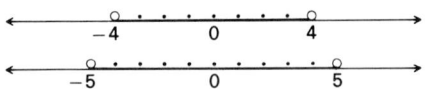

17. $x < 5 \cap x > -5$

19. $x \leq 7 \cap x \geq -5$

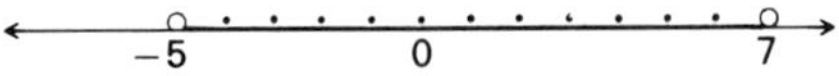

21. $\{\frac{5}{3}, -3\}$

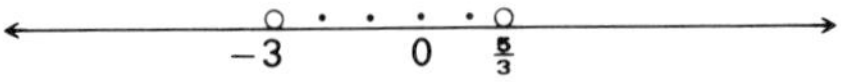

23. $x \leq 2 \cap x \geq -\frac{2}{5}$

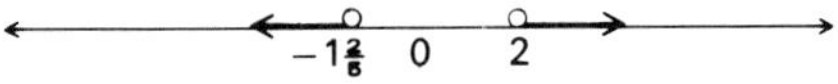

25. $\{x \mid -1 > x > -3\} \cup \{x \mid 3 > x > 1\}$

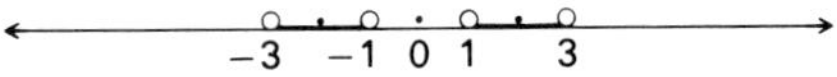

EXERCISE 5.6

1. $\{(2, 2), (4, 0), (5, -1)\}$
3. $\{(3, 1)\}$
5. $\{(3, 3), (4, 1), (4, 2), (4, 3), (3, 2)\}$
7. $\{(0, 3), (2, 2), (2, 3), (4, 1), (4, 2), (4, 3)\}$
9. $\{(-2, 2), (-2, 3), (-2, 4), (0, 2), (0, 3), (0, 4)\}$
11. $\{(-1, 0)\}$
13. $\{(1, 1), (2, 1), (-1, -1)\}$
15. $\{(3, 1), (3, 0), (6, 1), (6, 0)\}$
17. 4 hamburgers, 4 soft drinks
19. $\{(1, 5), (1, 4), (1, 3), (1, 2), (1, 1), (2, 5), (2, 4), (2, 3), (2, 2), (2, 1), (3, 4), (3, 3), (3, 2), (3, 1), (4, 3), (4, 2), (4, 1), (5, 3), (5, 2), (5, 1), (6, 1), (6, 2), (7, 1), (8, 1)\}$

EXERCISE 5.7

1.

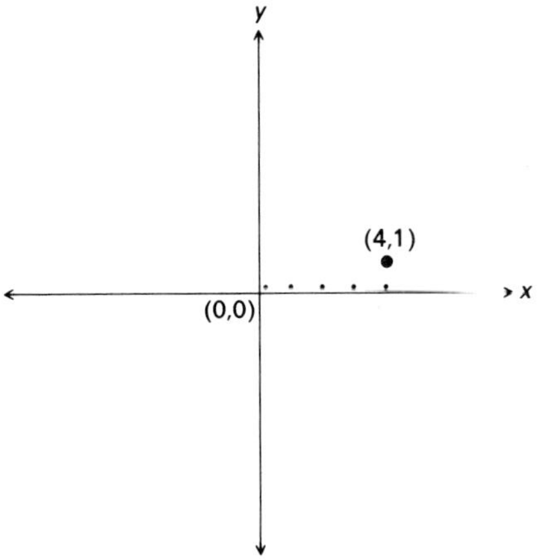

3.

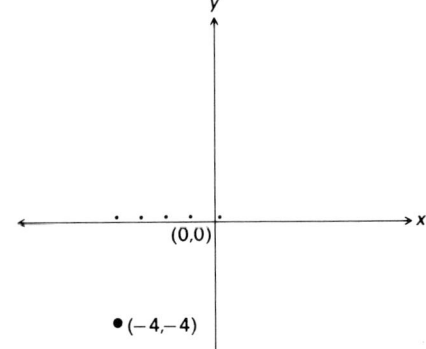

5.

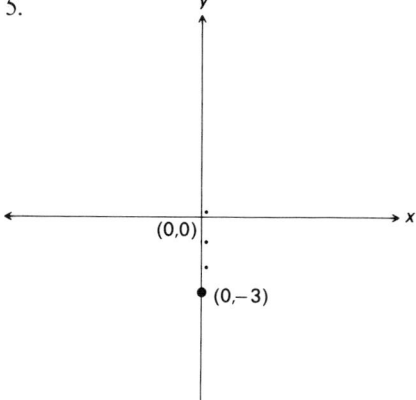

[Graph showing points (0,0) and (0,−3) on y-axis]

7.

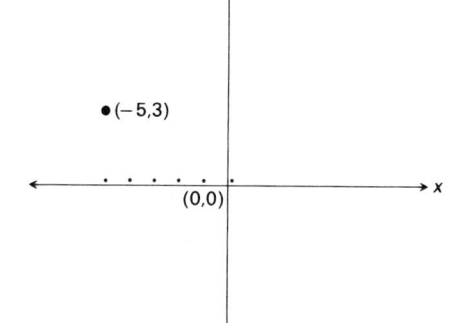

[Graph showing point (−5,3) and (0,0)]

9.

[Graph showing points (−3/8, −1) and (0,0)]

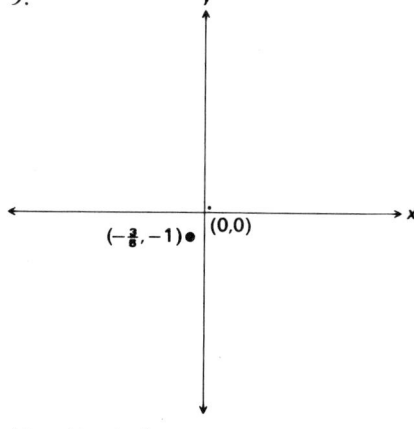

11. $A(-1, 1)$
13. $C(5, 0)$
15. $E(-9, 0)$
17. $G(-4, -6)$
19. $I(6, 5)$
21. I
23. I
25. II
27. I
29. True
31. True

EXERCISE 5.8

X AND Y INTERCEPT

1. $2x - 3y = 6$

x	y
0	-2
3	0
6	2

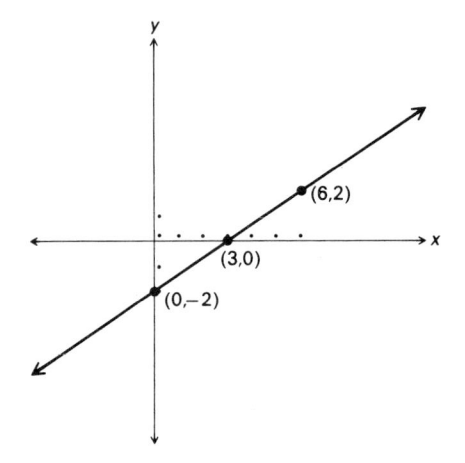

3. $3x - 2y = -12$

x	y
0	6
-4	0
-2	3

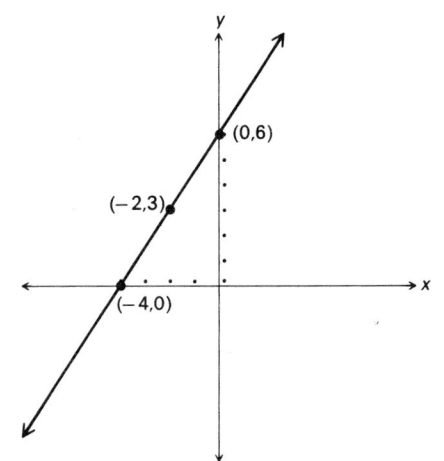

5. $2x = 6$

x	y
3	0
3	5
3	2

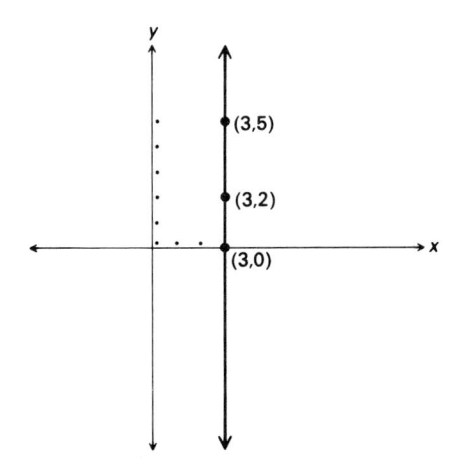

7. $2x - 4y = 8$

x	y
4	0
0	-2
6	1

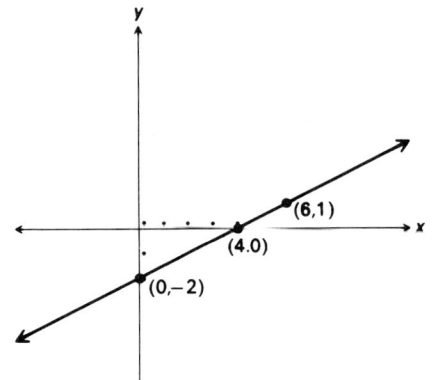

Odd Numbered Answers

SLOPE INTERCEPT

9. $y = 2x - 3$

   Slope = $\frac{2}{1}$
   y intercept is $(0, -3)$

11. $\dfrac{x + y}{2} = 0$

    Slope = $-\frac{1}{1}$
    y intercept = $(0, 0)$

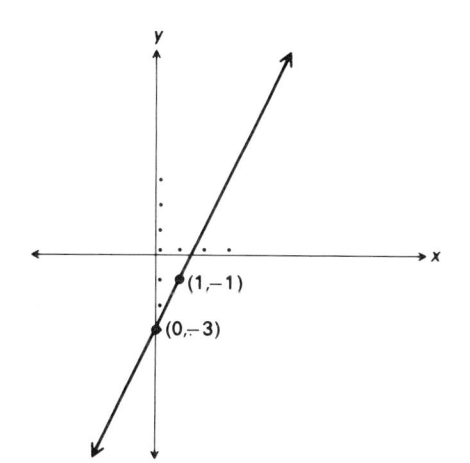

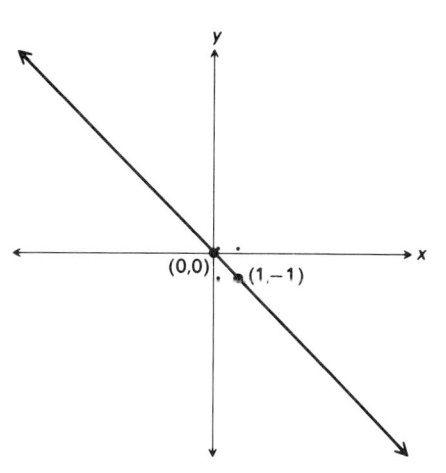

13. $3x = -6$
    Slope is undefined
    x intercept = $(-2, 0)$

15. $2x - 4y = 2$
    Slope = $\frac{1}{2}$
    y intercept = $(0, -\frac{1}{2})$

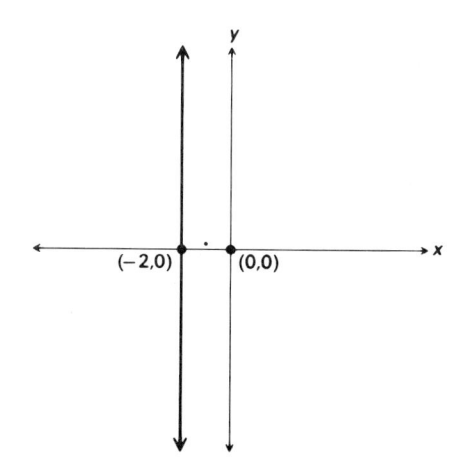

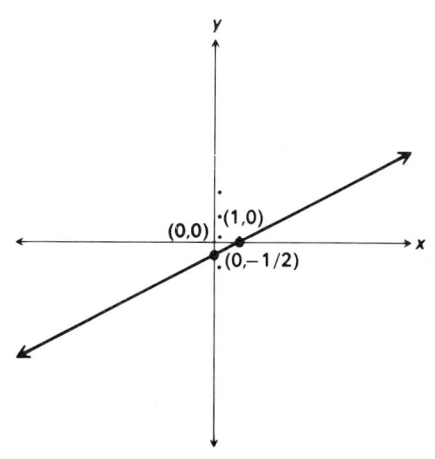

INEQUALITIES

17. $2x - 3y > 6$

x	y
0	-2
3	0

19. $x - 3y < -3$

x	y
0	1
-3	0
3	2

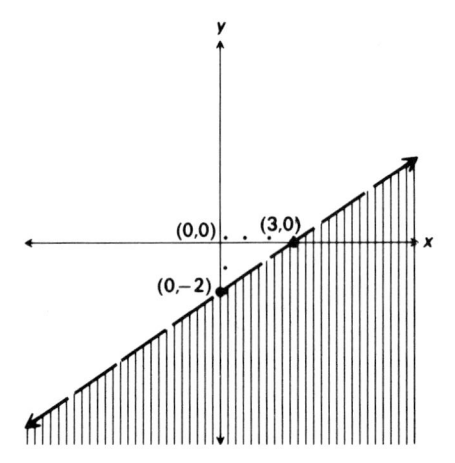

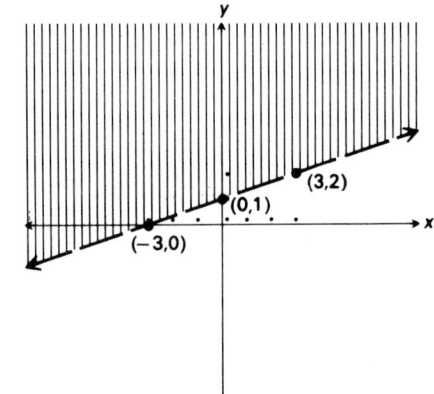

21. $y < -2x$

x	y
0	0
-2	4
1	-2

23. $x + 3y \geqslant 0$

x	y
0	0
3	-1
6	-2

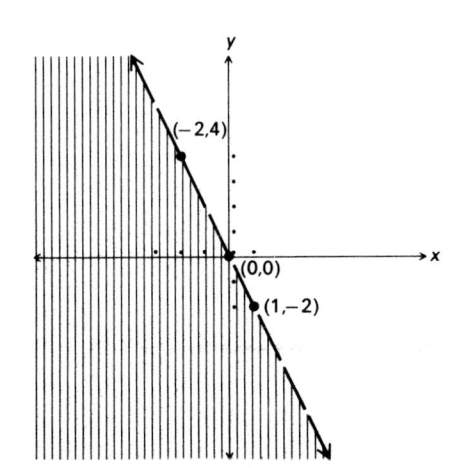

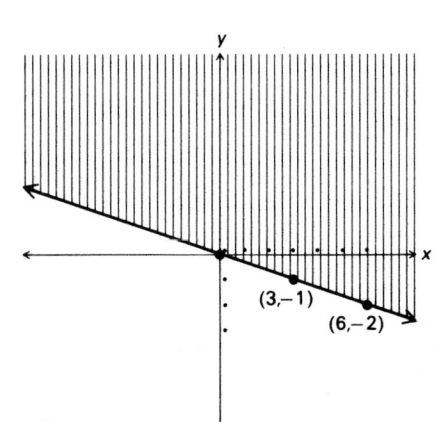

25. $3x - 2y \leq 1$

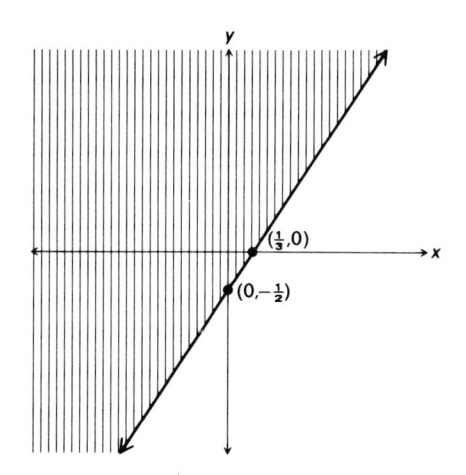

x	y
$\frac{1}{3}$	0
0	$-\frac{1}{2}$

27. $y = 2x + 2$ 29. $y = \frac{2}{3}x + 4$ 31. $y = \frac{7}{3}x + \frac{9}{2}$

REVIEW EXERCISES 5.1

1. $\{4\}$
3. $\{1, 3, 4\}$
5. $\{0, 5\}$
7. $\{3, -1, -2\}$
9. $T\{(2, 0)\}$; $F\{(0, 0), (0, 2), (2, 2)\}$
11. $\{6\}$
13. $\{6\}$
15. $\{-6\}$
17. $x < 10$
19. $x \leq 4$

21. $\{10, -10\}$

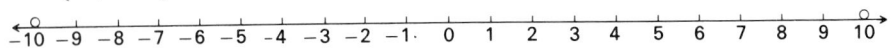

23. $x \geq 4 \cup x \leq -4$

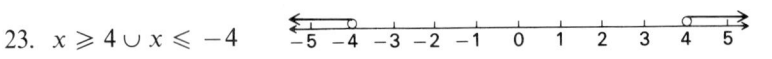

25. $x \leq 4 \cap x \geq -5$

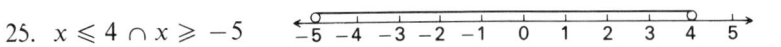

27. 9 pints
29. Joe $11.50, Don $8.50
31. 92%

SELF QUIZ 5.1

1. $x = 3$ 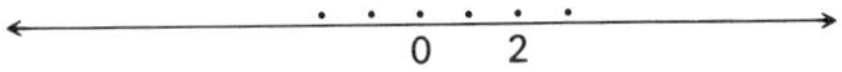
3. $x = 3$ 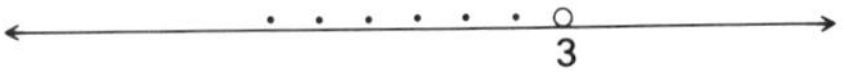
5. $x \leq 5 \cup x \geq -3$ 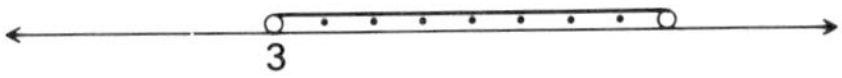
7. $4,000 at 6%, $6,000 at 8%
9. Milkshake 35 cents, sandwich 65 cents
11. 3 lbs. of 85 cent candy, 2 lbs. of 50 cent candy

EXERCISE 5.9

1. $x + y = 4$
   $2x - 3y = 2$

x	y
2	2
0	4
4	0

x	y
−1	0
0	$\frac{2}{3}$
4	2

3. $2x - y = 7$
   $x + 3y = 0$

x	y
$\frac{7}{2}$	0
0	−7
4	1

x	y
2	0
0	$\frac{2}{3}$
−1	1

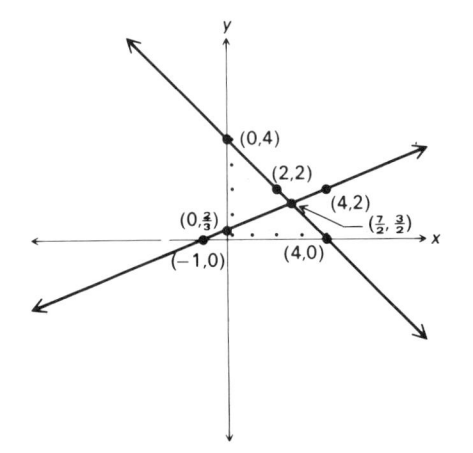

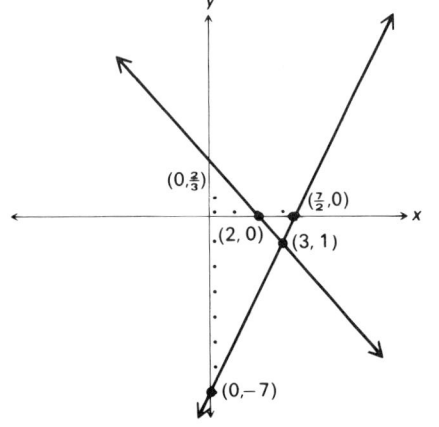

Odd Numbered Answers 279

5. $x + 4y = 27$
   $x + 2y = 21$

x	0
27	0
0	$\frac{27}{4}$
1	6

x	y
21	0
0	$\frac{21}{2}$
1	10

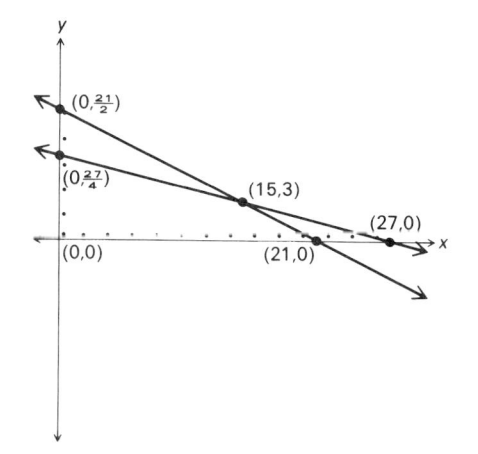

7. $3x + 2y = 5$
   $9x + 6y = 7$

x	y
$\frac{5}{3}$	0
0	$\frac{5}{2}$
3	-2

x	y
$\frac{7}{9}$	0
0	$\frac{7}{6}$
2	$-\frac{11}{6}$

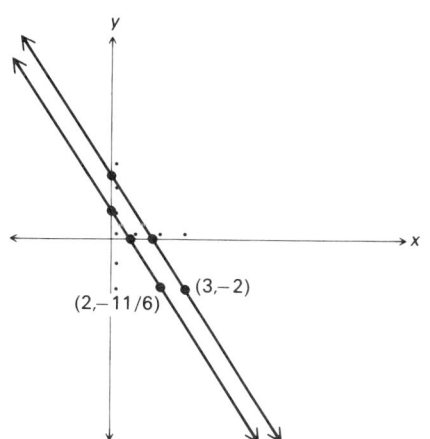

9. $2x - 3y = 6$
   $x - \frac{3}{2}y = 4$

x	y
3	0
6	2
0	-2

x	y
0	$-\frac{8}{3}$
4	0
$\frac{11}{2}$	1

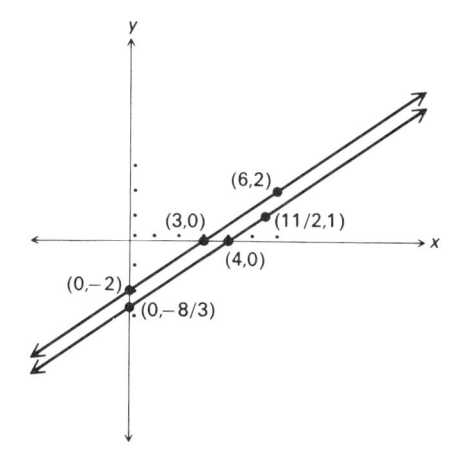

EXERCISE 5.10

1. $x = 2, y = 2$
3. The set of real numbers (identical lines)
5. $x = 8, y = 3$
7. $x = 2, y = 1$
9. $x = 5, y = 5$
11. $x = 1, y = 1$
13. The set of real numbers
15. The set of real numbers
17. Hamburgers 42¢, sodas 17¢
19. 16 ft. wide, 24 ft. long
21. house payment $125, car payment $75
23. 59¢ doz. eggs, 81¢ lb. bacon
25. 1.15 qts. of 86% alcohol, .85 qts. of 60% alcohol

EXERCISE 5.11

1. $(1, 1)$
3. $(\frac{9}{7}, \frac{6}{7})$
5. $(6, 3)$
7. $(6\frac{3}{5}, 4\frac{2}{5})$
9. $(\frac{16}{3}, \frac{17}{3})$
11. Dick 283.3 mil., Cathy 616.7 miles
13. Son $4,000, daughter, $6,000
15. 5.6 lb. of $1.75 per lb., tea 2.4 lbs. of $1.25 per lb.

EXERCISE 5.12

1. $x - 2y > 4$
   $2x + 3y < 6$

x	y
0	-2
4	0

x	y
0	2
3	0

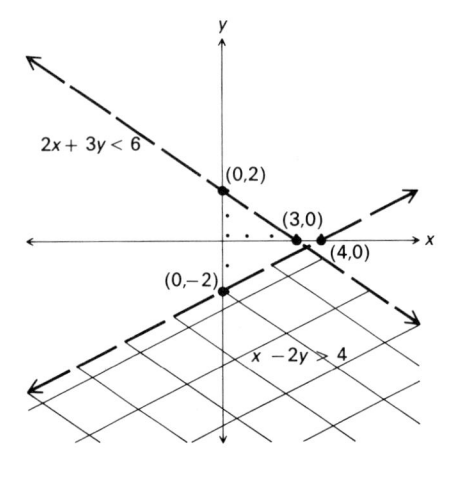

3. $5x - y \leq 10$
   $2x + 3y > 6$

x	y
0	-10
2	0

x	y
0	2
3	0

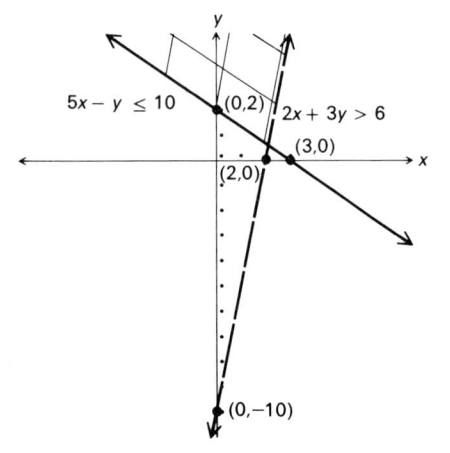

Odd Numbered Answers 281

5. $\frac{1}{2}x + \frac{1}{3}y > 6$
   $\frac{2}{5}x - \frac{3}{2}y < 1$

x	y
0	18
1.2	0

x	y
0	$-\frac{2}{3}$
$2\frac{1}{2}$	0

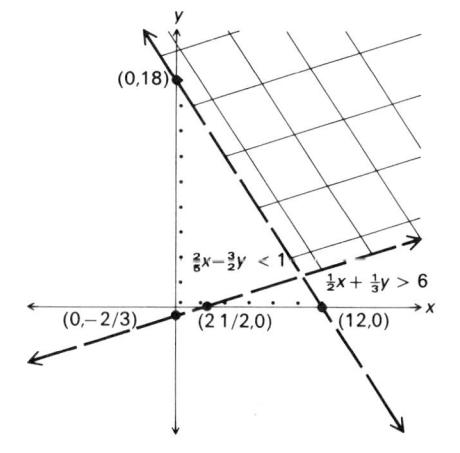

7. $2x - 3y \leq -12$
   $y \leq 4$
   $x \geq -2$

x	y
0	4
-6	0

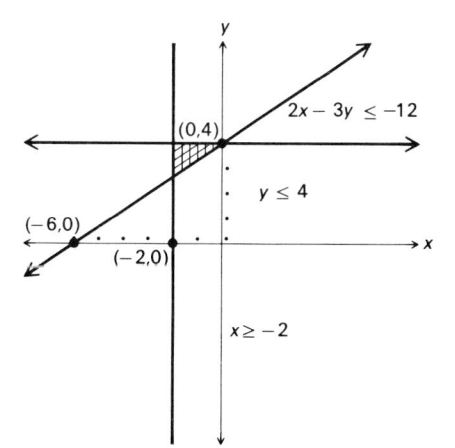

9. $x > y$ $y \leq 4$
   $x \geq 0$ $y \geq 0$

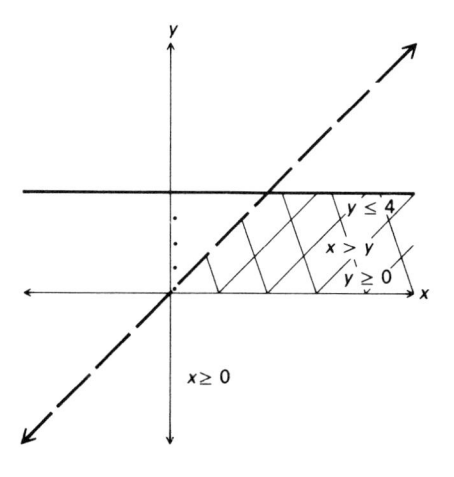

11. $3x + 4y \leq 12$
    $5x + y \geq 10$
    $x \geq 1$
    $y \geq 0$

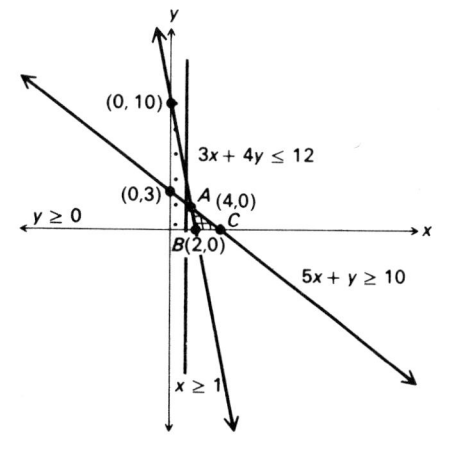

Vertices	$P = 4x + y$
$A(\frac{28}{17}, \frac{30}{17})$	$8\frac{6}{17}$
$B(2, 0)$	8
$C(4, 0)$	16

13.

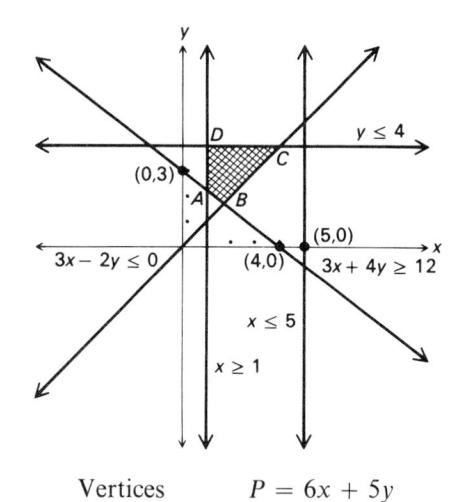

Vertices	$P = 6x + 5y$
$A(1, \frac{9}{4})$	$17\frac{1}{4}$
$B(\frac{4}{3}, 2)$	18
$C(\frac{8}{3}, 4)$	36
$D(1,4)$	26

15.

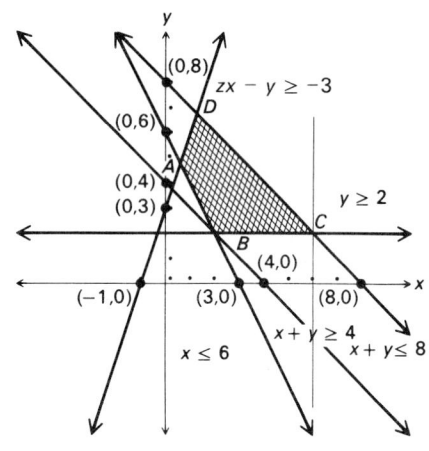

Vertices	$P = 2x - y$
$A(\frac{3}{5}, \frac{24}{5})$	$-\frac{18}{5}$
$B(2, 2)$	2
$C(6, 2)$	10
$D(\frac{5}{4}, \frac{27}{4})$	$-\frac{17}{4}$

17. 40 women and 60 men.
19. Machine A operates 1 hour and machine B operates $9\frac{1}{3}$ hours.

EXERCISE 5.13

1. Domain $\{0, 2, 5, 7\}$ Range $\{0, 3, 8, 11\}$
3. Domain $\{-3, -3, -1, 0, 1\}$ Range $\{1, 2, 3, 4, 5\}$
5.

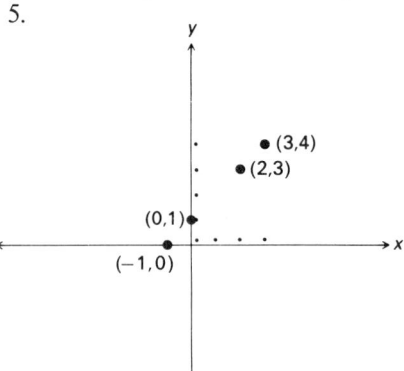

7.

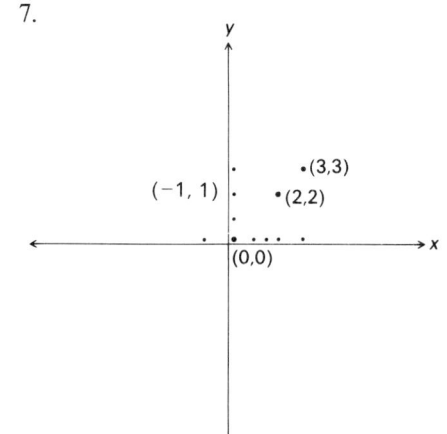

9. $L = \dfrac{A}{W}$

11. $y = 2x$

13.

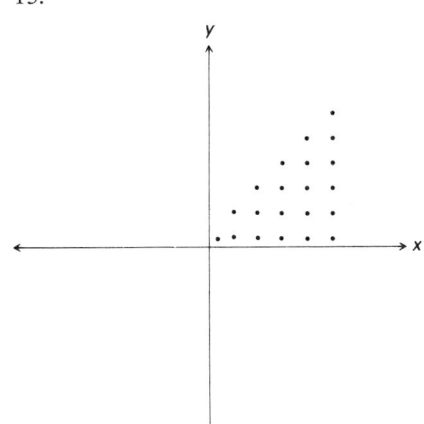

15.

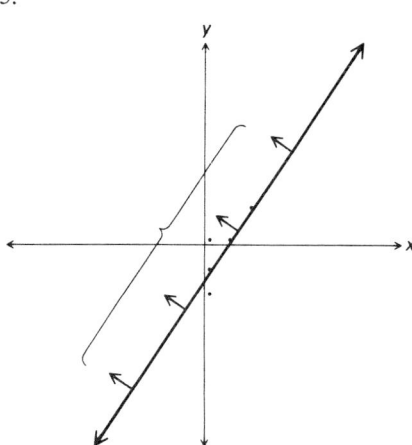

EXERCISE 5.14

1. $f(x) = 2x + 3$
3. $f(x) = .5x$
5. not a function
7. $f(x) = 16x$
9. $f(n) = 15n$
11. $P(x) = 62.5x$; $x =$ depth in feet
13. $D(t) = 65t$
15. $R(n) = 2n + \$5.00$

REVIEW EXERCISE 5.2

1. $\{(0, 5), (1, 3), (2, 1)\}$
3. $\{(-1, 5), (-1, 3), (0, 5), (0, 3), (3, 5), (3, 3), (3, 0)\}$

5.

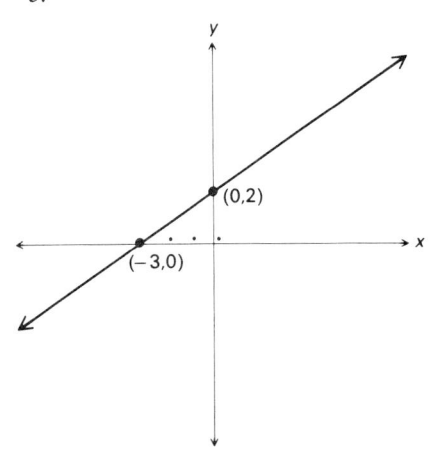

7.

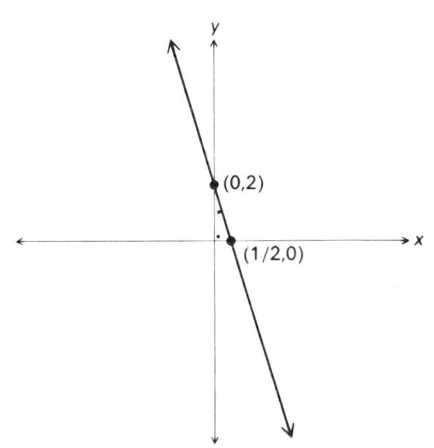

9.

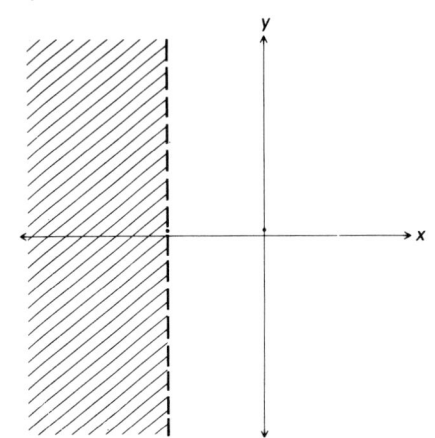

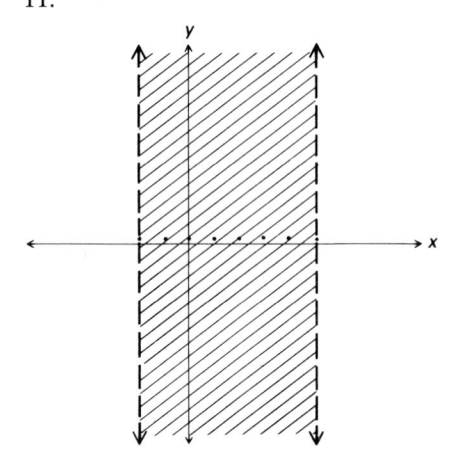

11.

13. $y = -2x + \frac{1}{2}$
15. $\{(\frac{12}{5}, -\frac{12}{5})\}$
17. $\{(2, -3)\}$
19. $\{(6, -5)\}$
21. $\{(5, -3)\}$

23.

25.

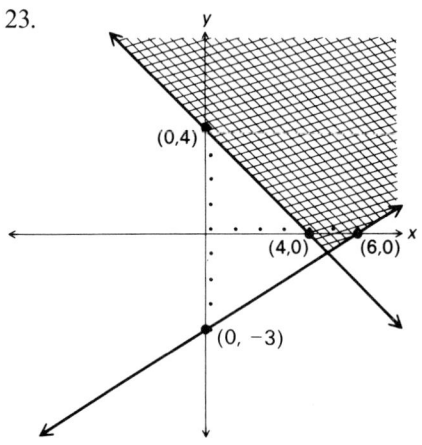

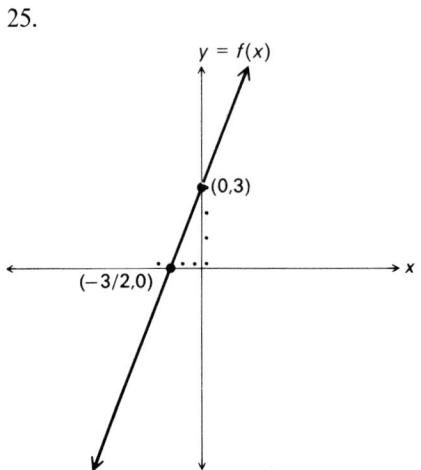

27. 9 tablets, 6 pencils
29. 6 quarts of milk, 4 quarts of ice cream

SELF QUIZ 5.2

1. $\{(0, 6)(3, 0)\}$

5.

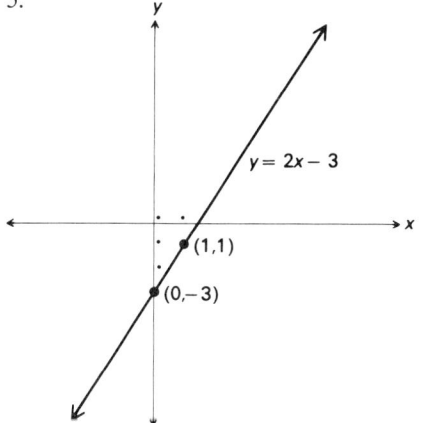

3. $\{(0, 4), (0, 2), (0, 0), (6, 0), (6, 2), (6, 4), (12, 4)\}$

7. $\{(3, 1)\}$

9.

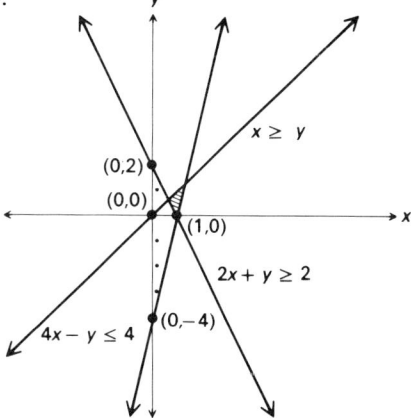

EXERCISE 6.1

1. $2 \cdot x$
3. $5 \cdot y$
5. $\frac{2}{3} \cdot y$
7. $x \cdot y$
9. $.7 \cdot a \cdot b$
11. $3 \cdot (x + 1) \cdot (x + 1)$
13. $11 \cdot 1$
15. $2 \cdot x \cdot x$
17. $3 \cdot x \cdot x \cdot x \cdot y \cdot y$
19. $6 \cdot a \cdot a \cdot b \cdot b \cdot b \cdot \frac{1}{2}$ or $3 \cdot 2 \cdot a \cdot a \cdot b \cdot b \cdot b \cdot \frac{1}{2}$
21. 6
23. $\frac{1}{2}$
25. $(y + 2)$
27. -1
29. a^3
31. y^5
33. $4b^3$
35. $6(xy)^4$ or $6x^4y^4$
37. $2(s - 1)^3$
39. 9
41. 1
43. 4
45. 6
47. 23
49. a) 36 sq. in.
    b) 2.25 sq. ft.
    c) 196 sq. yds.
    d) $4r^2$
51. a) $12.00
    b) $132.00
    c) $6.25

EXERCISE 6.2

1. $20r^3s^2$
3. $8x^2$
5. $-30xyz$
7. $2x^4y^5z^4$
9. $-125a^2b^2c^2$
11. x^3y^5

13. $.216a^4b^4$
17. $10x^3w^3z^4$
21. $4a^4 - 2a^3$
15. $4x^3y^2$
19. $46x^7y^7z^6$
23. a) $w(w + 20) = w^2 + 20w$
    $w(w + 30) = w^2 + 30w$
    b) $2w^2 + 50w$

EXERCISE 6.3

1. $4x^6$
5. $-50m^3n^4$
9. $-.5m^5n^6$
13. $17x^2y^2$
17. $a^8b^7 + .5a^6b^7$
3. $8x^5$
7. $36m^5n^4$
11. $1.8a^6b^5c^6$
15. $m^3 - 16m^8$
19. $8a^3b^4c^4 - 32a^6b^5c^4$

EXERCISE 6.4

1. $-6x^5y^3z^4$
5. $2a^3 + 4a^2b + 2ab^2$
9. $-a^4 + a^3 - 10a^2$
13. $2a^5b^4 - 2a^4b^3 - 2a^2b^7$
17. $4x^2 + 4xy + 2x + 5y - 15y^2$
21. $a^4 + 3a^3 + 5a^2 + 2a - 1$
25. Area $= x^2 - 400$ sq. ft. (x = width)
3. $-5x^2 + 15x + 20$
7. $6a^2 + 5a - 6$
11. $-2x^2 + 15x - 25$
15. $3x^4 - 20x^2 + 25$
19. $6x^4 + x^3 + 3x - 2$
23. Area $= x^3 + 3x$ sq. ft. (x = width)
27. Width 10 inches, length 15 inches

EXERCISE 6.5

1. $7ab$
5. $\dfrac{6b^2}{5a^2}$
9. -7
13. $\dfrac{s}{2r^2}$
17. $6a^6b^3$
3. $5b^3$
7. 9
11. $\dfrac{3y^2}{5}$
15. $\dfrac{xy}{2}$
19. $x^{a-b}y^{b-a}$

EXERCISE 6.6

1. $x + 2y$
5. $t^2 - 2t + 1$
9. $2a^3b^2 + \frac{3}{2}a^2b - 3a$
3. 7
7. $3x + y + 2$
11. $\dfrac{2a^2b + 3a + b^2}{5}$

EXERCISE 6.7

1. $x + 2$
3. $x + 4$
5. $5a - 4$
7. $5a - 3b$
9. $x - 4 R 32$
11. $x^2 - xy + y^2$
13. $16m^2 + 12mn + 9n^2$
15. $6a - 7 R 3$
17. $2a^2 + 3a - 2R - 10$
19. $3a^2 - 4a + 5$
21. $x - 4$
23. $x^2 + 2x + 4$
25. 12

EXERCISE 6.8

1. 11
3. 16
5. 4
7. 17
9. $|x + y|$
11. $\frac{1}{2}$
13. $\dfrac{3x^2}{y^4}$
15. $-\frac{33}{29}$
17. 5
19. $\dfrac{\sqrt{2}}{2}$

EXERCISE 6.9

1. $3(x^2 - 4)$
3. $5(x^2 + 2y^2)$
5. $3a^2(2 + 3a)$
7. $6a^2(2 + b)$
9. $9b^2(b - 3a^3)$
11. $x(1 + 3yz)$
13. $3t^2(2 + 3r^2 t)$
15. $4x^2 y^2 (2x^3 y + 3x^2 - 4y^2)$
17. $25x(1 - 2x)$
19. $3x^2(x^2 + 5)$

EXERCISE 6.10

1. $(x - 4)(x + 4)$
3. $(5 - 4x)(5 + 4x)$
5. $(1 - 3a)(1 + 3a)$
7. $(-3 + ts)(3 + ts)$
9. $(.3a + .4)(.3a - .4)$
11. $(.9 - t)(.9 + t)$
13. $-4a^2(a - 2)(a + 2)$
15. $2ab^2(ab - 6)(ab + 6)$
17. $(a^n - 1)(a^n + 1)$
19. $(x + y - 1)(x + y + 1)$

EXERCISE 6.11

1. $(x + 2)(x + 2)$
3. $(m - n)(m - n)$
5. $(2t - 1)(2t - 1)$
7. $(1 - 5a)(1 - 5a)$
9. $(5a - 3)(5a - 3)$
11. $(6x + 5y)(6x + 5y)$
13. $(a^2 - 1)(a^2 + 1)$
15. $(a - 3)(a + 3)(a - 3)(a + 3)$
    $= (a - 1)(a + 1)(a^2 + 1)$
17. $(t^3 - 4)(t^3 - 4)$
19. $(12a - 5b)(12a - 5b)$

EXERCISE 6.12

1. $(x + 4)(x - 1)$
3. $(3x - 2)(2x + 3)$
5. $(m + 8)(m - 3)$
7. $(t - 6)(t + 2)$
9. $(a - 10)(a + 3)$
11. $(ax - 3)(ax + 2)$
13. $(t + 4s)(-t + s)$
15. $(a + 4)(5a - 4)$
17. $(xy + 1)(xy - 10)$
19. $(2x + 3)(x + 4)$

EXERCISE 6.13

1. $3, -3$
3. 3 (multiplicity of 2)
5. $\frac{1}{2}$ (multiplicity of 2)
7. $\frac{1}{2}, -2$
9. $9, -8$
11. $\frac{4}{3}, -\frac{5}{4}$
13. $8, -2$
15. $\frac{8}{3}, -\frac{7}{2}$
17. $4, -3$
19. $\frac{8}{3}, -\frac{7}{2}$
21. Width 6 feet, length 16 feet
23. 400 feet
25. 20 head
27. 70 Shares

EXERCISE 6.14

1. $x = 2 + \sqrt{7}$ or $x = 2 - \sqrt{7}$
3. $x = \dfrac{-5 + \sqrt{5}}{2}$ or $x = \dfrac{-5 - \sqrt{5}}{2}$
5. $x = \dfrac{-2 + \sqrt{5}}{2}$ or $x = \dfrac{-2 - \sqrt{5}}{2}$
7. $x = \dfrac{-1 + \sqrt{6}}{2}$ or $x = \dfrac{-1 - \sqrt{6}}{2}$
9. $x = \dfrac{3 + \sqrt{15}}{2}$ or $x = \dfrac{3 - \sqrt{15}}{2}$
11. $x = \dfrac{5 + \sqrt{13}}{6}$ or $x = \dfrac{5 - \sqrt{13}}{6}$
13. $x = \dfrac{-7 + \sqrt{17}}{8}$ or $x = \dfrac{-7 - \sqrt{17}}{8}$
15. $x = 3 + i$ or $x = 3 - i$
17. $x = \dfrac{-2 + i}{3}$ or $x = \dfrac{-2 - i}{3}$
19. $x = \dfrac{5 + i\sqrt{5}}{2}$ or $x = \dfrac{5 - i\sqrt{5}}{2}$
21. Width 6 feet, length 9 feet.
23. 5 hrs; $7\frac{1}{2}$ hrs.
25. 60 mph going; 50 mph returning.

Odd Numbered Answers

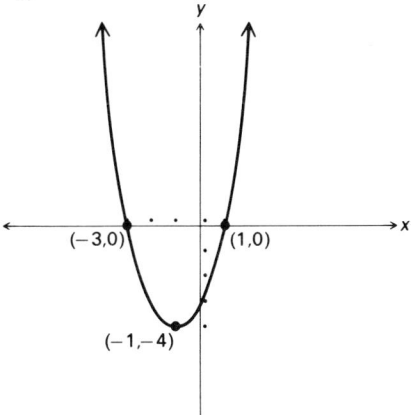

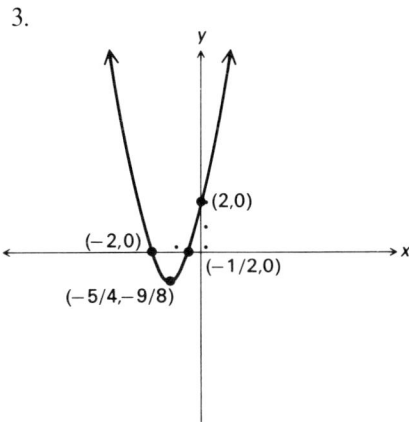

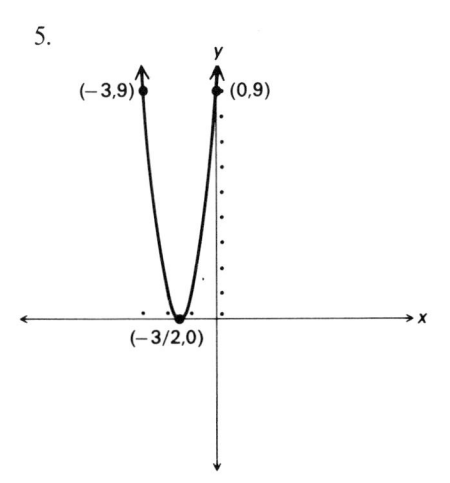

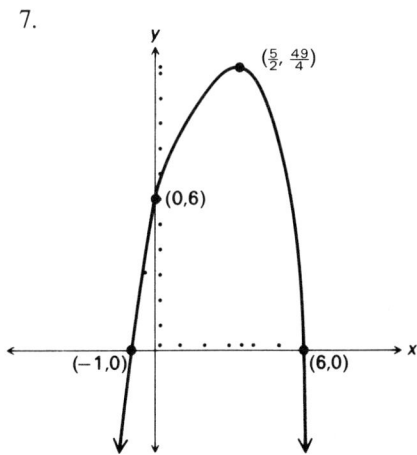

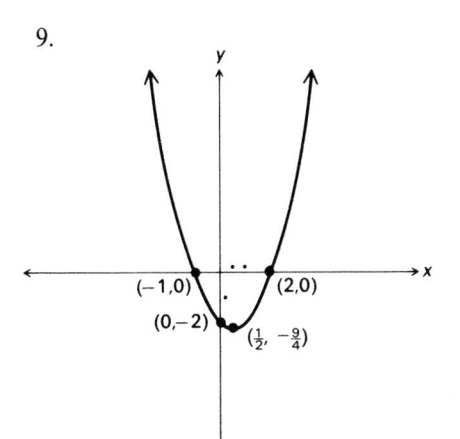

EXERCISE 6.15

1. Parabola opening upward with x-intercepts $(-3,0)$ and $(1,0)$, vertex $(-1,-4)$.

3. Parabola opening upward with x-intercepts $(-2,0)$ and $(-1/2, 0)$, vertex $(-5/4, -9/8)$, and point $(2,0)$ marked.

5. Parabola opening upward with vertex $(-3/2, 0)$, points $(-3, 9)$ and $(0, 9)$.

7. Parabola opening downward with x-intercepts $(-1,0)$ and $(6,0)$, y-intercept $(0,6)$, vertex $(5/2, 49/4)$.

9. Parabola opening upward with x-intercepts $(-1,0)$ and $(2,0)$, y-intercept $(0,-2)$, vertex $(\frac{1}{2}, -\frac{9}{4})$.

11. $x = 2$
13. 4 weeks
15. 2 five cent increases (for 40 cents fare)

REVIEW EXERCISE 6.1

1. 11
3. -7
5. 65
7. $30x^4y^3$
9. $16a^7b^7$
11. $2m^3 + 4m^2n + 2mn^2$
13. $7xy$
15. $3x^2 - x + 2$
17. $2x^2 + 3xy + y^2$
19. 12
21. $\frac{4}{5}$
23. $(2x - 3)(2x + 3)$
25. $(x + y - 2)(x + y + 2)$
27. $(5x - 3)(5x - 3)$
29. $(x + 2)(x + 4)$
31. $\{-1, -4\}$
33. $\{-3, 4\}$
35. $\{-\frac{5}{3}, 2\}$

39.

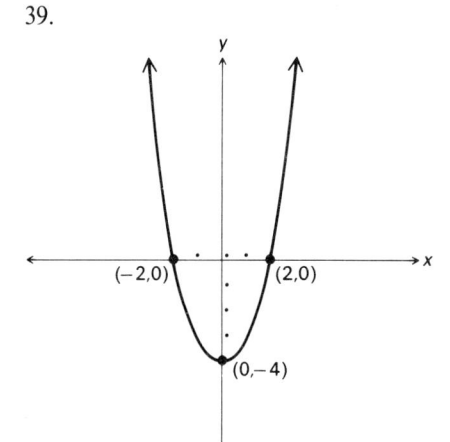

[Graph of a parabola with x-intercepts at $(-2, 0)$ and $(2, 0)$, and vertex at $(0, -4)$.]

41. $L = 18, W = 5$
43. 24 rows, 30 seats
45. 8 inches, 12 inches

SELF QUIZ 6.1

1. -1
3. $2x^3 - 6x^2y - 4xy^2$
5. 12
7. $(3x - 2)(3x + 2)$
9. $\{1, -4\}$

11. $\{1, -3\}$

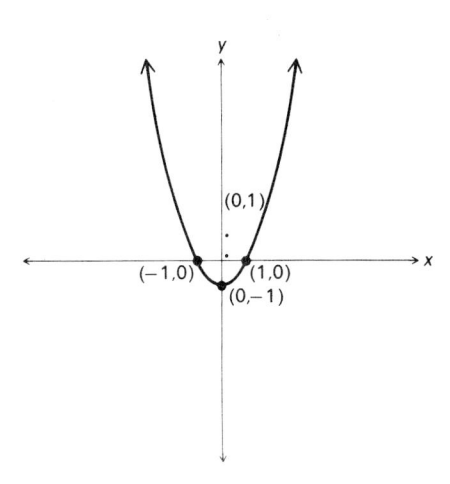

(graph of upward parabola with vertex at $(0,-1)$, passing through $(-1,0)$, $(0,1)$, $(1,0)$)

EXERCISE 7.1

1. Common notion 1 is equivalent to the transitive property of equality. Common notion 2 and 3 are equivalent to the additive property of equality.
3. By use of the real number line.
5. $10\sqrt{2}$
7. Problem 5 disproves the proposed theorem by use of a counter-example.

EXERCISE 7.3

1. Area $= \dfrac{8 \cdot 6}{2} = 24$ sq. ft.

3.

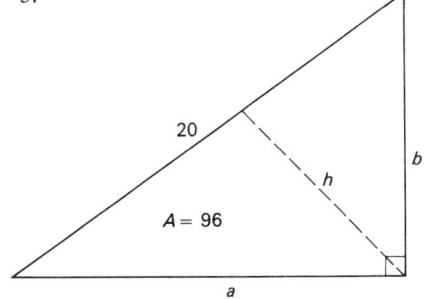

$$\frac{20 \cdot h}{2} = 96$$

$$b = 9.6$$

$$\frac{a \cdot b}{2} = 96$$

$$a = \frac{192}{b}$$

$$\frac{(192)^2}{b} + b^2 = 400$$

$$(192)^2 + b^4 = 400b^2$$

$$\therefore, b^2 = 144$$

$$\text{or } b^2 = 256$$

$$b = 12$$

$$\text{or } b = 16$$

$$h = 12 \text{ to the longest side.}$$

5. Let L = length of wire

$s = \dfrac{L}{4}$ of square

$s^2 = \dfrac{L^2}{16}$ area of square

$s = \dfrac{L}{3}$ of triangle

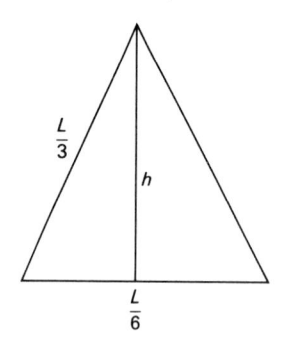

$h^2 = \dfrac{L^2}{9} - \dfrac{L^2}{36}$

$h^2 = \dfrac{4L^2 - L^2}{36}$

$h = \dfrac{L}{6}\sqrt{3}$

$\dfrac{L}{6} \cdot \dfrac{L}{6}\sqrt{3}$ = Area of triangle

$\dfrac{L^2\sqrt{3}}{36}$ = Area of triangle

$\dfrac{\text{Area of Square}}{\text{Area of Triangle}} = \dfrac{L^2/16}{L^2\sqrt{\frac{3}{36}}}$

$= \dfrac{36L^2}{16\sqrt{3L^2}}$

$= \dfrac{36}{16\sqrt{3}}$

The square is larger than the triangle in the ratio approx. 5.1 to 4.
7. No. But they are convenient.
9. a) 5 b) $\sqrt{2}$
   c) $\sqrt{97}$ d) $\sqrt{85}$

EXERCISE 7.4

1. a) 4π sq. units b) $\dfrac{\pi}{4}$ sq. units.
   c) 2.5π sq. units

3. $\dfrac{25\pi}{2} + (20 - 5\sqrt{3})10 + 5\sqrt{3} \cdot 5$

   $+ \dfrac{\pi \cdot 100}{6} = \dfrac{175\pi}{6} + 200 - 25\sqrt{3}$

5. a) $S = 4\pi r^2$
      $S = 4\pi (4000)^2$
      $S = 64{,}000{,}000\pi$ sq. mi.
   b) $2{,}560{,}000\pi$ sq. mi.

7. $\dfrac{d^2(4-\pi)}{4} \cdot \dfrac{1}{8} \cdot 300{,}000$

EXERCISE 8.2

1. $Pr(E) = \frac{5}{15} = \frac{1}{3}$
   b) $Pr(E) = \frac{5}{14}$
   c) $Pr(E) = \frac{10}{15} = \frac{2}{3}$

3. $Pr(E) = \frac{1}{2}$

5. a) Outcome of the red die   b) $Pr(E) = \frac{1}{36}$

		1	2	3	4	5	6
Outcome of the green die	1	1, 1	1, 2	1, 3	1, 4	1, 5	1, 6
	2	2, 1	2, 1	2, 3	2, 4	2, 5	2, 6
	3	3, 1	3, 2	3, 3	3, 4	3, 5	3, 6
	4	4, 1	4, 2	4, 3	4, 4	4, 5	4, 6
	5	5, 1	5, 2	5, 3	5, 4	5, 5	5, 6
	6	6, 1	6, 2	6, 3	6, 4	6, 5	6, 6

c) $\Sigma = 1$

7. a) $S = \{(h, 1), (h, 2), (h, 3), (h, 4), (h, 5), (h, 6),$
      $(t, 1), (t, 2), (t, 3), (t, 4), (t, 5), (t, 6)\}$
   b) $Pr(E) = \frac{3}{12} = \frac{1}{4}$
   c) $Pr(E) = \frac{3}{12} = \frac{1}{4}$

9. a) $\frac{4}{52}$
   b) $\frac{1}{2}$
   c) $\frac{1}{2}$
   d) 0
   e) $\frac{12}{52} = \frac{3}{13}$

11. $\frac{20}{51}$

EXERCISE 8.3

1. $4 \times 5 = 20$
3. $15 \times 17 \times 12 = 3060$
5. $7! = 7 \cdot 6 \cdot 5 \cdot 4 \cdot 3 \cdot 2 \cdot 1 = 5040$
7. $6 \times 4 \times 5 \times 3 = 360$
9. $13 \cdot 12 \cdot 11 \cdot 10 \cdot 9 \cdot 8 \cdot 7 \cdot 6 \cdot 5 = 259{,}459{,}200$
11. $10 \cdot 9 \cdot 8 \cdot 7 = 5040$

EXERCISE 8.4

1. $P(9, 3) = \dfrac{9!}{(9-3)!} = 504$

3. $P(11, 6) = \dfrac{11!}{(11-6)!} = 332{,}640$

5. $P(15, 9) = \dfrac{15!}{(15-9)!} = 1{,}816{,}214{,}400$

7. a) $P(6, 4) = \dfrac{6!}{(6-4)!} = 360$
   b) $6^4 = 1296$
   c) $3P(5, 3) = \dfrac{3 \cdot 5!}{(5-3)!} = 180$

9. a) $4P(4, 3) = 96$
   b) $4 \cdot 5^3 = 600$

11. $P(6, 3) = 120$

EXERCISE 8.5

1. $C(12, 4) = \dfrac{12!}{(12-4)!4!} = 495$

3. a) $C(12, 9)$
   b) No, $C(12, 3) = C(12, 9)$

5. $C(5, 1) + C(5, 2) + C(5, 3) + C(5, 4) + C(5, 5) = 31$

7. $C(20, 4) \cdot C(14, 3)$

9. $C(15, 6) \cdot C(9, 5) \cdot C(4, 4)$

11. $C(5, 3) + C(6, 3)$

EXERCISE 8.6

1. $Pr(E) = \dfrac{C(13, 3)}{C(52, 2)}$

3. $Pr(E) = \dfrac{C(20, 3) \cdot C(10, 2)}{C(30, 5)}$

   b) $Pr(E) = \dfrac{C(20, 1) \cdot C(10, 4)}{C(30, 5)}$

5. a) $Pr(E) = \dfrac{C(13, 4)}{C(52, 4)}$
   b) $Pr(E) = \dfrac{C(4, 4)}{C(52, 4)}$
   c) $Pr(E) = \dfrac{C(26, 4)}{C(52, 4)}$

7. a) $Pr(E) = \dfrac{C(10, 3)}{C(20, 3)}$
   b) $Pr(E) = \dfrac{C(4, 2) \cdot (6, 1)}{C(20, 3)}$

9. $Pr(E) = \dfrac{4 \cdot C(13, 3)}{C(52, 3)}$

EXERCISE 8.7

1. $Pr(E) = \frac{1}{8}$
    b) $Pr(E) = \frac{1}{8} + \frac{1}{8} + \frac{1}{8} = \frac{3}{8}$
3. a) $Pr(E) = \frac{1}{10} \cdot \frac{3}{10} = \frac{3}{100}$
    b) $Pr(E) = \frac{1}{10} + \frac{3}{10} - \frac{3}{100} = \frac{37}{100}$
5. a) $Pr(E) = \frac{4}{15}$
    b) $Pr(E) = \frac{2}{15}$
    c) $Pr(E) = \frac{7}{15}$
7. a) $Pr(E) = \frac{2}{5}$
    b) $Pr(E) = \frac{2}{15}$
    c) $Pr(E) = \frac{13}{15}$
9. a) $Pr(E) = \frac{5}{16}$
    b) $Pr(E) = \frac{11}{16}$
    c) $Pr(E) = \frac{7}{16}$

EXERCISE 8.8

1. $E(A) = \$2.50$
3. No. $E(A) = \$6.00$
5. $E(A) = 12\frac{1}{2}$
7. Yes. $E(A) = \$0.77$
9. $E(A) = 0$
11. Yes, for the dealer

SELF TEST 8.1

1. $Pr(E) = \frac{16}{52}$
3. $P(6, 4) = \dfrac{6!}{2!}$
5. a) $P(4, 3) = \dfrac{4!}{1!}$
    b) $P(4, 3) + P(4, 2) + P(4, 1)$
7. a) $C(7, 4) = \dfrac{7!}{3!4!} = 35$
    b) $Pr(E) = \frac{1}{35}$
    c) $Pr(E) = \frac{1}{15}$
9. No, $E(A) = \$1.67$

EXERCISE 8.9

1. a) $\bar{x} = 4$, $M = 3.5$, mode 3
   b) $\bar{x} = 7$, $M = 6$, mode 5
   c) $\bar{x} = 7.5$, $M = 6$, mode not unique
3. Answers not unique
5. $\bar{x} = 19.4$ in.
   b) $M = 19.2$ in.
7. $\bar{x} = 5.27$
   b) $M = 5.3$
9. $\bar{x} = \$33$
   b) $M = \$25$

EXERCISE 8.10

1. a) $s^2 = 16$, $s = 4$
   b) $s^2 = 22.67$, $s \doteq 4.76$
   c) $s^2 = 22.86$, $s \doteq 4.78$
   d) $s^2 = 1250$, $s \doteq 35.35$
3. $\bar{x} = 2.5$, $s^2 \doteq .77$, $s \doteq .88$
5. $\bar{x} = 10.87$, $s \doteq .028$
7. $\bar{x} = 5.3$ lbs, $s \doteq .62$ lbs.
9. $\bar{x} = 1.5$, $s \doteq 1.2$

EXERCISE 8.11

1. a) $13.59 + 34.13 = 47.72$
   b) $.50 + 34.13 = 84.13\%$
   c) $1 - 68.26 = 31.74$
   d) $Pr(E) = .1359$
3. a) 4,560,000
   b) $Pr(E) = .1586$
5. $Pr(E) = .6826$
7. $Pr(E) = .6826$
9. $Pr(E) = .8413$

EXERCISE 9.1

1. a) $6 \times 10^2 + 7 \times 10 + 5 \times 10^0$
   b) $2 \times 10^3 + 3 \times 10^2 + 0 \times 10^1 + 0 \times 10^0$
3. a) 1001000
   b) 1001011001
   c) 1010010011
   d) 10001010111
5. a) $7 + 3 = 10 = 1010_2$
   b) $7 + 3 + 11 = 21 = 10101_2$
   c) $21 + 31 = 52 = 110100_2$
   d) $5 + 5 + 11 + 23 = 44 = 101100_2$
7. a) 1001
   b) 1111
   c) 1001101
   d) 1101001

9. A table of some negative powers of 2 is as follows:
$2^{-1} = \frac{1}{2} = .5$
$2^{-2} = \frac{1}{4} = .25$
$2^{-3} = \frac{1}{8} = .125$
$2^{-4} = \frac{1}{16} = .0625$
$2^{-5} = \frac{1}{32} = .03125$
$2^{-6} = \frac{1}{64} = .015625$
$2^{-7} = \frac{1}{128} = .0078125$
$2^{-8} = \frac{1}{256} = .00390625$
$2^{-9} = \frac{1}{512} = .001953125$
$2^{-10} = \frac{1}{1024} = .0009765625$
$2^{-11} = \frac{1}{2048} = .0048828125$
$2^{-12} = \frac{1}{4096} = .000244140625$

We select the decimal representatives of powers of 2 as follows:

$$\begin{array}{rl} \text{We require } 1 \times 2^{-1} & = .500000 \\ \text{We require } 1 \times 2^{-6} & = .015625 \\ \text{We require } 1 \times 2^{-8} & = .00390675 \\ \text{We require } 1 \times 2^{-12} & = .000244 \\ \hline \text{Total} & .519775 \end{array}$$

Hence, $.52 = .100001010001_2$

EXERCISE 9.2

1. a) $7 \times 8^2 + 1 \times 8 + 7 \times 8^0$.
   b) $6 \times 8^2 + 3 \times 8^0$.
   c) $5 \times 8^2 + 2 \times 8 + 1 \times 8^0$.
   d) $6 \times 8^2 + 3 \times 8 + 5 \times 8^{-2}$
3. $8^0 = 1$
   $8^1 = 8$
   $8^2 = 64$
   $8^3 = 512$
   $8^4 = 4096$

a) $8^3 \overline{\smash{\big)}\, 565}\ \ 1$
   $\underline{512}$
   53

   $565 = 1065_8$

   $8 \overline{\smash{\big)}\, 53}\ \ 6$
   $\underline{48}$
   5 rem

b) $8^2 \overline{\smash{)}\begin{array}{r} 3 \\ 230 \\ 192 \\ \hline 38 \end{array}}$ $230 = 346_8$

$8 \overline{\smash{)}\begin{array}{r} 4 \\ 38 \\ 32 \\ \hline 6 \text{ rem} \end{array}}$

c) $8^4 \overline{\smash{)}\begin{array}{r} 1 \\ 5631 \\ 4096 \\ \hline 1535 \end{array}}$

$8^3 \overline{\smash{)}\begin{array}{r} 2 \\ 1535 \\ 1024 \\ \hline 511 \end{array}}$

$8^2 \overline{\smash{)}\begin{array}{r} 7 \\ 511 \\ 448 \\ \hline 63 \end{array}}$

$8 \overline{\smash{)}\begin{array}{r} 7 \\ 63 \\ 56 \\ \hline 7 \text{ rem} \end{array}}$ $5631 = 12777_8$

5. a) $101_2 = 5_{10} = 5_8$
   b) $1101_2 = 13_{10} = 15_8$
   c) $11.11 = 3.75_{10} = 3.6_8$
   d) $.001 = .125_{10} = .1_8$
7. $.007_{16} \doteq .001709_{10}$ No.

EXERCISE A.1

1. a) Line 4 is incorrect:

        4   PRINT X, "IS THE SUM OF," A, "AND", B

   b) Lines 10, 20, 30 and 40 are incorrect.

        10 READ X, Y
        20 DATA 2, 4, 6, 8
        30 LET Z = X + Y
        40 PRINT Z
        45 GO TO 10
        50 END

c) Lines 7, 8 and 9 are incorrect
```
7   LET Y = X ↑ 3
8   PRINT "THE CUBE OF," X, "IS", Y
9   GO TO 6
```

3. a. LET A = B *(C + D)
    c. LET X = 2 * Z - 2 * Y
    d. LET Z5 = 2 * (5 + .03 * X)
    e. LET W7 = X2 * X7

5.
```
10  READ A, B, C, D, E, F
20  DATA 3000, .035, 5150, .022, 10310, .018
30  PRINT "JOHN OWES"; A * B
40  PRINT "MARY OWES"; C * D
50  PRINT "JIM OWES"; E * F
60  END
```

EXERCISE A.2

1.
10000	.01	100.
12000	.012	120.
16000	.025	400.

3.
```
5   PRINT "EMP", "GROSS", "TAX", "SS", "NET"
10  READ E, G
20  DATA 1, 500, 2, 1000, 3, 700, 4, 900, 5, 400
30  LET T = .10 * G
40  LET S = .05 * G
50  LET N = G - (S + T)
60  PRINT E, G, T, S, N
70  GO TO 10
80  END
```

5.
```
    PRINT "ITEM", "QUANTITY", "UNIT COST", "TOTAL COST"
10  READ I, Q, U
20  DATA
30  LET C + Q * U
40  PRINT I, Q, U, C,
50  GO TO 10
60  END
```

EXERCISE A.3

1. The printout is:

```
            TABLE OF POWERS OF 2
            EXPONENT                    2↑E
                0                         1
                1                         2
                2                         4
                3                         8
                4                        16
                5                        32
                6                        64
                7                       128
                8                       256
                9                       512
               10                      1024
```

3.  ```
    10 FOR I = 1 TO 100
    20 LET S = S + I
    30 NEXT I
    40 PRINT S
    50 END
    ```

5.  ```
    10 FOR I = 1 TO 10
    20 LET S = SQR(I)
    30 PRINT I, S
    40 NEXT I
    ```

Appendix C
Solutions (Even Numbered)

EXERCISE 1.1

2. b) Good books are friends and I never get lonesome.
   d) Two times four is equal to 8 and four times two is equal to 8.
   f) The commutative law applies and the distributive law applies.

EXERCISE 1.2

2. Fred is not a teacher and Fred is not a bum.
4. Ten is not larger than five.
6. I do not live in Ohio
8. Mr. Brown smokes cigars.
10. Paris is not the largest city in France.

EXERCISE 1.3

1. b) Hypothesis: John makes good grades and does not miss the exam.
      Conclusion: he will make an A.
      Already in if-then form.
   d) Hypothesis: the hurricane comes
      Conclusion: the wind blows
      If the hurricane comes then the wind blows.
   f) Hypothesis: A person is a politician.
      Conclusion: A person is honest.
      If a person is a politician then he is honest.
   h) Hypothesis: A person is a college student.
      Conclusion: A person is industrious.
      If a person is a college student then he is industrious.
   j) Hypothesis: A student procrastinates.
      Conclusion: The student should expect to fail.
      If a student procrastinates then he should expect to fail.
2. b) It is a theorem and it has not been proved.
   d) $x + 1 = 2$ and $x \neq 1$.

EXERCISE 1.4

I. 2. Yesterday was Sunday.
   4. Fred has fur.

II. 2. Mary does not own 100 oil wells.
    4. You can swim.

III. 2. If Jane is happy then she is polite.
    4. If a man marries then he is a good husband.

IV. 2. $p \wedge q \rightarrow r$
    4. 1. $p \rightarrow q$
       2. $\sim q \Rightarrow \sim p$

EXERCISE 1.5

I. 2.

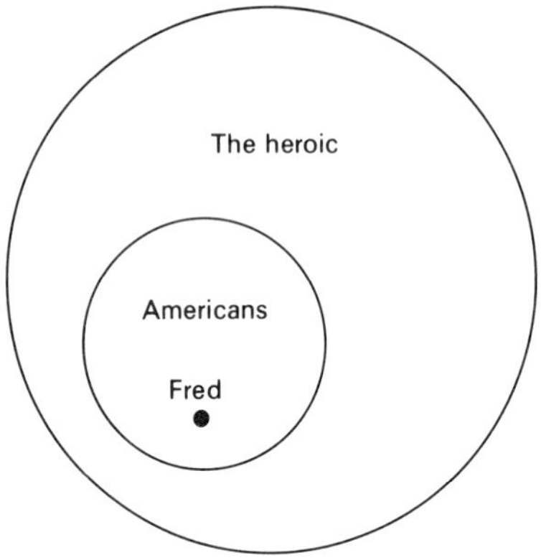
The heroic
Americans
Fred

The conclusion is correct.

4.

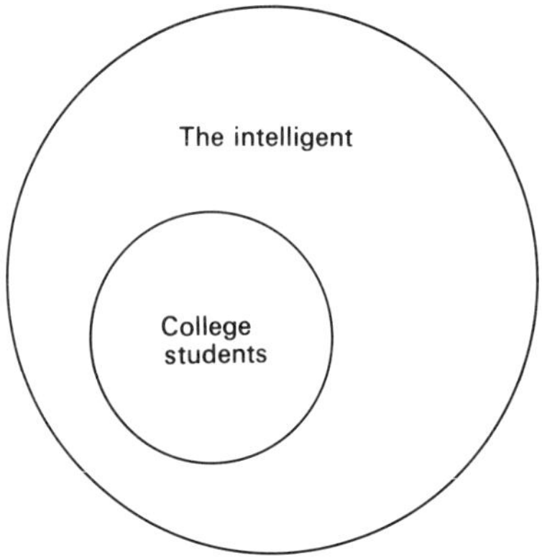
The intelligent
College students

The conclusion is incorrect.

6.

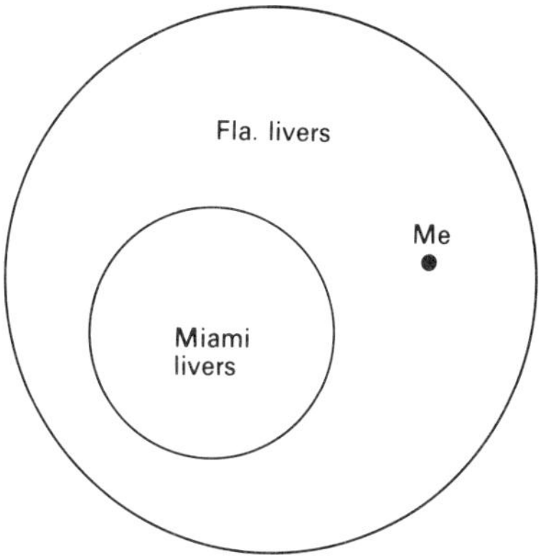
Fla. livers
Me
Miami
livers

The conclusion is incorrect.

8.

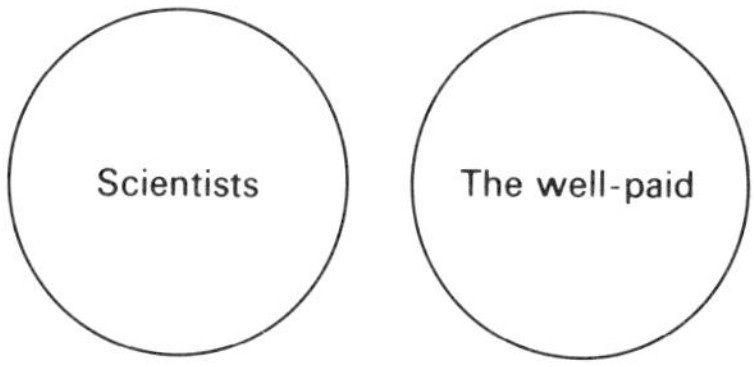
Scientists
The well-paid

The conclusion is incorrect

10.

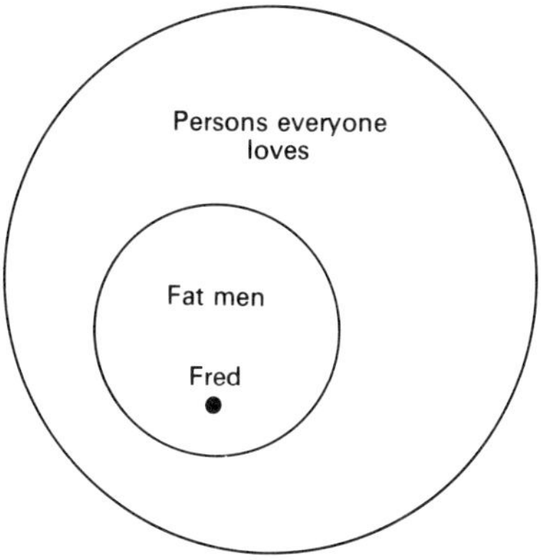
Persons everyone
loves
Fat men
Fred

The conclusion is correct.

II. 12. All squares are plane figures.
14. Some fat boys are not short boys.
16. The shirt needs laundering.
18. No prime number is both even and odd.
20. Some tall men are romantic.

EXERCISE 1.6

I. b) Converse: If it turns cold then it rains.
Inverse: If it does not rain then it does not turn cold.
Contrapositive: If it does not turn cold then it does not rain.

d) Converse: If Jones is President then the democrats win.
Inverse: If the democrats do not win then Jones will not be President.
Contrapositive: If Jones is not President then the democrats did not win.

II. b) If he is a dictator then he is undemocratic.
Converse: If he is undemocratic then he is a dictator.
Inverse: If he is not a dictator then he is not undemocratic:
Contrapositive: If he is not undemocratic then he is not a dictator.

d) If it is x then it is not y.
Converse: If it is not y then it is x.
Inverse: If it is not x then it is y.
Contrapositive: If it is y then it is not x.

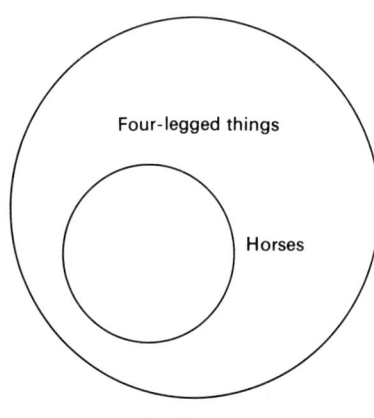

EXERCISE 1.7

Four-legged things

Horses

Implication

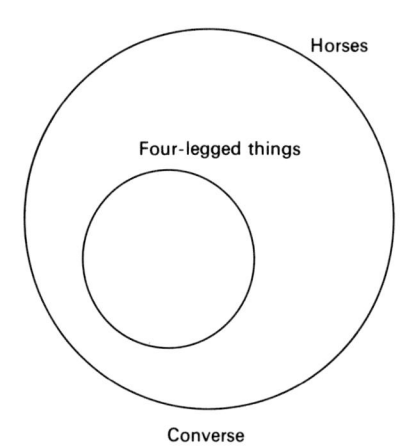

Horses

Four-legged things

Converse

EXERCISE 1.8

2. c)
4. a) If $2 + 2 \neq 4$ then ten is not larger than ten.
   b) If it is not an alligator then it does not bark like a dog
   c) If New York is not in Canada then Dallas is not in Texas.
   d) If the student is not antisocial then he is not brilliant.
6. Propositions (c) and (d) are equivalent to the given proposition.

EXERCISE 1.9

2. a)

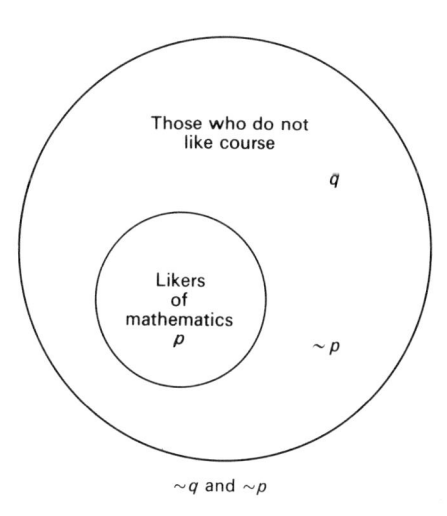

[Diagram: Large circle labeled "Those who do not like course" q, containing smaller circle "Likers of mathematics" p; region outside inner circle but inside outer is $\sim p$; region outside outer circle is $\sim q$ and $\sim p$.]

$\sim p$ is *not necessarily* included in $\sim q$. Argument invalid.

b)

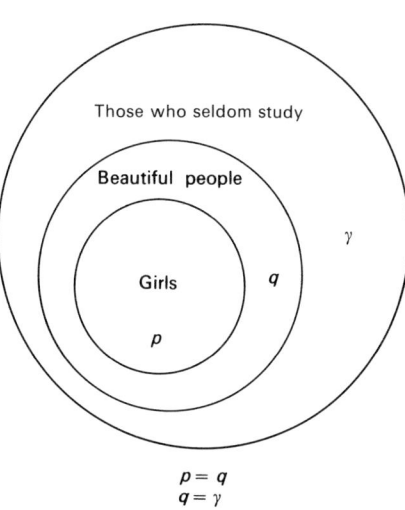

[Diagram: Three nested circles. Outermost "Those who seldom study" γ; middle "Beautiful people" q; innermost "Girls" p.]

$p = q$
$q = \gamma$
$\therefore p = \gamma$

γ is not included in p. The argument is invalid.

EXERCISE 2.1

2. all
4. a) $\{1, 2, 3\}, \{1, 2\}, \{1, 3\}, \{2, 3\}, \{1\}, \{2\}, \{3\}, \emptyset$
   b) $\{(1, 2), (2, 1)\}, \{(1, 2)\}, \{(2, 1)\}, \emptyset$
   c) $\{(B, B, B)\}, \{(G, G, G)\}, \{(B, B, B)\}, \{(G, G, G)\}, \emptyset$
   d) $\{(ss), (sf), (fs), (ff)\}, \{(ss), (sf), (fs)\}, \{(ss), (sf), (ff)\}, \{(ss), (fs), (ff)\},$
      $\{(ss), (sf)\}, \{(ss), (ff)\}, \{(ss), (fs)\}, \{(sf), (fs)\}, \{(sf), (ff)\}, \{(fs), (ff)\},$
      $\{(ss)\}, \{(sf)\}, \{(fs)\}, \{(ff)\}, \emptyset$
   e) $\{(AUR), (UAR), (RUA)\}, \{(AUR), (UAR)\}, \{(AUR), (RUA)\},$
      $\{(UAR), (RUA)\}, \{(AUR)\}, \{(UAR)\}, \{(RUA)\}, \emptyset$
6. Real numbers and counting numbers.
8.

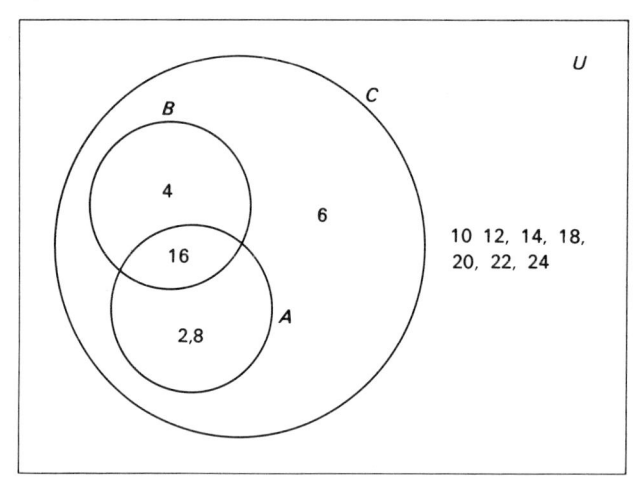

10. a) $A \subseteq B$ b) $x \in A$
    c) $(x_1, y_1) \in F$ d) $\{(B, B), (G, G)\} \subset \{(B, B), (G, G), (B, G)\}$

EXERCISE 2.2

2. a) $\{(s, s, s), (s, s, f), (s, f, s)\}$
   b) $\{(s, s, s), (s, f, s), (s, f, f), (f, s, s), (s, s, f)\}$
   c) $\{(s, s, s), (s, s, f), (s, f, f), (f, s, s)\}$
   d) $\{(s, s, s), (s, s, f), (s, f, s), (s, f, f), (f, s, s)\}$
   e) same as d.
   f) $\{(s, s, s), (s, s, f)\}$
   g) $\{(s, f, s), (f, s, s), (s, f, f), (f, s, f), (f, f, s)\}$
   h) $\{(s, s, f), (f, s, s), (s, f, f), (f, s, f), (f, f, s), (f, f, f)\}$
   i) $\{(s, s, s), (s, f, s), (f, s, f), (f, f, s), (f, f, f)\}$
   j) $\{(s, s, s), (s, s, f), (s, f, s), (s, f, f), (f, s, s), (f, s, f), (f, f, s), (f, f, f)\}$
4. a) 18
   b) none
   c) 13

Even Numbered Answers   307

   d) 10
6. a) $\{(B, B), (B, G)\}$
   b) U
   c) $\{(B, B), (B, G)\}$
   d) $\{(B, B), (B, G)\}$
   e) $\{(B, B), (B, G)\}$
   f) $\{(B, B), (B, G)\}$
8. a)

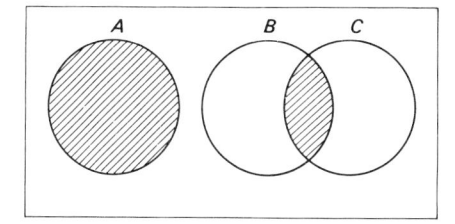

b)

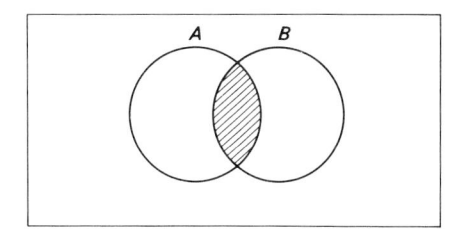

c)

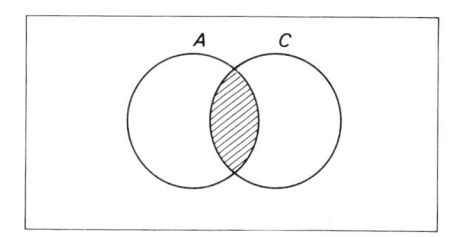

d)

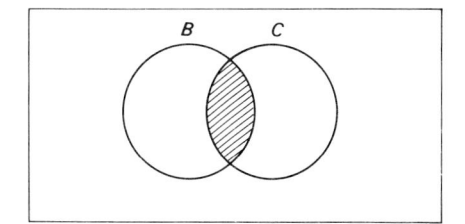

e)

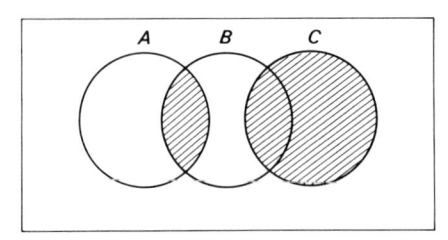

f)

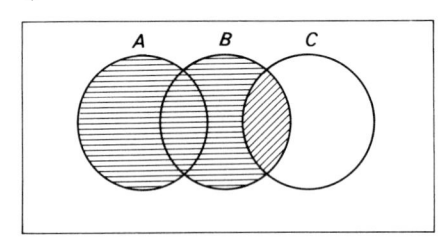

g)

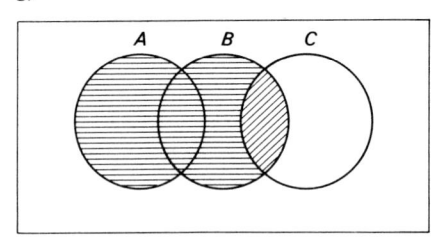

h)

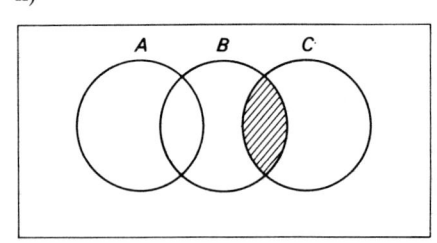

EXERCISE 2.3

2. The product of the number of elements in A and the number of elements in B is the number of elements in $A \times B$.
4. a) 105
   b) 105
   c) 105

EXERCISE 3.5

2. a) $-\frac{42}{10} = -\frac{21}{5}$
   b) $\frac{18}{5}$
   c) -1
   d) $+\frac{18}{70} = \frac{9}{35}$
   e) .01417

4. a) $\frac{12}{16}$
   b) $\frac{875}{1000}$
   c) not possible
   d) $\frac{20}{64}$
   e) not possible

6. a) .5625
   b) .25
   c) $.\overline{6}$
   d) .4558
   e) .231

8. No

10. a) $.16\overline{6}$
    b) .625
    c) $.11\overline{1}$
    d) .857
    e) 5.109

12. a) 2.5
    b) $-8.58\overline{3}$
    c) $-.483$
    d) 8.52

14. One-to-one correspondence

16. $\frac{11}{391} \stackrel{?}{=} \frac{21}{780}$
    $11 \cdot 780 \stackrel{?}{=} 391 \cdot 21$
    $8580 \neq 8211$

EXERCISE 3.6

4. The theorem is true for $n = 1$
   Assume true for $n = k$
   $1 + 3 + 5 + + 2k - 1 = k^2$
   Prove for $n = k + 1$
   $1 + 3 + 5 + \ldots 2k - 1 + 2(k+1) - 1 = k^2 + 2(k+1) - 1$
   $ = k^2 + 2k + 2 - 1$
   $ = (k+1)^2$

   The theorem is true for all n

6.

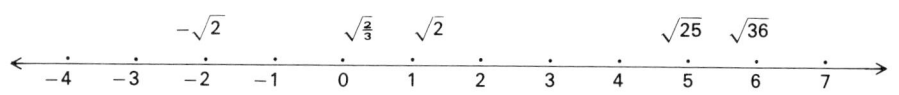

   $-\sqrt{2}$ at -2 to -1; $\sqrt{\frac{2}{3}}$, $\sqrt{2}$ between 0 and 2; $\sqrt{25}$, $\sqrt{36}$ at 5, 6

   Number line from -4 to 7.

8. a) Integer—real
   b) rational $\frac{1}{8}$—real
   c) 1 integer—real
   d) irrational—real
   e) rational real

EXERCISE 4.1

2. 5—hour clock addition is closed, associative, has an identity and each element has an inverse; hence, it forms an additive group.

4. a) 7   b) 4
   c) 2, 6 or 10   d) 4, 8 or 12
   e) 5   f) 10
   g) 3 or 9   h) 4
6. None

EXERCISE 4.2

2. a) 0   b) 2
   c) 0   d) 0
4. a) 7   b) 3
   c) 3   d) 4
   e) 7   f) 4
6. 4, 6, 8, 10, 12, 14

EXERCISE 4.3

2. a) $\begin{pmatrix} -3 & 8 \\ 7 & 16 \end{pmatrix}$ b) $\begin{pmatrix} x+3 & x+16 \\ x+9 & x-16 \end{pmatrix}$

   c) $\begin{pmatrix} 2x & x+10 \\ 2x & x \end{pmatrix}$ d) $\begin{pmatrix} 2 & 1 \\ 8 & 1 \end{pmatrix}$

4. a) 3×3 b) 2, 3, 11, 2, 3

6. $\begin{matrix} 50 \\ 10 \\ 25 \end{matrix}$ or (50 10 25)

EXERCISE 4.4

2. a) $\begin{pmatrix} 122 & 188 \\ 70 & 105 \end{pmatrix}$ b) $\begin{pmatrix} 122 & 188 \\ 70 & 105 \end{pmatrix}$

   c) $\begin{pmatrix} 126 & 182 \\ 76 & 107 \end{pmatrix}$ d) $\begin{pmatrix} 126 & 182 \\ 76 & 107 \end{pmatrix}$

4. a) $\begin{pmatrix} -\frac{1}{5} & \frac{3}{5} \\ -\frac{1}{5} & \frac{2}{5} \end{pmatrix}$ b) No

   c) No   d) No

6. No (in most cases)

EXERCISE 4.5

2.

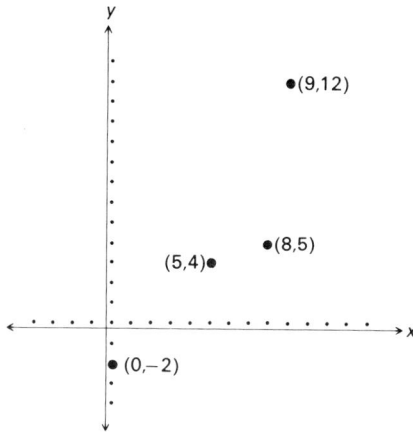

```
       y
       ↑
       :
       :            •(9,12)
       :
       :
       :       •(8,5)
       :  (5,4)•
       :
   ←───┼·········──────→ x
       :
       •(0,−2)
       :
       ↓
```

4. The pattern is shown in table for x

x	i	-1	$-i$	1
i	-1	$-i$	1	i
-1	$-i$	1	i	-1
$-i$	1	i	-1	$-i$
1	i	-1	$-i$	1

If x in the number i^x is divisible by 4, $i^x = 1$; if the remainder is 1, $i^x = i$; if remainder is 2, $i^x = -1$; remainder of 3, $i^x = -i$.

6. Yes. $(2 + \sqrt{3}, 0)$

8. a) Yes b) No. An infinite number would have the same magnitude.

10. a) $(a, b) + (c, d) = (a + c, b + d)$
    $(c, d) + (ab) = (c + a, d + b)$
    $\quad a + c = c + a$
    $\quad b + d = d + b$

    ∴ Complex numbers are commutative for addition.

    b) $(a, b) \times (c, d) = (ac - bd, ad + bc)$
    $(c, d) \times (a, b) = (ca - db, cb + da)$
    $\quad\quad ca = ac$
    $\quad\quad bd = db$
    $\quad\quad ad = da$
    $\quad\quad bc = cb$

    ∴ Complex numbers are commutative for multiplication.

EXERCISE 4.6

2. a) $\sqrt{13}$ b) $\sqrt{130}$
   c) 2   d) 2
   e) 2   f) 2
4. a) $\langle 3, 4 \rangle$ b) $\langle -2, -3 \rangle$
   c) $\langle 1, -1 \rangle$ d) $\langle -4, -3 \rangle$
6. a) 17   b) -1
   c) -16 d) 13
8. a) $\langle 2, 2 \rangle$ b) $\langle 2, 4 \rangle$
   c) $\langle \frac{2}{3}, 1 \rangle$ d) $k = 0$
   e) $8k + 10k = 9$
             $18k = 9$
                $k = \frac{1}{2}$

EXERCISE 4.7

2.

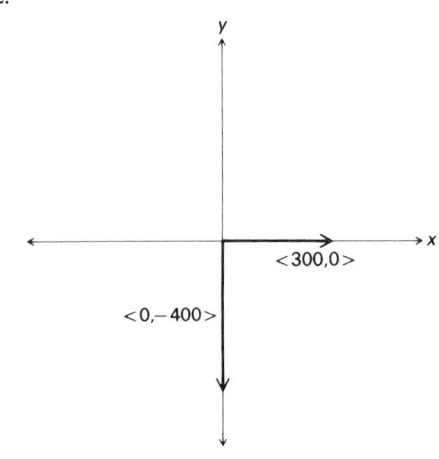

$\langle 300, 0 \rangle$
$\langle 0, -400 \rangle$

4.

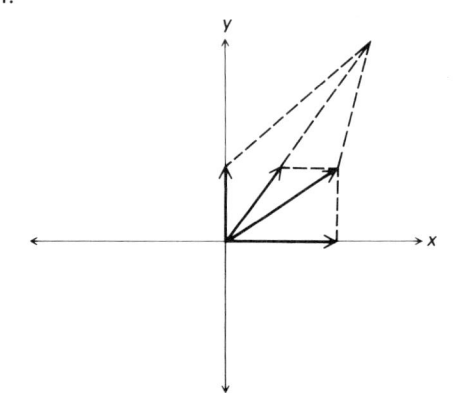

The resultant is a vector in the northeast direction.

EXERCISE 5.1

2. -7
4. 155
6. 35
8. 110
10. 37.6992
12. $95°$
14. 300

EXERCISE 5.2

2. $\{4\}$

4. $\{6, 7\}$

6. $\{0, 1, 2\}$

8. $\{5, 6, 7\}$

10. $\emptyset$

12. $\{1, 2, 3, 4 \ldots\}$

14. $\{-1, -2\}$

16. $(1, 1)F, (1, 2)F, (2, 1)F, (2, 2)F$

18. $(4, 0)T, (4, 1)T, (7, 0)T, (7, 1)T,$
    $(0, 0)F, (0, 1)F$

20. $(0, 0, 2)T, (0, 3, 2)T,$
    $(1, 0, 2)F, (1, 3, 2)F$

22. $(2, 3) F, (3, 3) T$

24. $(a)T, (b)F$

EXERCISE 5.3

2. 5
4. 4
6. 8
8. -10
10. -8
12. 4
14. 6.8
16. $\frac{1}{2}$
18. 1
20. 1
22. 0
24. -2
26. $\ell = \frac{P - 2w}{2}$
28. $a = S - Sr$
30. $W = 6, \ell = 9$
32. 6, 18
34. 3, 6
36. 360 mph; 400 mph.
38. Purse $18, shoes $20, dress $36
40. Co. $A = 20$; Co. $B = 40$; Co. $C = 60$

EXERCISE 5.4

2. $-x > y$
4. $x \geq y$
6. $xz > yz$
8. F, let $x = -2$ and $y = -1$
10. F
12. T

14. $x < 2$

16. $x < \frac{1}{2}$

18. $x > -2$

20. $x \geq 7$

22. $x \leq 6$ and $x > -5$

24. $450

26. 40 calories
28. Camera $100, radio $50, projector $90
30. $135 per month

EXERCISE 5.5

2. -1
4. 8
6. 0
8. 28
10. -18

12. $\{2, -2\}$

14. $\{4, -4\}$

16. $x > 6 \cup x < -6$

18. $\{4, -6\}$

20. $\{6, -9\}$

22. $x \geq 3 \cup x \leq -2$

24. $x > -1 \cup x < 1$

EXERCISE 5.6

2. $\{(3, 2)\}$
4. $\{(-3, 2)\}$
6. $\{(1, -1), (1, 0), (1, 1), (2, -1), (2, 0), (2, 1), (3, 1)\}$

Even Numbered Answers   315

8. ∅
10. {(−1, 1), (−1, 2), (0, 0), (0, 1)}
12. {(4, 9)}
14. {(10, −3) (10, −4)}
16. {(4, 4), (1, 6), (7, 2)}
18. 2 hamburgers, 5 soft drinks
20. {(3, 4), (3, 3), (4, 3), (8, 1), (7, 1), (6, 2), (6, 1), (5, 3), (5, 2), (2, 5), (2, 4), (1, 5)}

EXERCISE 5.7

2.

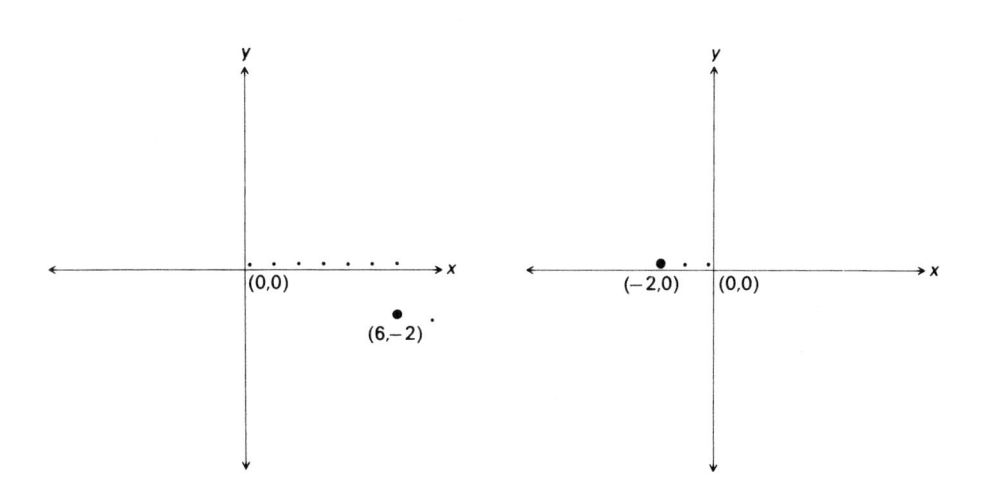

[Graph showing points along positive x-axis from (0,0) and point (6,−2)]

6.

[Graph showing points between (−2,0) and (0,0)]

4.

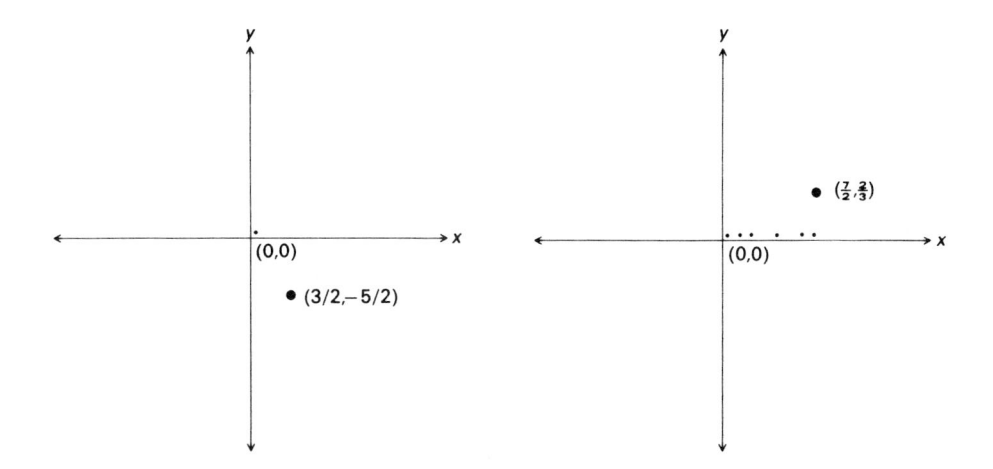

[Graph showing point (0,0) and point (3/2,−5/2)]

8.

[Graph showing points near (0,0) on x-axis and point (7/2, 4/3)]

316   Appendix C   Selected Answers

10.

(0,0)

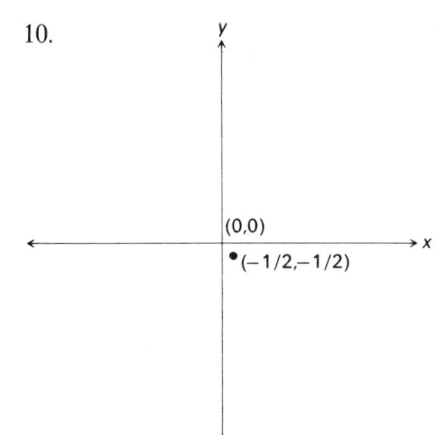

•(−1/2,−1/2)

12. $B(2, 3)$
14. $D(0, -4)$
16. $F(0, 6)$
18. $H(-8, 5)$
20. $J(8, -7)$
22. III

24. On positive x axis; not in any quadrant
26. I
28. On positive x axis; not in any quadrant
30. True
32. True

EXERCISE 5.8

2. $4x - y = 8$

x	y
2	0
0	−8
3	4

(3,4)
(2,0)
(0,−8)

4. $5x - 3y = 10$

x	y
2	0
0	$-\frac{10}{3}$
3	$\frac{5}{3}$

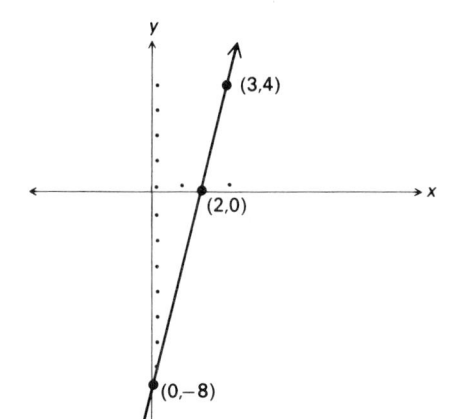

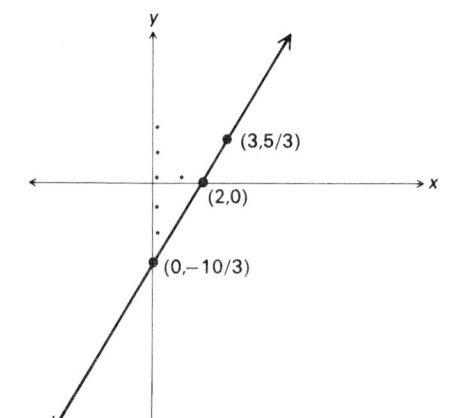

(3,5/3)
(2,0)
(0,−10/3)

Even Numbered Answers 317

6. $3x = 4y$

x	y
0	0
4	3
-4	-3

8. $-2x + \frac{1}{2}y = 1$

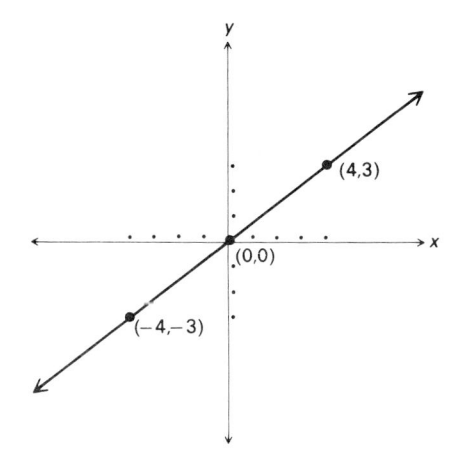

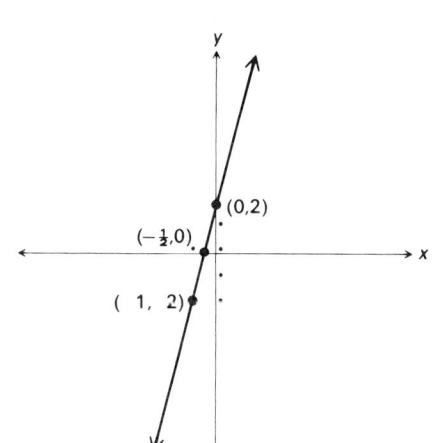

x	y
$-\frac{1}{2}$	0
0	2
-1	-2

10. $y = -\frac{1}{2}x + 2$
    Slope $= -\frac{1}{2}$
    y intercept $= (0, 2)$

12. $3x - 2y = 0$
    Slope $= \frac{3}{2}$
    y intercept $= (0, 0)$

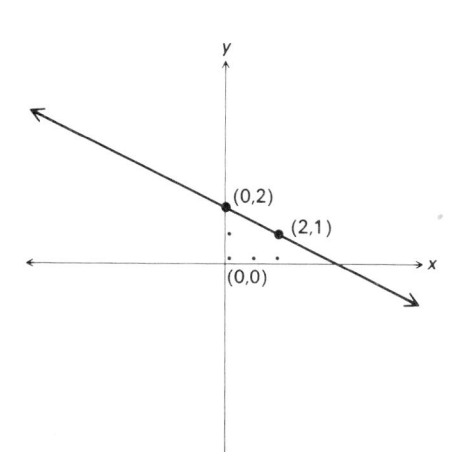

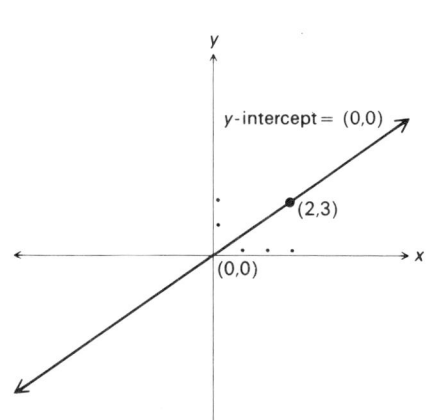

318   Appendix C   Selected Answers

14. $\frac{1}{3}x - \frac{1}{2}y = 1$
    Slope = $\frac{2}{3}$
    y intercept = $(0, -2)$

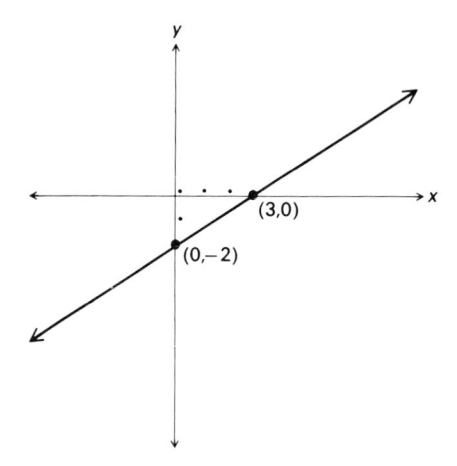

16. $3x \quad \frac{1}{2}y - 4$
    Slope = $\frac{6}{1}$
    y intercept = $(0, -8)$

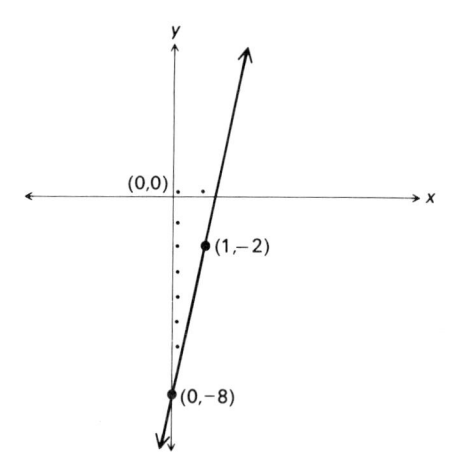

18. $4x + 3y \geq -1$

x	y
$-\frac{1}{4}$	0
0	$-\frac{1}{3}$
-1	1

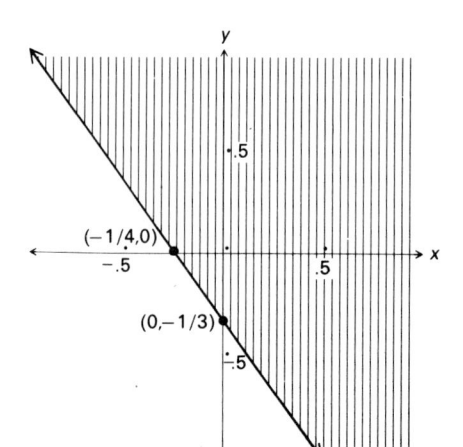

20. $\frac{1}{2}x - \frac{1}{3}y \leq 0$

x	y
0	0
6	9

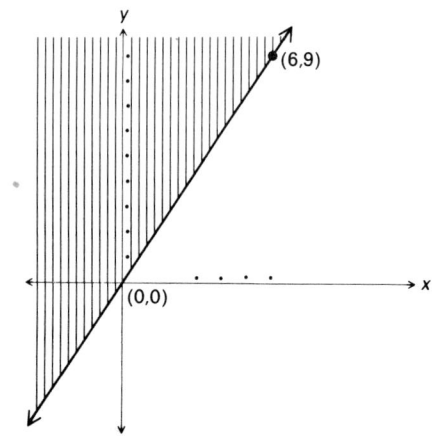

Even Numbered Answers 319

22. $x > 0$ and $y > 0$

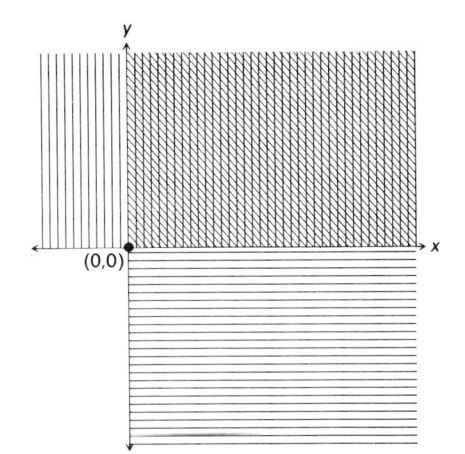

24. $x > 0$ or $y > 0$

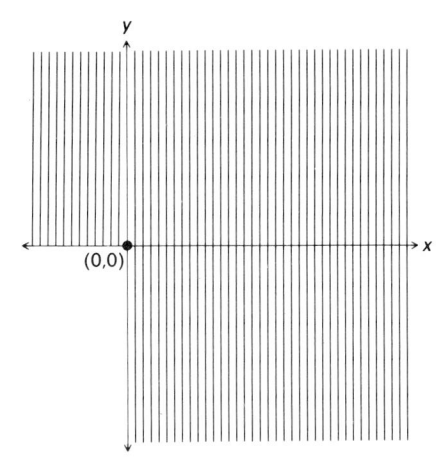

26. $x < 0$ and $y > 0$

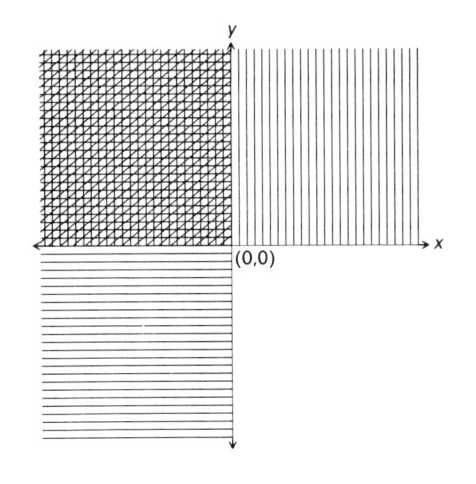

28. $y = 3x + 5$
30. $y = \frac{-5}{2}x + 3$

REVIEW EXERCISE 5.1

2. $\{2\}$

4. $\{3, 4\}$

6. $\{5, 6\}$

8. $T \{(0, 1), (1, 2)\}$, $F \{(0, 0), (0, 2), (1, 0), (1, 1), (2, 0), (2, 1), (2, 2)\}$

10. a) T
    b) F

320   Appendix C   Selected Answers

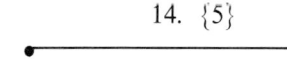

12. $\{3\}$ 14. $\{5\}$

16. $x > -4$

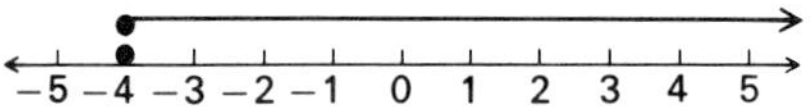

18. $x \leq -3$

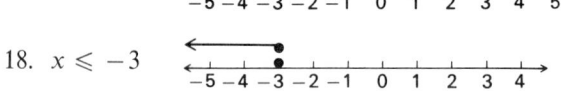

20. $x > -6$

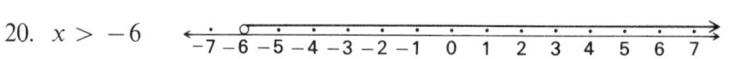

22. $\{3, -4\}$

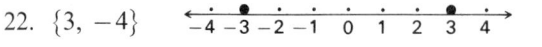

24. $x \leq 3 \cap x \geq -3$

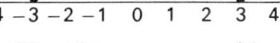

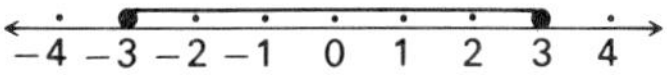

26. Sue 9, Sam 3   28. $25   30. Students 1200, adults 800

SELF QUIZ 5.1

2. $x = \{2, 4, 6\}$

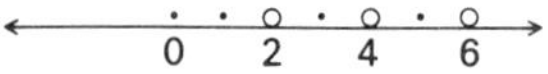

4. $x > -3$

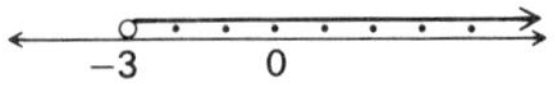

6. $x > -2$

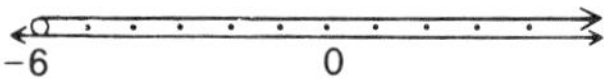

8. Purse $22, shoes $28, dress $50
10. 81

EXERCISE 5.9

2. $2x - y = 6$
   $x + 3y = 10$

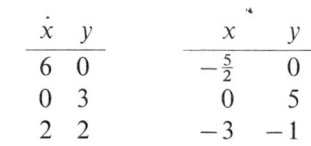

x	y
3	0
0	-6
4	2

x	y
10	0
0	$3\frac{1}{3}$
4	2

4. $x + 2y = 6$
   $2x - y = -5$

x	y
6	0
0	3
2	2

x	y
$-\frac{5}{2}$	0
0	5
-3	-1

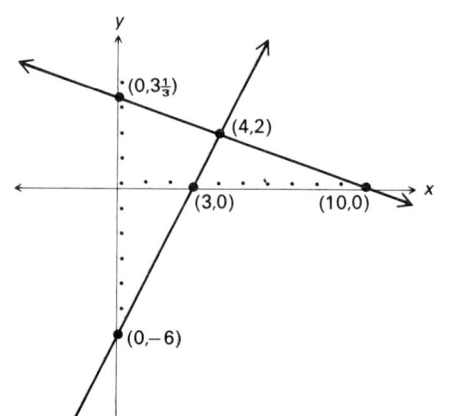

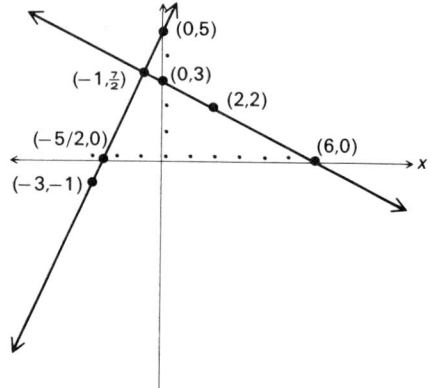

Even Numbered Answers 321

6. $5x + 2y = 20$
   $3x - 2y = 4$

x	y
4	0
0	10
2	5

x	y
$\frac{4}{3}$	0
0	-2
2	1

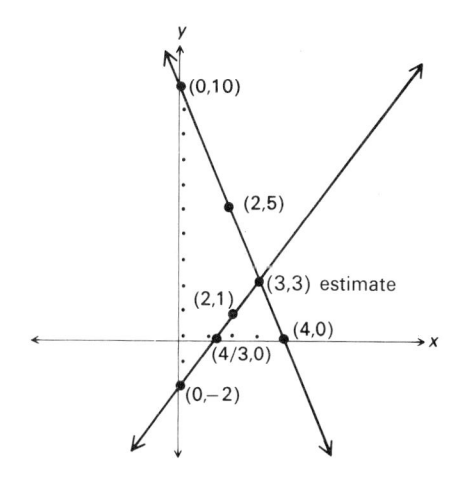

8. $x + 2y = 3$
   $2x + 4y = 6$

x	y
3	0
0	$\frac{3}{2}$
1	1

x	y
3	0
0	$\frac{6}{4}$
1	1

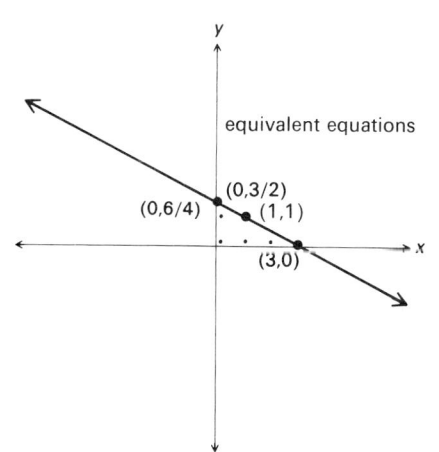

equivalent equations

10. $x - 3y = 0$
    $2x - y = 0$

x	y
0	0
3	1

x	y
0	0
2	4

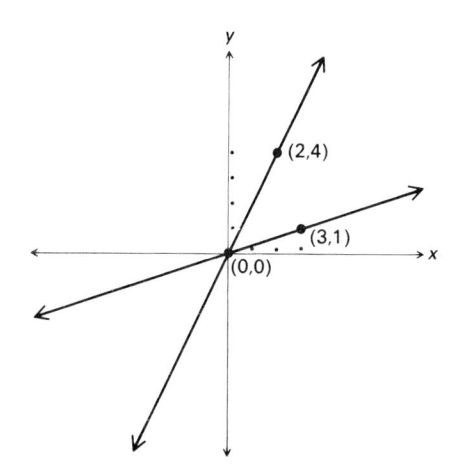

Appendix C Selected Answers

EXERCISE 5.10

2. $x = 2, y = 1$
4. $\emptyset$ (parallel lines)
6. $x = 2, y = -3$

8. $x = 2, y = 2$
10. $x = 4, y = 2$
12. $x = \frac{7}{9}, y = \frac{2}{3}$
14. $\emptyset$

16. $x = -\frac{5}{2}, y = 20$
18. 23, 48
20. 31 doz. medium sized eggs, 20 doz. large sized eggs
22. Mary 11 yrs., John 25 years
24. 125 children, 250 adults
26. stocks $4,666.67, bonds, $5,333.34

EXERCISE 5.11

2. (1, 2)
4. (3, 2)
6. (5, 2)
8. (7, 3)
10. (7, 1)

12. 5.3 oz. of 65%, 2.7 oz. of 80%
14. Bats $3.00, baseballs $1.25

EXERCISE 5.12

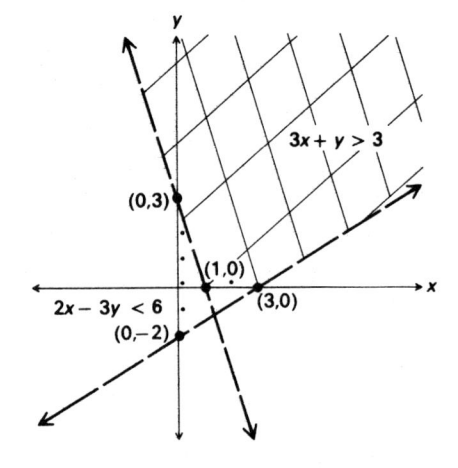

2. $x + y > 8$
    $2x - y > 4$

x	y
0	8
8	0

x	y
0	-4
2	0

4. $3x + y > 3$
    $2x - 3y < 6$

x	y
0	3
1	0

x	y
0	-2
3	0

6. $x - 2y > -1$
    $x < y$
    $3x + 4y < 12$

8. $3x - 2y \geq -6$
    $x \leq 2$
    $x + 3y \geq 6$

Even Numbered Answers 323

x	y 1		x	y 2		x	y
0	½		0	3		2	3
−1	0		4	0		−1	0

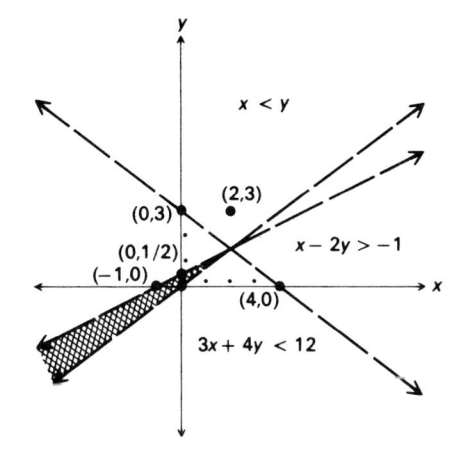

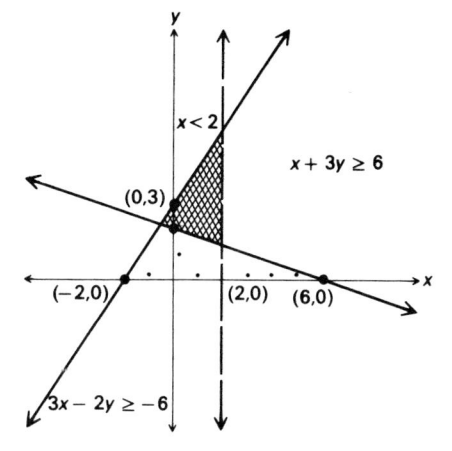

x	y 1		x	y
0	3		0	2
−2	0		6	0

10. $y < 2x + 1$
    $x + y < 3$
    $x + 3y > 3$
    $x < 2$

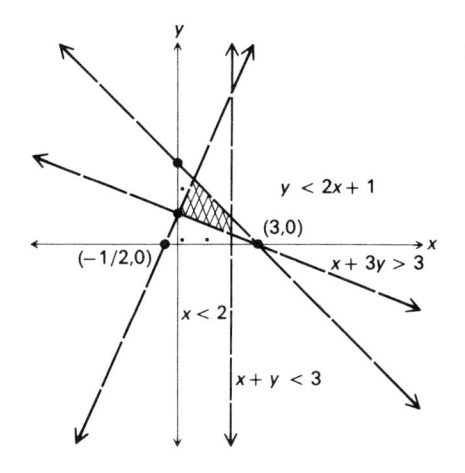

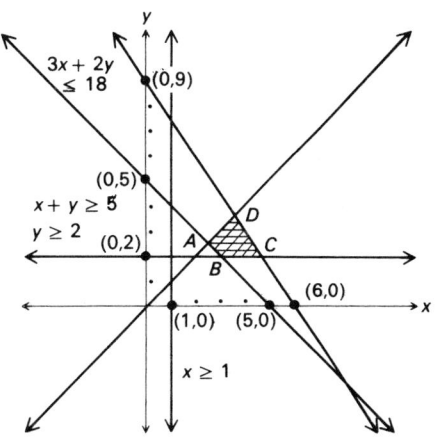

12. $x \geq 1$ $x + y \geq 5$
    $y \geq 2$ $3x + 2y \leq 18$
    $x \geq y$

x	y		x	y		x	y
−½	0		0	3		0	1
0	1		3	0		3	0

Vertices $P = 5x + 2y$
A $(\frac{5}{2}, \frac{5}{2})$ $17\frac{1}{2}$
B $(3, 2)$ 19
C $(\frac{14}{3}, 2)$ $27\frac{1}{3}$
D $(\frac{18}{5}, \frac{18}{5})$ $25\frac{1}{5}$

14.

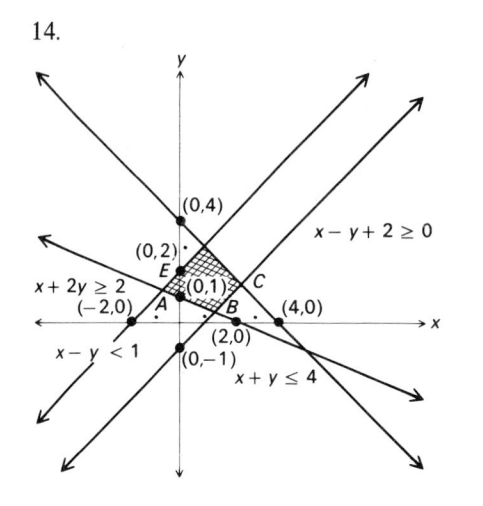

[Graph with lines $x-y+2 \geq 0$, $x+2y \geq 2$, $x-y < 1$, $x+y \leq 4$; points labeled $(0,4)$, $(0,2)$, E, $(-2,0)$, A, $(0,1)$, C, B, $(4,0)$, $(2,0)$, $(0,-1)$]

Vertices	$P = 10x + 12y$
A $(-\frac{2}{3}, \frac{4}{3})$	$9\frac{1}{3}$
B $(\frac{4}{3}, \frac{1}{3})$	$17\frac{1}{3}$
C $(\frac{5}{2}, \frac{3}{2})$	43
D $(1, 3)$	46

16. 4 regular and 6 heavy duty
18. $80,000 at 5%, $70,000 at 8%
20. 2 lb of beef; 1 lb of pork

EXERCISE 5.13

2. Domain $\{1, \frac{1}{2}, \frac{1}{4}, \frac{1}{8}\}$ Range $\{1, 2, 4, 8\}$
4. Domain $\{3, 4, 5, 6\}$ Range $\{-2, -3, 4, 5\}$

6. [Plot with points $(3, 15)$, $(2, 8)$, $(0, 0)$, $(-1, -1)$]

8. [Plot with points $(3, 15)$, $(2, 3)$, $(-1, 0)$, $(0, -1)$]

10. $C =$ (number of pounds) (price per pound)
12. $y = x + 1$

Even Numbered Answers 325

14.

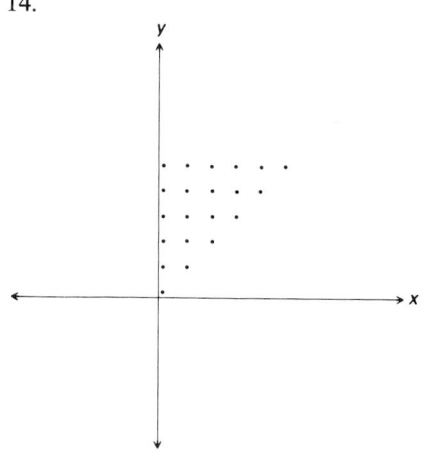

16.

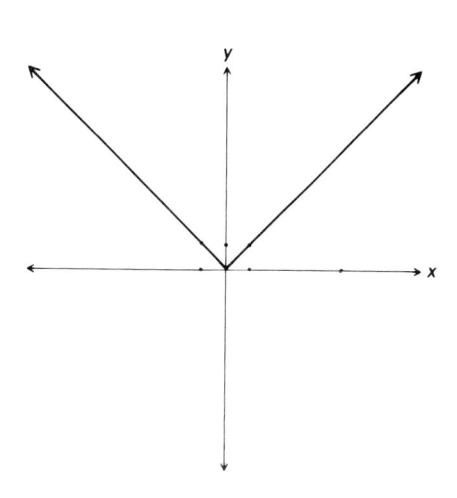

EXERCISE 5.14

2. $f(x) = 6 - x$
4. not a function
6. $f(x) = 12x$
8. $f(x) = 10x$
10. $C(n) = \dfrac{n}{10} + 5$
12. $V(e) = e^3$
14. $P(y) = 4y$

REVIEW EXERCISE 5.2

2. $\{(-2, 0), (0, 3), (2, 6)\}$
4. $\{(-1, 0), (1, -1)\}$
6. 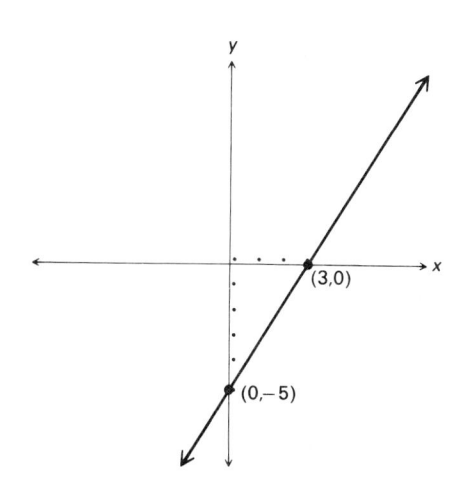
8.

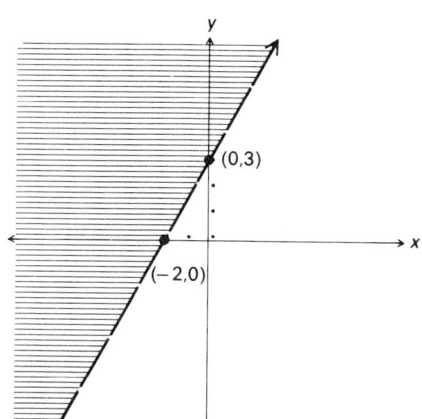

10.

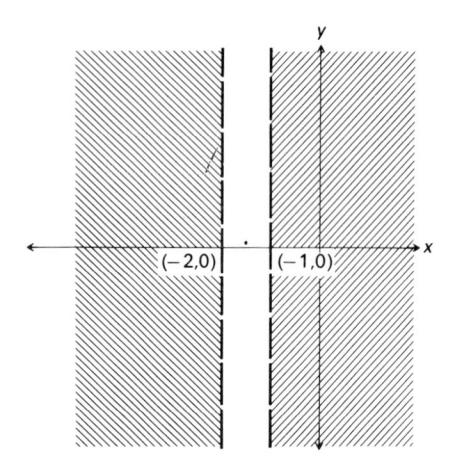

[Graph showing vertical dashed lines at x=-2 and x=-1 with shading outside the region between them, points (-2,0) and (-1,0) marked]

12. $y = \frac{3}{2}x - 2$
14. $y = x$
16. $\{(4, -2)\}$
18. $\{(3, 5)\}$
20. $(-\frac{16}{19}, -\frac{1}{19})$
22. $\{(\frac{1}{2}, -5)\}$

24.

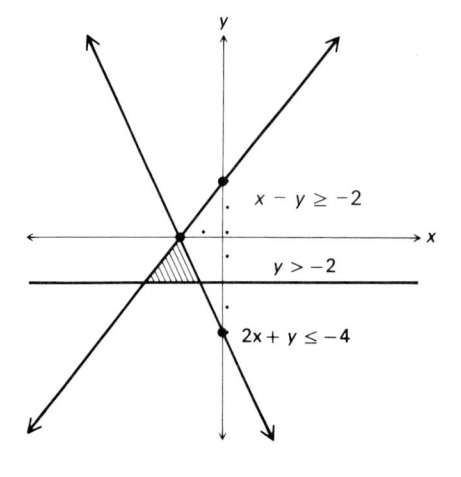

[Graph with three lines: $x - y \geq -2$, $y > -2$, $2x + y \leq -4$, showing a shaded triangular region]

26.

[Graph of a line through $(4,3,0)$ and $(0,-4)$]

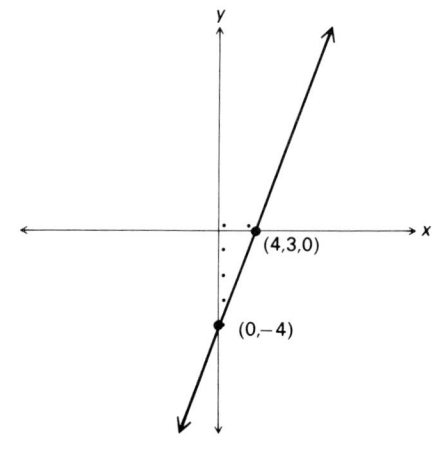

28. Tom $2.85, Sam $1.55

30. 4.5 lbs. @ .95; 5.5 lbs. @ .75

SELF QUIZ 5.2

2. $\{(4, 0)\}$
4.

[Graph showing line $3x - 4y = 12$ passing through $(4,0)$ and $(0,-2)$]

6.

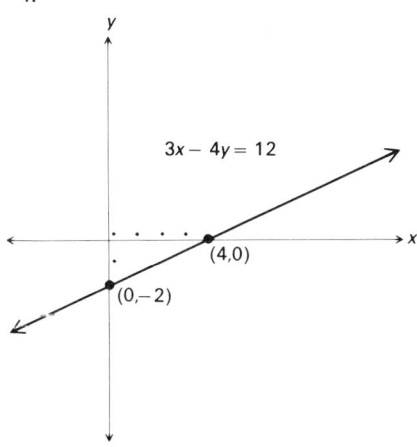

[Graph showing shaded region for $3x - 2y \geq -6$ with boundary line through $(0,3)$ and $(-2,0)$]

8. $\{(3, 1)\}$

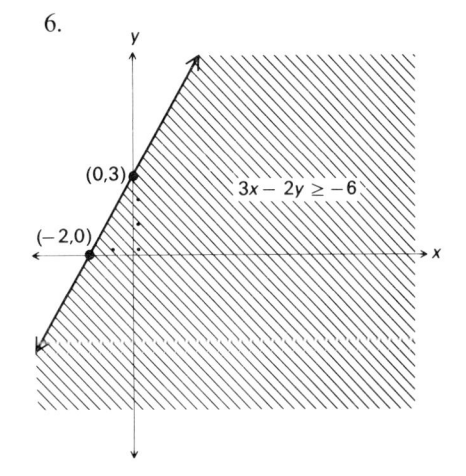

10. $(1, 0), (\frac{4}{3}, \frac{4}{3}), (\frac{2}{3}, \frac{2}{3})$

EXERCISE 6.1

2. $3 \cdot s$
4. $\frac{1}{2} \cdot x$
6. $.3 \cdot x$
8. $3 \cdot x \cdot y$
10. $2 \cdot (x + y)$
12. $3 \cdot a \cdot (x + y)(x + y)$
14. $12 \cdot 1$ or $6 \cdot 2$ or $3 \cdot 4$
16. $6 \cdot x \cdot y \cdot y$ or $3 \cdot 2 \cdot x \cdot y \cdot y$
18. $a \cdot b \cdot \frac{1}{2}$
20. $2 \cdot a \cdot b \cdot c \cdot c \cdot \frac{1}{2}$
22. 1
24. $2y$
26. 3
28. y
30. b^3
32. s^n
34. $3b^3$
36. $(x + 1)^2$
38. 3
40. 9
42. $\frac{9}{2}$
44. 0
46. 76
48. 33
50. a) π
    b) 10π
    c) $\dfrac{5\pi}{2}$
52. a) $\dfrac{32\pi}{3}$
    b) $\dfrac{256\pi}{3}$
    c) $\dfrac{\pi}{6}$
    d) $\dfrac{32\pi s^3}{3}$

EXERCISE 6.2

2. $6a^3b^6$
4. $-6a^3b$
6. $144s^9$
8. $\frac{1}{4}g^3t^3$
10. $.00032x^5$
12. $-.06a^2b^3$
14. $-.64ab^4$
16. $3a^3b^3$
18. $41a^6b^{10}c^2$
20. $2x^6 + x^5 + 4x^4 + 4x^3$
22. $a^{m+n} + 2(ab)^m + b^{m+n}$
24. Let $x =$ length of radius of small circle. Then $2x =$ length of radius of large circle.
    a) $4\pi x^2$
    b) πx^2
    c) $3\pi x^2$

EXERCISE 6.3

2. $-27x^9$
4. $16a^7b^4$
6. $8a^4$
8. $-32a^{10}b^3c^3$
10. $[x^9y^6]$
12. $27n^5p^4q^7$
14. $-54ab^3c^3 - 45a^2b^2c^2d$
16. $.1m^7n^2 + m^6n^3 - .6m^5n^4$
18. 0
20. 0

EXERCISE 6.4

2. $-a^2b^2 + b^2c^2 - b^3$
4. $-8x^5 + 6x^4 - 4x^3$
6. $a^2 - b^2$
8. $2x^2 + 3xy - 2xy^2 - 3y^3$
10. $-4x^3y^2 + 10x^2y + 2x^2y^3$
12. $8a^2 - .48ab - 1.08b^2$
14. $2x^3 - x^2 - 10x + 8$
16. $-6a^8b^4 - 24a^7b^4 + 24a^5b^5 + 12a^3b^8$
18. $4x^4 + 8x^3 + 3x^2 + 10x + 8$
20. $-6x^4 - 7x^3 - 5x^2 + 10x + 8$
22. Area $= 2x^2 - 5x$ sq. ft. $x =$ width)
24. Area $= 2x^2 - 20x$ sq. ft. ($x =$ width)
26. a) Area $= 2x^2$ sq. ft.
    b) Area $= 2x^2 + 12x + 16$ sq.ft.
    c) Area $= 2x^2 + 12x + 16$
       $= 2x^2 + 2(6x + 8)$
    d) Width 30 ft., length 60 ft.

EXERCISE 6.5

2. $\dfrac{4b}{a}$
4. $\dfrac{-3y}{x^2}$
6. $\dfrac{3r^4}{4s^2}$
8. $\dfrac{12x}{y}$
10. $\dfrac{-26q^2}{p}$
12. $\dfrac{-2}{n}$
14. $-\dfrac{1}{abc}$
16. $\dfrac{y}{x^3}$
18. $2a^{m-1}b^{n-1}$
20. $\dfrac{3ay^{m-n}}{16}$

Even Numbered Answers

EXERCISE 6.6

2. $3x + 4$
4. 1
10. $3 - 2m^3n^5 + 4m^5n^4$
6. $8a^2 - 9a + 7$
8. $3x^2y^2 - xy + 4$
12. $\dfrac{2 + 6b - 4ab}{7b^2}$

EXERCISE 6.7

2. $a + 3$
4. $x - 2$
6. $n + 6p$
8. $3b + b$
10. $a + 3b$
12. $4a^2 + 2ab + b^2$
14. $m + 7$ R 3
16. $3a^2 + 2a - 6$ R 33
18. $3n^2 + 8n + 16$
20. $2n^3 + 3n^2 - 6n + 5$
22. $3x - 2$
24. 7
26. Width $= 4$, length $= 12$

EXERCISE 6.8

2. 18
4. 22
6. 5
8. $\dfrac{a^2}{10}$
10. 3
12. $\tfrac{7}{8}$
14. $\dfrac{\sqrt{2a^2}}{2}$
16. $4m^2n^4\sqrt{3}$
18. 5
20. $\tfrac{1}{2x}$

EXERCISE 6.9

2. $xy(x - y)$
4. $7x^3(1 - 3x)$
6. $5a(3a - c)$
8. $49x(x - 2)$
10. $n(3n + 13)$
12. $x^3y^3(13y - 17xy^2 + 25)$
14. $x(12x^2 + 13x + 24)$
16. $5a^3b^2(a^2 - 2ab^3 + 4b - 5a^2b^4)$
18. $4x^3y^4(xy - 1)$
20. $ab(ab + 7b + 6a)$

EXERCISE 6.10

2. $(2x - 3)(2x + 3)$
4. $(2x - z)(2x + z)$
6. $(6m - 1)(6m + 1)$
8. $(-2t + 3s)(2t + 3s)$
10. $(.5ab^2 - .6c^3)(.5ab^2 + .6c^3)$
12. $(x - \tfrac{1}{2})(x + \tfrac{1}{2})$
14. $3x^2(x - 3)(x + 3)'$
16. $x^2y(x^2 - y)(x^2 + y)$
18. $(a - b^n)(a + b^n)$
20. $(a + 2b - 2c)(a + 2b + 2c)$

EXERCISE 6.11

2. $(a + 3c)(a + 3c)$
4. $(t - 7)(t - 7)$
6. $(4x + 1)(4x + 1)$
8. $(x + 6y)(x + 6y)$

10. $(5x - 1)(5x - 1)$
12. $3(a - 9b)(a - 9b)$
14. $(4a + 5b)(4a + 5b)$
16. $(t - 2s^2)(t + 2s^2)$
18. $2t(t - 2)(t - 2)$
20. $(11abc - 1)(11abc - 1)$

EXERCISE 6.12

2. $(x + 4)(x + 1)$
4. $(3n - 1)(n + 4)$
6. $(y + 4)(y + 2)$
8. $(4t - 3)(3t + 5)$
10. $(5a + 4)(3a - 5)$
12. $(4a - 1)(a - 2)$
14. $(2t + 3)(5t + 3)$
16. $(t + n + 7)(t + 4 - 2)$
18. $(xyz + 6)(xyz - 2)$
20. $(3x - 1)(x + 2)$

EXERCISE 6.13

2. $-6, -1$
4. -2 (multiplicity of 2)
6. $-\frac{1}{2}$ (multiplicity of 2)
8. $-\frac{1}{2}, 2$
10. $3, 2$
12. $\frac{5}{3}, -2$
14. 5 (multiplicity of 2)
16. $-\frac{3}{4}, -\frac{4}{3}$
18. $13, 14$
20. $-\frac{5}{3}, 2$
22. 30 Seconds
24. Height 8 feet base 12 feet
26. Decrease the area.
    $40'' \cdot 80'' = 3200 \, sq''$

EXERCISE 6.14

2. $x = 4 + 2\sqrt{6}$ or $x = 4 - 2\sqrt{6}$
4. $x = \frac{3}{2}$ or $x = -\frac{4}{5}$
6. $x = \dfrac{3 + \sqrt{11}}{6}$ or $x = \dfrac{3 - \sqrt{11}}{6}$
8. $x = \dfrac{1 + \sqrt{7}}{3}$ or $x = \dfrac{1 - \sqrt{7}}{3}$
10. $x = \dfrac{4 + \sqrt{10}}{3}$ or $x = \dfrac{4 - \sqrt{10}}{3}$
12. $x = \dfrac{-9 + \sqrt{21}}{10}$ or $x = \dfrac{-9 - \sqrt{21}}{10}$
14. $x = 2 + i$ or $x = 2 - i$
16. $x = \dfrac{-5 + i}{2}$ or $x = \dfrac{-5 - i}{2}$
18. $x = \dfrac{-1 + 2i}{3}$ or $x = \dfrac{-1 - 2i}{3}$
20. $x = \dfrac{5 + i\sqrt{11}}{6}$ or $x = \dfrac{5 - i\sqrt{11}}{6}$
22. Width 70 feet, depth 120 feet
24. 36 feet square.

EXERCISE 6.15

2.

4.

6.

8.

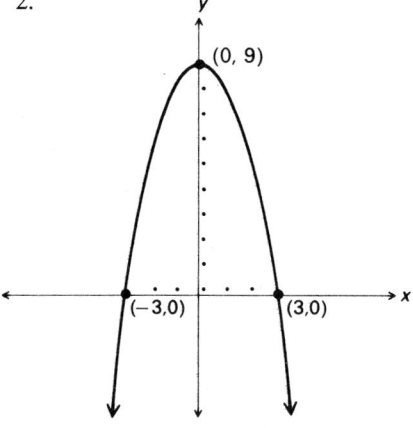

10.

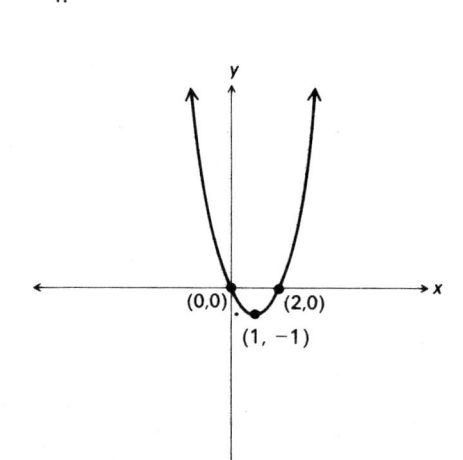

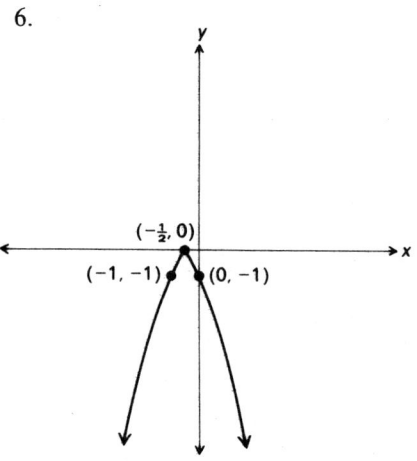

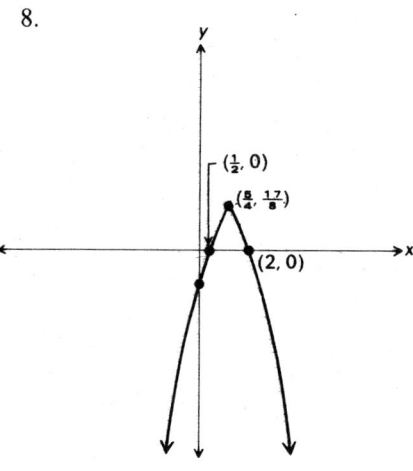

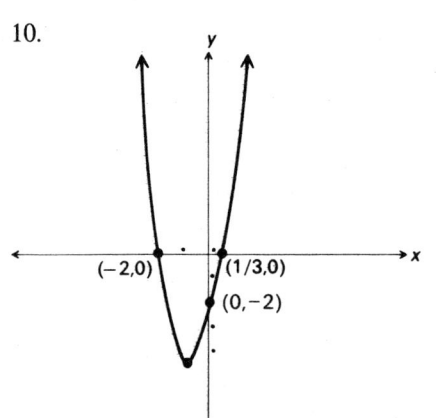

12. 97 or 98 tickets

14. $42\frac{1}{2}$ cents

REVIEW EXERCISE 6.1

2. -6
4. 1
6. $24x^3y^2$
8. $6x^8y^5$
10. $a^6b^5c^6$
12. $2x^2 - 3x - 2$
14. $\dfrac{4}{xy^2}$
16. $\dfrac{2x^2 + 3xy + y^2}{5}$
18. $3x^2 - 2xy + 5y^2$
20. -15
22. $\dfrac{7x}{8y}$
24. $(.5 - x)(.5 + x)$
26. $(2x + 1)(2x + 1)$
28. $(x - 6)(x - 1)$
30. $(2x - 3)(x - 4)$
32. $\{-\frac{1}{3}, \frac{1}{3}\}$
34. $\{8, -\frac{7}{6}\}$
36. $\{1 + \sqrt{5}, 1 - \sqrt{5}\}$
38. $\left\{\dfrac{-1 + \sqrt{7}}{2}, \dfrac{-1 - \sqrt{7}}{2}\right\}$
40.

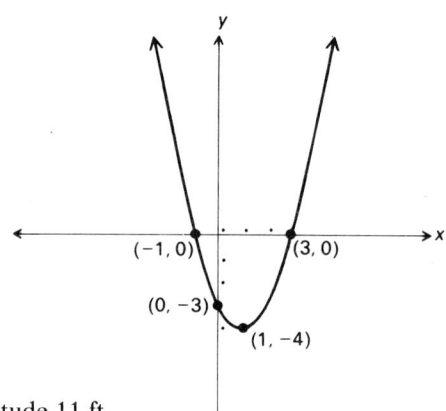

42. 12.68 ft.
44. base 16 ft. altitude 11 ft.

SELF QUIZ 6.1

2. 2
4. $\dfrac{3x}{y}$

Even Numbered Answers 333

6. $\dfrac{9x^2}{5y}$

8. $(2x - 1)(x + 2)$

10. $\sqrt{2}, -\sqrt{2}\}$

EXERCISE 7.1

2. $\sqrt{a^2 + b^2}$, 5; 12; $4\sqrt{11}$

6. Let $s = 2$
$d^2 = s^2 + s^2 = 8$
$d = 2\sqrt{2}$

EXERCISE 7.3

2.

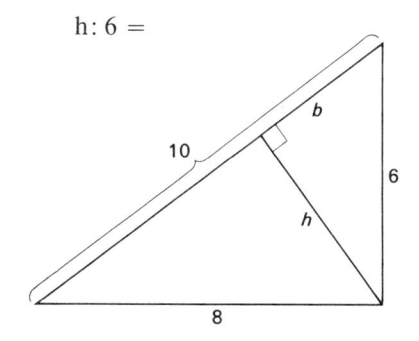

h: 6 =

$\text{Area} = \dfrac{8 \cdot 6}{2} = 24$

$\text{Area} = \dfrac{10 \cdot h}{2} = 24$

$10 \cdot h = 48$

$h = \tfrac{48}{10}$

4. $A = \left(\dfrac{6 + 8}{2}\right)4 = 28$ sq. ft.

6.

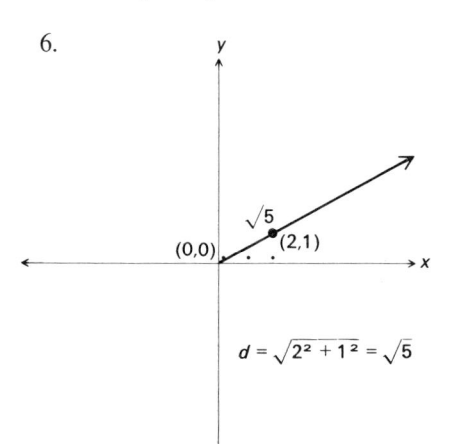

$d = \sqrt{2^2 + 1^2} = \sqrt{5}$

8.

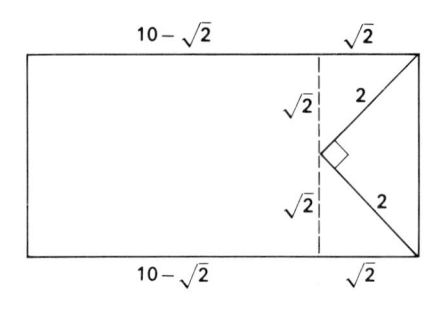

$$A = (10 - \sqrt{2})2\sqrt{2} + \frac{2\sqrt{2}\sqrt{2}}{2}$$
$$A = 20\sqrt{2} - 4 + 2$$
$$A = 20\sqrt{2} - 2$$

10.

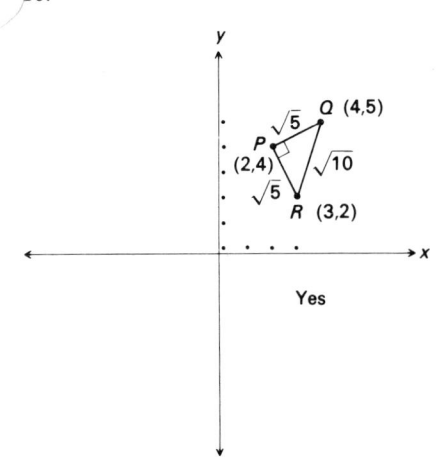

$\overline{PQ} = \sqrt{5}$
$\overline{PR} = \sqrt{5}$
$RQ = \sqrt{10}$

EXERCISE 7.4

2. a) 4π units
   b) π units
   c) 10π units
4. $27 + 3\sqrt{5}$ feet

8. Volume = $394\frac{2}{3}\pi$ cu. units
   Weight = $\frac{4}{3}\pi(296)(128)$ pounds

EXERCISE 8.2

2. a) $Pr(E) = \frac{1}{2}$
   b) $Pr(E) = \frac{1}{3}$
   c) $Pr(E) = \frac{5}{6}$
4. a) $Pr(E) = \frac{6}{11}$
   b) $Pr(E) = \frac{5}{11}$
   c) $Pr(E) = \frac{1}{11}$
   d) $Pr(E) = 1$
6. $Pr(E) = \frac{10}{250} = \frac{1}{25}$
8. $Pr(E) = \frac{1}{6}$
   b) $Pr(E) = \frac{2}{6}$
10. a) $S = \{(S, K), (S, R,), (S, B), (K, R), (K, B), (R, B)\}$
    b) $\frac{1}{6}$
    c) $\frac{1}{2}$
    d) $\frac{1}{6}$
    e) $\frac{1}{6}$
12. a) $\frac{1}{9}$
    b) $\frac{1}{9}$
    c) $\frac{5}{9}$
    d) $\frac{4}{9}$

EXERCISE 8.3

2. a) $9 \times 8 = 72$
   b) $9 \times 9 = 81$
4. $3^5 = 243$
6. $4 \cdot 5 \cdot 4 = 80$
8. $6 \cdot 7 \cdot 4 = 168$
10. $9! = 362,880$

EXERCISE 8.4

2. $P(10, 10) = \dfrac{10!}{(10-10)!} = 3,628,800$

4. $P(7, 7) = \dfrac{7!}{(7-7)!\, 2!} = 2520$

Appendix C Selected Answers

6. $P(7, 7) = \dfrac{7!}{(7 - 7)!} = 5040$
8. $P(4, 4) + P(4, 3) + P(4, 2) + P(4, 1) = 64$
10. $P(12, 3) = 1320$
12. $2(P(6, 6)(P(4, 4))) = 34{,}560$

EXERCISE 8.5

2. $C(12, 9) = \dfrac{12!}{(12 - 9)!\, 9!} = 220$
4. No. Order is important.
6. $C(52, 13) = \dfrac{52!}{(52 - 13)!\, 13!}$
8. $C(7, 4) \cdot (3, 3)$
10. $C(10, 2) \cdot C(8, 3) \cdot C(5, 5)$

EXERCISE 8.6

2. $Pr(E) = \dfrac{C(10, 1)}{C(25, 1)}$
4. $Pr(E) = \dfrac{C(5, 2)}{C(10, 2)}$
   b) $Pr(E) = \dfrac{2[C(5, 1) \cdot C(5, 1)]}{C(10, 2)}$
6. a) $Pr(E) = \dfrac{C(10, 2)}{C(20, 2)}$
   b) $Pr(E) = \dfrac{C(4, 1) \cdot C(6, 1)}{C(20, 2)}$ or $\dfrac{C(6, 3) \cdot C(10, 1)}{C(20, 2)}$ or $\dfrac{C(6, 1) \cdot C(10, 10)}{C(20, 2)}$
8. $Pr(E) = \dfrac{[P(3, 3) \cdot P(2, 2)]}{P(5, 5)}$
10. $Pr(E) = \dfrac{C(1, 1)}{C(4, 1)} \cdot \dfrac{C(1, 1)}{C(3, 1)} \cdot \dfrac{C(1, 1)}{C(2, 1)} \cdot \dfrac{C(1, 1)}{C(1, 1)}$

EXERCISE 8.7

2. $Pr(E) = \frac{3}{6} + \frac{3}{6} - \frac{2}{6} = \frac{2}{3}$
4. $Pr(E) = \frac{1}{3} + \frac{1}{3} - \frac{1}{9} = \frac{5}{9}$ or $Pr(E) = 1 - \frac{2}{3} \cdot \frac{2}{3} = \frac{5}{9}$
6. a) $Pr(E) = \frac{1}{8}$
   b) $Pr(E) = \frac{1}{8}$
   c) $Pr(E) = \frac{3}{8}$
   d) $Pr(E) = \frac{1}{4}$

Even Numbered Answers 337

8. a) $Pr(E) = \frac{1}{15}$
   b) $Pr(E) = \frac{1}{10}$
   c) $Pr(E) = \frac{1}{5}$
10. Yes, $Pr(E) = \frac{1}{1024}$

EXERCISE 8.8

2. No, $0.60 each
4. $E(A) = \$4.17$. He should expect to pay more than $E(A)$
6. $E(A) = \$14,000$
8. Yes, $E(A) = 0$
10. $E(A) = \$31.67$

SELF TEST 8.1

2. a) $\{g, b\}$
   b) $\{(g, g), (g, b), (b, g), (b, b)\}$
   c) $\{(ggg), (ggb), (gbg), (gbb), (bgg), (bgb), (bbg), (bbb)\}$
4. $P(9, 5) = \dfrac{9!}{4!}$; no repetition allowed. 9^5 repetitions allowed.
6. a) $C(50, 5)$
   b) $Pr(E) = \dfrac{C(5, 5)}{C(50, 5)}$
8. a) $C(52, 5)$
   b) $Pr(E) = \dfrac{C(26, 5)}{C(52, 5)}$

EXERCISE 8.9

2. a) $\bar{x} = \$12,020$
   b) $M = \$7,000$
   c) median
4. The term "all employees" would include the officials whose earnings are usually high and constitutes extreme values.
6. a) The mean is an average value.
   b) Yes
8. 92 or greater
10. a) $\bar{x} = 9.54$
    b) $M = 9.3$
    c) median: 10.6 sec. is on extreme value for this race.

EXERCISE 8.10

2. a) $\bar{x} = 5, s^2 = \frac{5}{3}, s \doteq 1.3$
   b) $\bar{x} = 16, s^2 = 8.5, s \doteq 2.9$
   c) $\bar{x} = 5, s^2 = 2.67, s \doteq 1.63$
4. $\bar{x} = 5.2$ lbs., $s \doteq .43$ lbs.
6. $s^2 = 3.86$ in., $s \doteq 1.96$ in.
8. $\bar{x} = 67, s \doteq 2.8$
10. a) $\bar{x} = 2, s \doteq 1.9$
    b) Spelling: 18 made higher grades in spelling while 25 made higher in arithmetic.

EXERCISE 8.11

2. a) $.1359 + .0214 + .0013 = .1586$
   b) $.0214 + .0013 = .0227$
   c) $.3413 + .3413 + .1359 = .8185$
4. a) 81.85%
   b) $Pr(E) = .0013$
6. $Pr(E) = .6826$
8. $Pr(E) = .0227$
10. $Pr(E) = .1587$

EXERCISE 9.1

2. a) $101_2 = 1 \times 2^2 + 0 \times 2^1 + 1 \times 2^0 = 5$
   b) $10101_2 = 1 \times 2^4 + 1 \times 2^2 + 1 \times 2^0 = 21$
   c) $1 \times 2^1 + 1 \times 2^0 + 1 \times 2^{-1} + 1 \times 2^{-2} = 3.75$
   d) $1 \times 2^{-4} + 1 \times 2^{-6} = \frac{1}{16} + \frac{1}{64} = \frac{5}{64} = .078125$
4. a) 1010   b) 10101
   c) 110100   d) 101100
6. a) 10.00   b) 1010.10
   c) 1.0111   d) 110.111
8. No. A "binary" point.
10. Since fewer symbols are required for each numeral in bases higher than 2 the number of electric impulses required for a computation may be reduced. Also programming may be simplified. This question cannot be answered beyond doubt without a knowledge of how a computer operates.

EXERCISE 9.2

2. a) $72_8 = 7 \times 8 + 2 \times 8^0 = 58$
   b) $635_8 = 6 \times 8^2 + 3 \times 8 + 5 = 413$
   c) $.05_8 = \frac{5}{64} = .078125$
   d) $603.05 = 6 \times 8^2 + 3 \times 8^1 + .078125 = 408.078125$

4. a) $5_8 = 101_2$
   d) $201_8 = 128 + 8 = 136_{10} = 10001000_2$
   c) $2.004 = 2\frac{4}{512} = 2\frac{1}{128} = 10.0000001$
   d) $501.1 = 3 \times 8^2 + 8 + \frac{1}{8} = 11001000.001$
6. a) $AAA = 1010\ 1010\ 1010$
   b) $8FA = 1000\ 1111\ 1010$
   c) $9AB = 101\ 1010\ 1011$
   d) $F00F = 1111\ 0000\ 1111$
8. a) .001 base 2
   b) .111 base 2
   c) .808 base 10

EXERCISE A.1

2. a) Printout is:

    ```
    8   IS THE SUM OF 3 AND 5
    16  IS THE SUM OF 7 AND 9
    24  IS THE SUM OF 11 AND 13
    ```

   b) Printout is:

    ```
    6
    14
    ```

   c) Printout is:

    ```
    THE CUBE OF 1 IS 1
    THE CUBE OF 2 IS 8
    THE CUBE OF 3 IS 27
    THE CUBE OF 4 IS 64
    THE CUBE OF 5 IS 125
    THE CUBE OF 6 IS 216
    THE CUBE OF 7 IS 343
    THE CUBE OF 8 IS 512
    THE CUBE OF 9 IS 729
    THE CUBE OF 10 IS 1000
    ```

4. All except B, F and G

EXERCISE A.2

2. Printout is:

    ```
    THE COST OF C1 IS 100
    THE COST OF C2 IS 120
    THE COST OF C3 IS 144
    THE TOTAL IS 364
    ```

4.
```
 5  PRINT "X", "Y"
10  READ X
20  DATA 4, 9, 16, 25, 36
30  LET Y = X↑2 + 2 * X↑.5 + 3
40  PRINT X, Y
50  GO TO 10
60  END
```

EXERCISE A.3

2. The printout is:

AMOUNT	PERCENTAGE
6	4
8	5.333
10	6.666
12	8
14	9.333
16	10.666
18	12
20	13.333
22	14.666
24	16

4.
```
 5  PRINT "NUMBER", "SQUARE"
10  FOR I = 1 TO 100
20  LET S = I ↑2
30  PRINT I, S
40  NEXT I
50  END
```

6.
```
 5  PRINT "NUMBER", "SQR ROOT"
10  FOR I = 2 TO 3 STEP .01
20  LET R = I ↑ .5
30  PRINT I, R
40  NEXT I
50  END
```

Glossary

Abscissa The first of the two coordinates of a point in the Cartesian plane.

Absolute Value The absolute value of a nonnegative number is the number itself. The absolute value of a negative number is the additive inverse of the number; $|5| = 5.$ $|-5| = -(-5) = 5$.

Algorithm Step-by-step procedure employed in solving a problem.

Analytic Geometry The expression and solution of geometric problems algebraically and vice versa.

Axiom An assumption or postulate.

Base In the number a^x, a is called the base. In 10^x, 10 is the base.

Binary A numeration system with 2 as its base; $101_2 = 5$.

Binary Operation An operation performed on a pair of elements from the same set yielding a unique element in the same set, e.g., $2 \times 3 = 6$.

Binomial A polynomial with two terms.

Bit Contraction of "binary digit"; 0 and 1.

Byte Several bits considered as a unit. In base 8 the byte is 3 bits; in base 16 the byte is 4 bits.

Cardinal Number The number of elements in a set.

Cartesian Plane A plane (consisting of the points) that may be put in one-to-one correspondence with the set of all ordered pairs of real numbers.

Class Mark The midpoint of an interval in statistics.

Coefficient The numerical part of a term. In $2x$, 2 is the coefficient. In general, the constant factors in a term as distinguished from the variables.

Complement Set A is the complement of set B if and only if A consists of all elements of the universal set that are not in B. The complement of B is symbolized by B'.

Complex Number A number of the form (a, b), where a and b are real numbers. May also be written in the form $a + bi$.

Composite Number A natural number $\neq 1$, which is not a prime number. $6 = 2 \cdot 3$; 6 is composite.

Congruent (Geometry) Figures that can be superposed so that they coincide. **(Algebra)** Two quantities that when divided by a quantity, called the modulus, give the same remainders.

Conjunctive Statement Simple statements connected by "and" or an equivalent connective such as "but."

Glossary

Constant A quantity whose value does not change during a mathematical operation.

Contrapositive The contrapositive of the implication $p \to q$ is $\sim q \to \sim p$.

Converse The converse of the statement $p \to q$ is $q \to p$.

Coordinate The first or second number in an ordered pair of numbers assigned to a point.

Coordinate Plane See Cartesian plane.

Counterexample An example that contradicts a statement.

Determinant A square array of elements symbolizing the sum of certain products of these elements.

$$D = \begin{vmatrix} a & b \\ c & d \end{vmatrix} = ad - bc$$

Deviation If s is an element of a sample S whose mean is M, then the deviation of s is $s - M$.

Digit A term applied to one of the integers 0, 1, 2, 3, ..., 9.

Directed Number A positive or negative number.

Disjoint Sets Sets that have no common elements.

Disjunctive Statement Simple statements connected by the connective "or," symbolized by $\vee$.

Domain The set of all first members of all ordered pairs of a relation.

Element A member of a set. $b \in B$ means "b is an element of the set B."

Empty Set A set that has no members, as symbolized by $\emptyset$.

Equality A mathematical relationship, symbolized by = and characterized by the reflexive, symmetric, transitive, additive, and multiplicative properties.

Equation A statement of equality between two quantities. Equations are of two types: identities and conditional equations.

Euler Circles Circles used to illustrate the relations between sets.

Experiment A planned course of action that has more than one outcome.

Exponent In the expression 2^x, x is the exponent.

Even Number A number of the form $2n$, where n is an integer.

Factor When used as a verb, the process of resolving an arithmetic or algebraic expression into factors whose product is the given expression. For example, $6 = 2 \times 3$. $x^2 - 2x - 3 = (x - 3)(x + 1)$. When used as a noun, 2 and 3 are factors of 6. $(x - 3)$ and $(x + 1)$ are factors of $x^2 - 2x - 3$.

Field A set of elements with two operations that possess eleven properties. Rational numbers, real numbers, numbers in mod 5 are examples of a field.

Finite Set A set that cannot be put into a one-to-one correspondence with a proper subset of itself. A set that has for some integer n, just n elements.

FORTRAN A computer language; contraction of the phrase "FORmula TRANslation."

Frequency The number of times an element appears in a sample.

Function A set of ordered pairs in which no two pairs have the same first element.

Graph A set of points in the Cartesian plane. May be a continuous graph of a set of discrete points. (Could it be the whole plant?)

Group A set of elements with a single binary operation that is closed and associative and that includes an identity element and inverse.

Half-Line A line terminated by a point in one direction and that extends indefinitely in the other direction.

Histogram Graphical representation of a frequency function. Frequency in each interval is indicated by the area of vertical bars.

Hypotenuse The side of a right triangle that is opposite the right angle.

Implication $p \rightarrow q$. If p is true, then q is true.

Index $\sqrt[n]{x}$, n is the index.

Inequality A sentence of the form $x > y$ or $x < y$.

Infinite Sets A set that has no last element. A set that can be put in a one-to-one correspondence with a proper subset of itself.

Integers The set consisting of $0, \pm 1, \pm 2 \ldots$

Intersection The set consisting of only those elements that belong to both of two given sets, A and B, as symbolized by $A \cap B$.

Inverse If a is a real number, then $-a$ is the additive inverse of a; that is, -5 is the inverse of 5 and 5 is the inverse of -5. If a $\in$ real number, $a \neq 0$, then the inverse of a for multiplication is $1/a$; that is, $\frac{1}{5}$ is inverse of 5, and 5 is inverse of $\frac{1}{5}$.

Irrational Number A real number that cannot be written in the form a/b ($b \neq 0$), where a and b are integers.

Isomorphic Two number systems are isomorphic when their elements can be put in one-to-one correspondence and the operations of one system are preserved in the other.

Klein Bottle A one-sided surface with no edges and no "inside" or "outside."

Matrix A rectangular array of elements; for example, $\begin{pmatrix} a & b & c \\ d & e & f \end{pmatrix}$.

Mean The arithmetic average of a sample.

Median The middle element of a sample.

Member Another name for an element that belongs to a set; $a \in A$ means a is a member (element) of the set A.

Memory That part of a computer in which data are stored.

Mobius Strip The one-sided surface formed by taking a long rectangular strip of paper and pasting its two ends together, after giving it a half-twist.

Mode An element of a sample whose frequency is greater than or equal to the frequency of any other element.

Modulus If $a \equiv b \pmod{C}$, then C is called the modulus of the relationship $\equiv$. This means that C divides $a - b$ without a remainder.

Monomial An expression with one term; $2x^2$.

Natural Numbers Counting numbers: 1, 2, 3, ...

Nonterminating Decimal A number that cannot be written exactly as a decimal fraction. May be rational or irrational, depending on whether repeating elements appear. Examples: .027027 ... , 25.1010010001 ...

Normal Curve A symmetrical distribution curve in which the mean, median, and mode coincide.

Null Set A set with no elements, the empty set $\emptyset$.

Numerals Symbols used to denote numbers, for example, Arabic numerals 1, 2, 3, etc. or Roman numerals I, II, III.

Octal Base 8 numeration.

Odd Number A number of the form $2n + 1$, where n is an integer.

Ordinal Number The order or position of a particular element in a set; that is, first, 22nd, etc.

Ordinate The second of the two coordinates or a point. In $P(x, y)$, y is the ordinate.

Origin The point on the number line assigned to the number zero, or the point on the Cartesian plane assigned to the pair (0, 0).

Parallelepiped A prism whose bases are parallelograms.

Parallel Lines Lines that do not intersect no matter how far extended.

Parallelogram A quadrilateral with its opposite sides parallel.

Perfect Number A number equal to the sum of its proper divisors.

Perpendicular Two lines which intersect to form a right angle (90°) are perpendicular to each other.

Polygon A plane figure consisting of n points, called vertices, and n sides. The sides have no common point except their endpoint.

Polynomial A general term that includes monomials, binomials, trinomials, etc.

Postulate An axiom or assumption.

Prime Number A natural number having exactly two factors: 1 and the number itself.

Program A sequence of statements written in computer language that instructs the computer to perform certain operations.

Proposition Any statement which asserts something that is either true or false.

Quadrant One of the four subsets of the coordinate plane into which the two axes separate the plane.

Quadratic An expression or equation of the second degree; $y = x^2$.

Quadratic Equation An equation of the form $ax^2 + bx + c = 0$.

Quadrilateral   A polygon having four sides.

Radical x is a radical.

Range   The replacement set for y in the ordered pair (x, y).

Rational Number   A real number that can be expressed in the form a/b, $b \neq 0$, and $a, b \in$ integers.

Ray   Union of half-line and the point that determines the half-line.

Real Number   A rational or irrational number.

Rectangle   A parallelogram with one angle—a right angle.

Relation   A set of ordered pairs.

Relationship   Equality, inequality, congruence, greater than, etc.

Sample   A set of known numerical facts to be statistically analyzed.

Sample Space   The set of all possible outcomes of an experiment.

Set   A collection of things.

Similar Triangles   Triangles whose angles are equal, where the ratio of the lengths of corresponding sides is the same.

Solution Set   A set of numbers that satisfies a given equation or inequality.

Standard Deviation   The positive square root of the variance.

Subset A is a subset of B if and only if every element of A is also an element of B.

Syllogism   The three-step arrangement. (1) p, (2) $p \to q$, (3) $\therefore q$.

Terminating Decimal   A decimal that can be written with a finite number of digits; that is, .25.

Theorem   A statement that has been proved.

Trapezoid   A quadrilateral that has two parallel sides.

Triangle   A polygon formed by connecting three points.

Union   The set consisting of members that belong to one or the other of two given sets A and B, symbolized as $A \cup B$.

Universe   The set of all things chosen for a particular study.

Variable   A quantity that can take on any of the numbers of some set. Usually designated in algebra by x, y, z.

Variance   The sum of the squares of the deviations divided by the number of elements, n.

Vector   A quantity that has both magnitude and direction.

Vector Space   A mathematical system whose elements are vectors; operations on the elements are characterized by specific postulates.

Venn Diagram   Geometric figures used to represent relations between sets.

Well-Defined Set   If A is a set it must be possible to decide whether any given object is an element of A. The set A is then a well-defined collection.

Symbols

$\wedge$	Conjunction	$>$	Greater than
$\vee$	Disjunction	$\geq$	Greater than or equal to
$\rightarrow$	Implication	$<$	Less than
$\sim$	Negation	$\leq$	Less than or equal to
$\{\ \}$	Set notation	$\oplus$	Group addition
$\in$	Is an element of	$\otimes$	Group Multiplication
$\notin$	Is not an element of	$\equiv, \cong$	Congruent
$\neq$	Not equal	$a + bi$	Complex number
$\subset$	Proper subset	(a, b)	Complex number
$\subseteq$	Subset	$\langle a, b \rangle$	Vector
$=$	Equals (Computer: replaced by)	$\sqrt{\ }$	Square root
		$\sqrt[n]{\ }$	nth root
$\leftrightarrow$	Equivalent, if and only if	$\|a\|$	Absolute value of a
$\emptyset$	Null or empty set	σ	Standard deviation
$/$	Complement of	$\angle$	Angle
$\cap$	Intersection	$\rightarrow$	Ray
$\cup$	Union	$\leftrightarrow$	Line
$\|$	Such that	$-$	Line segment
$\cdot, \times$	Multiplication	π	Pi
$+$	Addition or positive	a^2	a squared
$-$	Subtraction or negative	a^n	a to the nth power
$\div$	Division		

Notes

Notes

Index

A

Abelian group, 70, 74
Abscissa, 114
Absolute value, 109
Addition, 41
  associative, 45
  closure for, 44
  commutative, 45
  identity, 51, 59
  inverse, 51, 59
  of matrices, 82
  rational numbers, 57
  table, 42
  vector, 88
Additive property, 44, 73
Address, 232
Algebraic expressions, 99
Amicable, 53
Analog computer, 231
Angles, 195-197
Arguments, 8-11
Arithmetic mean, 219
Array, 81
Associative, addition, 45
  multiplication, 45
Axiom, 2
Axis, real, 76

B

Base, 146, 225
Biconditional, 18-20
Binary, operations, 43, 50, 70, 77
  system, 234-235
Bits, 235
Bytes, 239

C

Cardinal numbers, 40
Cartesian plane, 76
Cartesian product, 36
Chain rule, 8
Class mark, 341
Closure, for addition, 44
  for multiplication, 44
Coefficient, 146
Combinations, 208-211
Commutative, addition, 45
  multiplication, 45
Complement of sets, 33
Completeness, postulate, 65
  property, 65, 187
Complex numbers, 75-81
Composite numbers, 53
Conclusion, 8-11
Conditional, 16
Congruent, 73, 197
Conjunctive proposition, 3, 5, 9
Connective, 9
Constants, 100, 242-245
Continuity, postulate of, 65, 187
Contrapositive, 16-17, 24
Converse, 16-17
Coordinate system, 79
Correspondence, one-to-one, 40, 65
Counting, principle, 206-207
  numbers, 39-41
Cramer's rule, 131-133

D

Decimal, repeating, 61
Deductive, arguments, 8
  diagrams, 12-15
  reasoning, 2
Defective numbers, 53
Defined terms, 2
Derived implications, 15-18
Descriptive geometry, 199
Descriptive statistics, 219
Determinants, 132
Difference of a and b, 54
Digital computer, 231
Direction, angle, 87
  concept of, 50
Direct proof, 22-24
Disjoint sets, 31
Disjunctive propositions, 4, 5, 9
Disproof, 24-25
Distributive multiplication, 46
Divisibility tests, 53-54
Division, 57
Domain, 139-141
  of the variable, 100-105
Dot product, 92

E

Element set, 28
Elliptical geometry, 186
Empty set, 28
Equality, matrices, 82
    postulates, 43
Equivalent, 20-29
Euler, 12, 200
Euler's circles, 12-14
Excessive numbers, 53
Experiment, 202
Exponents, 146-148, 158-162

F

Factoring, 162-163
Field, 74
Finite set, 28
Fortran, 342
Fractional exponents, 159-162
Fractions, 39
Frequency, 343
Fundamental Rule of Inference, 9-11
Functions, 141-145, 163-167

G

Gibbs, J. Willard, 87
Greatest common divisor, 54-56
Greatest common factor, 162
Group, Abelian, 70, 74
Groups, 69-75

H

Half-line, 196
Histograms, 224
Hyperbolic geometry, 185
Hypothesis, 8

I

Identity element, for addition, 50
    for multiplication, 50
Identity, for addition, 51, 59
    for multiplication, 51, 59-60
    matrix, 82
Imaginary numbers, 77
Implication, 6-9
    biconditional, 18-20
    derived, 15-18
Independent events, 213
Indeterminate, 58
Indirect proof, 24
Inductive reasoning, 2
Inference, deductive, 8
Infinite set, 28
Inner product, 92
Integers, 49-52
Intersection of sets, 32
Intervals, 108
Inverse, 16-17
    for addition, 51, 59
    for multiplication, 59
Irrational numbers, 64
Isomorphic, 91

L

Length, 187
Line, real number, 65
Linear, equation, 116
    inequalities, 133
    programming, 136
Lowest common multiple, 54-56

M

Mathematical, axiom, 66
    expectation, 216
    induction, 65-68
Matrices, addition of, 82
    equality, 82
Matrix, 81
    algebra, 86
    multiplication, 83-86
    square, 82
Measurement, 219
Measures, of central tendency, 219
    of variation, 221
Median, 221
Mode, 221
Modular arithmetic, 71-75

Modulus, 73
Multiplication, 41
  associative, 45
  closure for, 44
  commutative, 45
  identity, 51, 59-60
  inverse, 59
  of powers, 149
  rational numbers, 57
  scalar, 89-91
  table, 43
Multiplicative, inverse, 59
  property, 44, 73

N

Natural numbers, 28, 44-49
Necessary conditions, 18-20
Negation, 5, 7, 11
Non-Euclidean geometry, 182, 184
Normal curve, 224-225
Null set, 28
Number, cardinal, 40
  complex, 75-81
  composite, 53
  counting, 39-41
  defective, 53
  excessive, 53
  imaginary, 77
  irrational, 64
  natural, 28, 44-49
  perfect, 52
  prime, 53
  rational, 56-63
  real, 39, 63, 65
  theory, 39
Numerology, 52

O

Octal numeration system, 238
One-to-one correspondence, 40, 65
Order, axiom, 107
Ordered pairs, 29, 36, 76, 86, 138, 163-165
Ordinal concept, 40
Ordinate, 114

Outcomes, 203, 206-207

P

Pairs, ordered, 29, 36, 76, 86, 138, 163-165
Perfect number, 52
Permutation, 208-210
Plane, Cartesian, 76
Polynomials, 151-158
Postulate, 2
  of continuity, 65
Prime number, 53
Principal root, 159
Probability, 201
Products, 41, 146
  dot, 92
  inner, 92
  vector, 89
Projective geometry, 199
Proof, 22-24
Proper divisor, 53
Propositions, 3
  conjunctive, 3, 5, 9
  disjunctive, 4, 5, 9
  simple, 3

Q

Quadrants, 76
Quadratics, 163-177
Quantifiers, 11

R

Range, 139-141, 221
Radicals, 159-162
Rational numbers, 56-63
  addition, 57
  division, 57
  multiplication, 57
  subtraction, 57
Ray, 196
Real numbers, 39, 63, 65
Reflexive property, 43, 73
Relations, 138-141
Remainder tables, 74

Repeating block, 61
Repeating decimal, 61
Rostor method, 139, 141
Rule, chain, 8
    Cramer's, 131-133

S

Sample space, 203
Scalar, 89-91, 96
Sets, Cartesian product, 36
    disjoint, 31
    element, 28, 208
    empty, 28
    finite, 28
    infinite, 28
    intersection, 32
    notation, 29
    null, 28
    operations, 32-36
    union of, 33
    universal, 29
    well-defined, 28
Similar, 197
Simple proposition, 3
Space, sample, 203
    vector, 91
Speed, 96
Standard deviation, 222
Subsets, 29
    proper, 30
    subtraction, 57
Sufficient condition, 18-19
Sum, 40
Symbolic representations, 8-11
Symmetric property, 43, 60, 73

T

Tables, addition, 42
    multiplication, 43
    remainder, 74
    truth, 20-22
Tautology, 21
Tests of divisibility, 53-54

Theorem, 2
Topology, 200
Transitive property, 44, 47, 73
Truth tables, 20-22
Truth values, 17-18

U

Undefined terms, 2
Union of sets, 33
Universal set, 29

V

Variables, 100, 104-109, 112-124, 242-245, 252
Variance, 222
Value, absolute, 109
Vectors, 86-98
    addition, 88
    product, 89
    space, 91
Velocity vector, 93, 96-98
Venn, diagrams, 30-32
    John, 30
Vertex, 136, 164, 174-175

W

Well-defined set, 28

X

X axis, 76
X intercept, 117

Y

Y axis, 76
Y intercept, 117

Z

Zero, 50
    as cardinal number, 58
    division, 58
    matrix, 82